Praise for *T*

"Absolutely brilliant work! The author has fit so many pieces together. The timeline intricacies, science and research—all put together! Impressive, something more people need to know about...ties in the multiple sciences to backup these mysteries are awe-striking! Dead bones don't lie; they tell a remarkable story. Most assuredly worth reading!"

—*Rev. Kayelizabeth V. Bartlett*

"Mark Rose has produced a fascinating study of the geologic and other scientific evidence supporting the biblical account of the flood of Noah. Anyone with a serious interest in Genesis or the plethora of flood stories found throughout the world should consider this book."

—*Dr. Mark Barclift, World Mission Area Director - Assemblies of God*

"I edit and write reviews for many Christian books, and I can honestly say that what you have written goes far and beyond anything I've ever read. It's as if you have left no stone uncovered. I truly believe that God is going to use this book to His glory and as a blessing to multitudes of people."

—*Brenda, CBM Reviews "10 Stars"*

"This book is an amazing resource for those seeking accurate answers on how God's Word, His creation, and scientific evidence are in alignment. It gives people hope that God's design and history are woven into the very fabric of our world. We are not a cosmic accident! Mark Rose does a masterful job of sharing the hope of the gospel through evidence seen in God's creation. Thank you! We will use this book to encourage students across our country who don't have a voice when defending their faith!"

—*C. R. Herb, Oregon Area Director, Young Life Ministries*

"It's obvious that Mark Rose has spent countless hours researching this controversial topic. His foundational arguments are difficult for non-believers and skeptics to refute. While it addresses heady theological academics, it's written in such a way that anyone can read and understand."

—*Russ Jones, Executive Vice President, USA Headline News*

"Just finished your book and what an excellent job you've done. I will continue in prayer for the effectiveness of your book. There are so many Christians who do not believe in the Flood because they don't have the facts...I deeply appreciate your research which enlightened and informed me one fact after another. I am sure I will be referring back to your book in my own defense of the Flood of Noah. I have highly recommended it to a few friends already. Thanks again, Mark..."

—*Allen Austin, author,* Genesis in Egypt

"Mark Rose does an incredible job at explaining not just biblical process of God's creation but scientific and logical. He uses terminology people can understand and puts perspective on a controversial subject. This book is great for anyone looking for an informative, honest read on the subject. We will be using this material for teaching in the future! Highly recommended."

—*Lisa Tag, Young Life Leader*

"I would highly recommend this book for Christians, nonbelievers, or folks who are on the fence about their faith. There is nothing better than when faith can be backed up by fact. The author does a wonderful and thorough job of researching and articulating facts in a way that everyone can read. I look forward to using this book with friends, family, and in ministry to spread God's truth. Well done, Mark Rose!"

—*Brian P., Ministry Leader, Young Life*

"I felt compelled to let you know how much I am enjoying reading the book, *The Noah Code.* It is one of the best books I have ever read, so well written, so full of amazing history, facts and information. The description of the animals arriving to enter the Ark filled me with tears at the sheer magnificence of the Lord. It has helped to bolster my faith with the undeniable evidence that has been before our eyes all along. THANK YOU for such a wonderful book. I want to share it with family and friends. Blessings."

—*Laurie Rees, Trinity Broadcasting Network*

The Noah Code
Coding for Origins Truth

Mark Rose

Evidence for Creation and The Flood,
Considering the Future Judgment of Mankind

GENESIS ALIVE
Championing Origin's Truth

Genesis Alive LLC

To my grandchildren,
so they will forever
know the truth

"Have ye not read,
that He which made them
at the beginning
made them
male and female"
(Matt. 19:4)

Acknowledgments

There are a number of great folks who committed to see this project through, their support pivotal to the content quality and end result. Though initially started as the Noah Code Project, this adaptation is their harvest.

Helping with editing and graphics were Veronica Bruner and Tim Howard. Chris Herb and Liz Doyle contributed advice relating to generational applicability and formed the content advisory committee. Dr. Stephanie Rose provided editing suggestions, critique and content.

And finally Ryan Kinnaman, an engineering major who understands the issue at hand and the positive effect of good origins thought, gave his reliable tenacity and support vital to completion of this volume.

Note to the student reading this volume –

The information herein is life-changing. Once you read it, you will never feel the same about God, origins, creation, the Flood, the future or Jesus Christ again. You will sit back in awe, because you will know the truth about the true character of God, Jesus Christ, heaven and even Noah. You will understand why the Flood happened, why God is coming back someday in the near future, and how to be ready for that day.

You will learn things about the earth you never even thought of. Your faith will soar; your love for God will soar. You will get it. You will be "always ready to have an answer" for those who don't believe in God. You will be ready to go to heaven and be happy and expecting, not ashamed, to meet Jesus, who like Noah did for those he saved, is preparing a place for you, His treasure. You are the treasure for whom He died, the one for whom He's building a mansion right now. He will be there, keys in hand, to show you your new home and be excited to show off every room and the view to you. That's what He's doing right now, building the place and waiting for you...

Table of Contents

Table of Figures

Introduction

The story of Noah's Flood is among the most widely known in human history. Though it's a biblically solid account, we find the Church has largely sidelined the narrative to the nursery school and credited Noah with saving the furry creatures from disaster and little more. Surprisingly, the Flood story is known in history as far back as records exist, as defined in Funk and Wagnall's *Dictionary of Folklore, Mythology and Legend*: *"A world cataclysm during which the earth was inundated or submerged by water: A concept found in almost every mythology in the world."* These accounts now number in the hundreds, as Wagnall's correctly observes "almost every" culture has a version. Interestingly enough, each account names our main character in their best language, that is, Noah.

The following are a few examples recorded from around the world: in Mexico, Noah becomes *Coxcox,* "When mankind was overwhelmed with the deluge, none were preserved." From Sumar, *Utnapishtim* builds an Ark when warned by God of an imminent flood. From Egypt we have *Tem* and/or *Nue* who "was responsible for the primeval flood." From Alaska we have *"Yako"* who long ago, before Denali the High One was raised to the sky, one Yako dwelt in the land, [building a] Magic Canoe…covered with pitch." From Hawaii, *Nu'nu;* from China, *Fuhi,* "his wife, three sons and daughters, the only survivors of a great flood."

So how does this old tale relate to us today? Modern society generally accepts that geology, archeology and the related sciences have disproved the literal flood account, but why did so many cultures make every effort to preserve the story? Could the scientists have missed something? There's a long standing proverb among geologists, which proposes that "the rocks don't lie," and despite modern scientific interpretations, we find a good number of competent scientists far from ready to dismiss the biblical account.

Historically, this controversy is nothing new. For example in 1865, over 600 scientists of the British Association signed a statement condemning the idea that observations in the present (through a geology system coined as "uniformity") could disprove biblical history and strictly warning that science is limited in this regard. They maintained evidence of the past yet interpreted in the present may be easily overturned, and thus is tentative regarding *origins*. Many of these men were the founders of the disciplines of geology, archeology, zoology and other sciences. They wrote volumes and spent years in the field, many writing that the rocks and fossils do align with the Flood account. These men understood that science has great value in matters of operational uses and discovery, but not so much concerning origins in particular, seeing that a single finding could upend a theory about the past in a moment.

A recent example of such was the overturning of the long coveted astronomical substance "dark matter" in 2013. For over 30 years, astrophysicists maintained this unseen and undetectable material held entire galaxies together, the concept becoming near universal in acceptance in the eyes of the general public. Think of it: a substance that's undetectable and unseen by scientific experiment given the allegiance of so many scholarly men for all these years! It took a Peruvian team of astrophysicists to demolish the theory, their exhaustive study of the Milky Way Galaxy concluding: "There's no dark matter around here." In another development, the CERN particle laboratory in Switzerland announced another shocking 2013 conclusion that after searching for months, dark matter was undetected. You see with no dark matter, the galaxies and universe may be quite young, as those tight spiral galaxies are expanding and unraveling at a shocking rate and should be scattered about by now!

Capping the dark matter un-discovery was the fulfillment of the Standard Chart in 2013 by the detection of the "God Particle" also at CERN. Of course, the non-existent dark matter particle has not vanished from the textbooks nor the minds of the faithful, the trusting public patiently believing given the "some day we will find it" excuse. The point being we must recognize science has limits concerning origins, and man should beware of making religions of such beliefs, just as the members of the British Association warned those many years ago. The Bible has answers for these questions, as man was not present to observe such matters, but God was!

Most in our modern society think themselves objective and somewhat scientific, uninterested in following false ideas. They tend to trust the "authorities" who may be quite biased and most concerning have an agenda. In truth, origins science speculates about the un-witnessed past with evidence found in the present.

The 2014 discovery of ringwoodite water reservoirs in earth's crust is a prime example. Here was found all the additional water needed for a global flood, answering the no-water argument put forth by geophysicists for decades. Quoting the chief researcher on this project; "We should be grateful for this deep reservoir, if it wasn't there, it would be on the surface of the earth, and *mountain tops would be the only land poking out.*" They calculate that the North American basins alone hold water equivalent to *three* of earth's oceans. Thus we find another of many examples toppling long held anti-biblical notions supposedly from "science."

In this volume, I hope to show the objective that science and the Bible *do* agree in respect to origins, despite the persuasive power of the media and the claims of "institutional science" today. In a repeat of the 1865 initiative, fast forward to 2001, more than 700[1] scientists signed a similar decree rejecting the tenants of evolution in general, responding specifically to the PBS "Evolution" television series that promoted this theory as fact. Summarizing this list of objectors, member scientists from the following institutions signed on: National Academies of Science in Russia, Czech Republic, Hungary, India (Hindustan), Nigeria, Poland, Russia and the United States. Signers also included professors or researchers from Cambridge, British Museum of Natural History, Moscow State University, Masaryk University in Czech Republic, Hong Kong University, University of Turku in Finland, Autonomous University of Guadalajara in Mexico, University of Stellenbosch in South Africa, Institute de PalÃ, Ontologie Humaine in France, Chitose Institute of Science & Technology in Japan, Ben-Gurion University in Israel, MIT, the Smithsonian, Princeton, and many more. This list has been enlarged in the last years.

So why does this matter? As evolutionary thought has so thoroughly infiltrated every level of science and education today, the net effect has been the near destruction of the validity of the Bible as a voice concerning origins or even morality for that matter. As this new data has come to light, society must now face the fact that the former paradigm was patently in error and has taken our generation far off course. In addition, if the Flood *did* occur as literally outlined in Genesis, secular science must either change stories or face invalidation regarding origins thought. Catastrophism is now the story of our times, which is simply another word describing the Flood! Within these pages, I hope to show the thoughtful how well the evidence fits the findings of the field geologically, especially when interpretations include the biblical model, and further, the real and practical effect when the two are joined.

Most all agree the Bible's most important value is that of its moral message. The author considers the Bible *the* anchor of moral truth for mankind. Without this foundation, how does society determine right or wrong? What document better defines moral behavior and humankinds conduct? If the Bible be undermined, who can now make these moral definitions—man? If man substitutes himself as rule-maker in place of God, *any* moral code maybe called into question, which I propose is exactly what occurred in Noah's day with its terrible consequences. History has taught us that free floating morality quickly undermines the family unit and eventually the nation. One must ask the question, is such happening in our world today?

The fact is that there *is* a Creator who has wired humans a certain way. History has taught us if we tamper with these moral absolutes, society will eventually self-destruct. Working in aviation in my early years, more than once I witnessed terrible accidents brought upon by crews defying known basics. Flying in the Arctic allowed little margin for error, and seeing crew after crew lost (many in flames) because they thought themselves wiser than a regulation or manufacturer was a terrible and avoidable waste. The conclusion—best follow the directives closely, if you want to live!

Could it be that society today is heading in the same direction as Noah's time, abandoning traditional values for some new moral code that will end the same? The Bible graphically shows us the consequential result of rejecting God's moral standards. The bottom line being this: God is Creator, *He* makes the rules, and tampering with them leads to disastrous results. In this volume I first attempt to show that the literal Genesis narrative is patently honest and reliable, and secondly, suggest the ultimate means whereby Noah obtained favor and a unique relationship with the Creator Himself, a means available to anyone today.

In the end we find Noah, one of the greatest leaders of all time, successful in his role in mankind's preservation, his experience speaking a practical message ahead in time for us today.

"Doth not wisdom cry out? And understanding put forth her voice? She standeth in the top of high places, by the way in the places of the paths. She crieth at the gates, at the entry of the city, at the coming in at the doors. Unto you, O men, I call; and my voice is to the sons of man. O ye simple, understand wisdom: and, ye fools, be ye of an understanding heart. Hear; for I will speak of excellent things; and the opening of my lips shall be right things. For my mouth shall speak truth. Before the mountains were settled, before the hills was I brought forth: When he prepared the heavens, I was there, when he appointed the foundations of the earth: Now therefore hearken unto me, O ye children: for blessed are they that keep my ways. Hear instruction, and be wise, and refuse it not" (The Bible, Book of Proverbs, Chapter 8 KJV).

Mark D. Rose
July 2015 Albany, Oregon

[1] http://www.discovery.org/articleFiles/PDFs/100ScientistsAd.pdf

1

Preliminary Evidence of Providence

Fig. 1 The "Very Good" First Earth

To put the subject of Creation, Noah and the Flood in perspective, we shall first take a short tour through the subject of origins from a biblical standpoint. First, the materialists tell us the earth self-formed billions of years ago after a mass of gas and dust self-collected in space. Further, they propose these loose particles assembled into all the perfect spheres of our solar system, also creating the special planet we inhabit today. After these sphere forming events, the substances supposedly self-sorted again, forming the oceans, rivers, lakes, and land masses we enjoy today, all by unguided means.

Like the earth, evolution also claims life self-formed from dead chemicals. This theory suggests life of every variety sprang forth by chemical ac-

1

cidents over great eons of time. All agree these biochemical agents had no prior existence. The simplest life form (the evolutionist tells us) is the bacteria, presently known to be entirely complex and far from simple, along the way somehow activating into a living thing. The evolutionist also claims (without any outside assistance) that life bloomed into the plethora of forms we see today completely by accident. Moreover, they claim the origin of DNA and its coding came about by random means, the common mechanism proposed being time and unexplainable chemistry.

To the contrary, we now know DNA is an independent entity within the cell, incorporating millions of correctly ordered chemicals in tape form. DNA is understood to be the most compact data storage system in the known universe. DNA is designed with the intent to remotely control the moment by moment operation of the cell machine. Further, this compound is the com-mon denominator of all life, change the DNA in a given cell and you change the life form, like switching programs on your computer. Compounding the problem for accidental origin, we have the cell exactly duplicating all this data and bio-machinery in seconds, leaving us with only one solution to ex-plain these complexities—that of Intelligence. Not intelligence measured by IQ, but from the Creator of the brain that designed thinking in the first place, allowing man to have consciousness and comprehension of the matter.

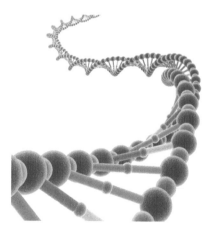

Fig. 2 The DNA information tape, using a 3 *billion* letter "codon" alphabet to "code" for people

Man and all his laboratories find such operations impossible to replicate, so a new term has been coined to describe the origin of such capability, that is, *Super-Intelligence*. The DNA and the cell mechanisms so directed must have evolved (if evolution is true) in perfect *parallel* for a cell to operate, a mathematical impossibility. Such makes the evolutionary explanation illogical. To defy mathematics and believe in the impossible, one must embrace a faith that these things occurred by *chance, without any assistance.*

In support of creation by a deity, we must not forget that DNA instructional commands use the same language convention in *all living things* and have so since the beginning of biological time. These systems need no perfecting today, so how did evolution mindlessly form them without a succession of trial and error? The materialist maintains these developed through multiple accident and chance processes, but how and when did those processes occur, since they have never been observed, changed nor become more efficient since the very beginning? Cell operation is now and has always been in *stasis, operating with near perfection billions of times daily.*

If we have an engineer and a factory, each must communicate to function. This is referred to as a *language convention.* A computer has a language convention (like DOS or Mac), and none of us would expect them to have come about by accidents, but this is exactly what the evolutionist asks one to believe. (Note that late breaking research has determined that DNA actually uses two unrelated codes superimposed one on the other, called duons, this allowing more data to be transcribed into a single section.[1])

For software and hardware to operate together as in computers, no one would dispute that each require *intelligence* acting on matter to function. One then must ask, if evolution has been so prolific in life creation, why have the basic mechanisms of DNA and all other cellular components in life have no known ancestral precursor? We know animals change and adapt—this is called micro-evolution. The Creator designed the DNA with *variability* to allow for such adaptations as the environment changes. This self-change capability is an amazing design feature, not a result of chance. Gene variability is incapable of transitioning a worm into a trilobite or an ape into a man. Each *kind* employs a separate DNA program. By experience, accidents make nothing; this law also holds true concerning the complex world of biologic origins as well. So on the strength of reason and logic, evolution is impos-sible; it's a belief system based on faith, not *science.*

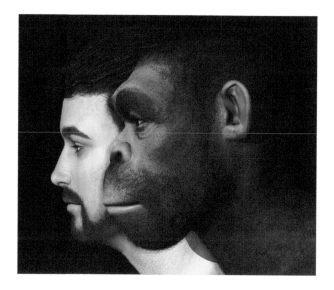

Fig. 3 Man has genes equal to 20 each, 500 page books,
completely different than apes

Chimp-Human Non-Similarity

Most everyone has heard of *Australopithecus Aphaeresis*, or "Lucy," a small orangutan type creature unearthed by Dr. Donald Johansson in the 1970s. Heralded by the media and science institutions as the last and final link between man and ape, few heard that Johansson (after intense cross-examination for months by his peers)[2] finally admitted to adding parts (knee joints)* to his box of bones they found in a completely different location. This was vital because Lucy needed a knee and hip that was near human to be an upright walker. The creature also needed straight appendages (hers were curved like monkeys), shorter arms, a larger skull, a different pelvis and a hundred other changes. It turns out Lucy was simply another species of orangutan or baboon, yet made it into the papers, textbooks and the minds of millions as proof of evolution, the "missing-link" between ape and man.

*Late breaking news about the "Lucy" find:
http://christiannews.net/2015/04/23/evolutionary-embarrassment-part-of-famous-ape-man-skeleton-actually-came-from-baboon/

A close relationship between man and ape DNA code matter has been lately advocated, comparing billions of codon sections (or letters) using a percentage factor where 1% of 3 billion codons equals 3 million *differences*—no small sum. Late reports claim the gap between man and apes is

1-1.5%.[3] But other studies report this gap is much wider, closer to 6% or larger.[4] A 2014 investigation of the human sequence by Brian Thomas, Drs Nathaniel Jeanson and Jeffery Tomkins* of The Institute for Creation Research determined that early Human Genome project administrators had compared *known* similar gene sections, sometimes leaving out the DNA sec-tions unique to man, throwing the results. Parts of these sections or genes are found to be equivalent to twenty 500 page books of human-specific information! The ICR study comparing the *entire* human genome determined that the difference is actually around 900,000,000 codons or closer to 30%![5]

Note the August 2014 issue of *Scientific American* ran an article adhering to the 1% Man/Ape dissimilarity figure, just in time for students entering school that year. Interestingly enough, in 2006 the same periodical published an article suggesting a gap of 6%, a figure that was never refuted![6]**

*Brian Thomas, Institute for Creation Research: www.icr.org/article/evaluating-human-chimp-dna-myth-new/ Nathanial Jeanson Acts & Facts Vol. 43 No. 12, December, 2014
**J.R. Minkel, *Human-Chimp Gene Gap Widens from Tally of Duplicate Genes, Scientific American* Dec 19, 2006 "There's a bigger genetic jump between humans and chimps than previously believed."

A final note on DNA comparisons: a banana contains approximately 55% of human DNA and a cow said to have 80%—so much for compar-isons! All man's efforts fall short to construct even a cell of grass, and if somehow such was accomplished, we could expect the effort to cost millions and employ teams of scientists working tirelessly around the clock, thus effecting *intelligence on matter*, like God!

Junk DNA, Fusion and Adam and Eve

Surprisingly, the percentage of DNA that codes to create the living parts of things is quite small compared with the remainder used for other purposes. Leading evolution proponents such as standing NIH (National Institutes of Health) Director Francis Collins, Professor John C. Avise, and radical anti-creation skeptic Richard Dawkins (that propose human/ ape ancestry) argue this non-coding DNA material is unused and therefore supports evolutionary randomness, not the work of a wise creator.

These evolutionists assert that the existence of such material suggests mindless eons of mutational mistakes, leaving a variety of random genetic material as "proof" of evolution and great periods of time. On the contrary, research shows "non-coding" DNA material has many all important func-

5

tions, and is not "junk" at all. Such has now been found to perform many important life processes, including of late - heart development! In other words, these folks have it all wrong.

The second argument relates to Chromosomal Fusion. Humans appear to have 47 chromosomes verses 48 found in apes, so evolutionists propose this finding supports common ancestry between man and apes. As in the case of the purported "junk" DNA, the argument fails under the weight of study and proves nothing concerning man's common ancestry with apes but actually points to a common *creator*. Due to the popularity of these concepts, we shall pursue them in defense of the actions of Providence.

All DNA Has a Job to Do

In his 2006 book *The Language of God,* Francis Collins states that [human DNA provides] "powerful support for Darwin's theory of evolution, that is descent from a common ancestor with natural selection operating on randomly occurring variations."[7] Many scientists refute this statement, say-ing evidence from DNA does not establish Collins's conclusions about human evolution at all.[8] Contrary to both Collins and Dawkins (also a junk DNA advocate), a casual overview of the literature shows they're wrong. For example Casey Luskin, researcher at the Discovery Institute in Seattle and co-author of the 2012 book *Science & Human Origins*, shows that there's a wealth of evidence to the contrary.

Luskin quotes biologist Richard Sternberg, who surveyed the literature and found that AREs (the non-coding DNA) include over 20 known critical functions. Here are seven examples:
1 Repairing DNA
2 Assisting in DNA replication
3 Regulating DNA transcription
4 Aiding in folding and maintenance of chromosomes
5 Controlling RNA editing and splicing
6 Helping to fight disease
7 Regulating embryological development[9]

University of Chicago geneticist James Shapiro agrees with Sternberg, asserting, "One day, we will think of what used to be called 'junk DNA' as a critical component of truly 'expert' cellular control regimes."[10] In 2007, the Washington Post noted that the ENCODE Project[11]* (a consortium of over 300 scientists) reported: "The vast majority of the 3 billion 'letters' of the human genetic code are busily toiling at an array of *previously invisible* tasks" [emphasis added]. And further, there is "convincing evidence that the genome is pervasively transcribed, such that the majority of its bases can be found in primary transcripts, including non-protein-coding transcripts."[12]

Not to be outdone, Pro-evolution Professor John C. Avise published *Inside the Human Genome: A Case for Non-Intelligent Design*, where he mentions the "junk DNA" concept. Avise comments along the line that these "pseudo-genes" don't appear to be designed by a "wise engineer" and that they lay scattered "like useless molecular cadavers." Such absolute statements are contrary to the findings of the *300 plus* scientists contributing to the ENCODE project, who report the science shows precisely the *opposite* when peering into their microscopes!

Jonathan Wells in his book *The Myth of Junk DNA* (Discovery Institute Press, 2011) notes that in 2010 "American biologists[13] reported that the expression of two human genes is increased by transcription of their related pseudogenes." The team concluded, "Pseudogenes have an intrinsic biological activity" in controlling gene integration. In 2006, scientists from Spain reported non-protein-coding RNAs "regulate virtually all aspects of the gene expression pathway, with profound biological consequences."[14] In 2009, Japanese biologists noted that "We have identified probably only a few of the many potential functional mechanisms" [of the non-coding gene matter] and further, "Research in the recent few years has identified *an unexpectedly rich variety of mechanisms* by which non-coding RNAs act"[15] [emphasis added] 180° from Professor Avice's assertion of *"A Case for Non-Intelligent Design."*

Luskin also mentions the *Nature* article: "Biology's new glimpse at a universe of non-coding DNA—what *used* to be called 'junk' DNA"[16] demonstrates the tide has reversed on the junk advocates. Dr. Collins lately admits he will no longer use the term "junk" in reference to these organics, but regardless of this retraction, his writings such as his influential book *The Language of God* and others live on, promoting views supporting human evolution as fact based upon suppositions, not real science.

According to Dr. Terry Luskin, "In reality, junk DNA is an increasingly *outdated way* to look at non-coding DNA, and its usefulness in proving common ancestry of humans with apes is highly suspect," further stating "Collins uses terms like 'inexorably' and 'inescapable,' but the fact remains that the evidence he presents based on genetics simply does not show what he claims." Summarizing, he said, "Collins's arguments from junk DNA are being eroded with each passing month by new studies uncovering a myriad of functions for non-coding DNA."[17]

Harvard graduate and PhD geneticist Dr. Nathan Jeanson sums up the psuedogene/Junk DNA argument, commenting about evolutionary scientists who persist to dispute the final conclusions of the 2012 ENCODE* Project[18] findings state, "not because the [ENCODE] experiments were flawed, but simply because the project's results were *inconsistent with evolutionary expectations*. The idea of a species having large amounts of junk DNA seems to be a relic of the past."[19]

We hope so, but as long as well known evolutionary scientists have the ear of the sympathetic media and the lectern and are publishing books, we can expect their agenda advancing to a trusting public, despite the preponderance of evidence to the contrary.

*Over 300 scientists contributed The ENCODE project report. For more see link: www.mythofjunkdna.com

Fig. 4 Your Polymerase Team working around the clock for your welfare—hardly accidental but devastating to evolutionary theory

The Polymerase Enzyme: the End of Evolutionary Biology?

In 2014, researchers discovered previously unknown functions of the "Polymerase"[20] enzyme, finding this active marvel vital to gene health. The cited PNAS report summarized:

> *"Mammalian genomes encode about 16 distinct DNA polymerases that participate in different aspects of DNA replication, DNA repair, recombination, or bypass of DNA damage."*

This late breaking research determined these enzymes *purposely and intentionally* act to repair damaged DNA sections and a myriad of other functions. The jobs these enzymes accomplish is crucial. When a damaged portion is encountered, mRNA replication work somehow temporarily ceases, and the lesion is bypassed and signposted by a process called "translesion synthesis" initiated by these mindless bio-machines. Now considering computer technology in analogy, if such a system was implemented to secure data storage reliability (as in the case of RAID back-up hard disk arrays), we would applaud the genius who designed such, hardly expecting the software to magically appear after having been crafted by time and chance processes. However, in the biological world, one is instantly expected to check logic at the door and believe the impossible.

Reflecting about this biological repair system working away 24/7 for our well being, consider that if *mutations* are the integral part of the evolutionary process, why have the same organisms developed (supposedly by means of mindless evolution)? These mechanisms actually *negate* the driving force of evolution theory itself—mutations! Further, new research along the repair/edit capability has found that some bio-components actually "edit" the RNA on its way to recombine in the construction of proteins. Further demonstrating intelligence acting on matter, similar to final production-line options for a custom ordered automobile!

When we observe molecular life operating with this level of complexity, one can only marvel, is their origin truly by cosmic accidents?

It's amazing how scientists such as Dawkins, Collins, Ayala and Avice freely attribute such complexity and automation to mindless time and chance. It would seem illogical to ignore these new finds, as among this number are several competent and even brilliant scientists. It stands to reason (by discarding such evidence) these people have other motives; maybe it's along the lines of acceptance among the institutional elite or even political in nature. Has institutional science, with its prime directive to reject *any* evidence of a Creator, gone a bridge too far? Has their silent directive to keep the theologian out of science forced this abandonment of reason? In a practical sense, this author finds himself not brave enough to call any of his attractive daughters or wife a byproduct of mutations; in this fact, may we find common ground in the reasonable, lest the population of mankind suffer dearly for the sake of such "science"!

Mutations Are Real, but Generally not Good!

There are thousands of diseases caused by genetic mutations. So as the primary driving mechanism *for* creative evolution, mutations have a very poor batting average; and in truth, mutations are generally *destructive* not *constructive*. This constant stands in contradiction of evolution's most basic element, that of upward and positive design-making abilities, so key to its purported mechanism—natural selection and *mutations*. It makes far more sense to understand that a Creator designed DNA—the cell and these associated repair systems just as a matter of reason. They're no accident and must be reasoned to represent intentional, creative acts of a God!

Video: Human/Chimp DNA Contradictions: https://vimeo.com/102354414

Fig. 5 The Adam and Eve[21] controversy:
what does the science really tell us?

The Adam and Eve Controversy—Just Two or Thousands?

Population geneticist Dr. Francisco Ayala recently argued that modern genetics disprove that just two individuals started the human race as the Bible teaches. Ayala (a member of the National Academy of Sciences, decidedly pro-evolution organization) used sequence information from HLA genes in this study, concluding that there were 32 possible HLA types involved in human ancestry, possibly representing an initial population of 4,000 or so individuals and not just two. Ayala's findings were widely published as proof positive that the Bible was scientifically in error and therefore mythological regarding a *real* Adam and Eve. Other high level scientists also chimed in, such as BioLogos President Darrel Faulk, stating: "There was never a time when there was a single first couple, two people who were the progenitors of the entire human race."[23] Ayala's conclusions were widely published in the mainstream media, books and scientific articles, even in Christian circles. At the onset, it looked like an open and shut case against those who believe the Bible to be literal and authoritative as far as Adam and Eve go.

Challenging these finds we have MIT geneticist and microbiologist Dr. Ann Gauger, who became suspicious of Ayala's conclusions based on the object gene picked for his study. In her rebuttal found in the volume *Science & Human Origins* (Discovery Institute Press, 2012), Gauger states these genes were: "guaranteed to give an overestimate" of the host population size.[24] According to Gauger, previous research determined there were actually only seven such indicator genes, down from Ayala's 32. After an exhaustive study (sponsored by the Discovery Institute of Seattle, WA), Gauger made an amazing discovery. Her conclusion: "There are just *five* basic versions of the HLA haplotype. Three appear to be ancient, pre-dating any supposed evolutionary split between chimps and humans, and two are more recent (some time before or after the putative most recent common ancestor of primates and humans, depending on where you draw the line..) [and] it is possible that *four or fewer* of those haplotypes pre-date our supposed divergence from chimps." Her summary refutation:

> *This is a remarkable reversal...what once seemed to be a rock-solid argument against the existence of a first couple has now dwindled considerably...one thing is clear right now: Adam and Eve have not been disproven by science, and those who claim otherwise are misrepresenting the scientific evidence.*
> —Dr. Ann Gauger, 2012

Gauger's conclusion: "This is a remarkable reversal; what once seemed to be a rock-solid argument against the existence of a first couple has now dwindled considerably. *The genetic analysis indicates that a first couple is possible.* At the very least it is fair to say that HLA haplotype diversity cannot rule out two first parents."[25] Gauger goes on to summarize: "One thing is clear right now: Adam and Eve have not been disproven by science, and those who claim otherwise are misrepresenting the scientific evidence." (Cited ref. p. 121)

To date, Dr. Gaugers' claims stand undisputed, but it's no big deal to Ayala and colleagues, as the mainstream media seems content to keep the other side of the story under wraps. Likely the last thing Dr. Ayala and friends want is a debate, silence on the subject working quite well for them. The Bible tells us: *"One man's story seems true until another comes and questions him"* (Proverbs 18:7). Certainly Gauger and Luskin's exposés of these popularized accounts are telling, but as in the example of the Human-Chimp DNA non-alignments, their counter will likely remain sidelined by the media and generally ignored by institutional science.

The Motors

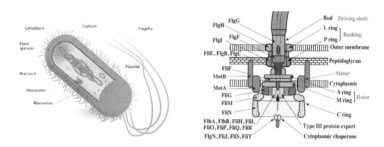

Fig. 6 Single cells are found to be unbelievably complex,
like this E. coli with its complex axial shaft motor, (RH) fueled by *protons!*

The simplest life forms known are the single cell prokaryotes, such as E. coli in the image above. These cells have one to six million codon letters in their DNA and use the same language convention common to all life forms. It has been known for years that E. coli and many other single cells incorporate *proton* (hydrogen ion) powered motors, found to be the most *efficient axial engine in the world*. Most have about 32 integrated parts versus approximately 24 used in electric motors designed by man. A new type, investigated by the Japanese[26] at Osaka University in 2012, the *MO-1* (*Pyrococ-cus furiosus*), shocked the science world when these were found to have *seven* such motors interconnected by a *24 gear drive!* Each motor incorporates components labeled "stator," "rotor" and "coils" (as in AC motors) and sport an anti-lock sensor system interconnected to each "coil."

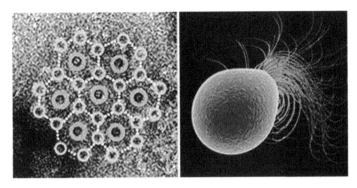

Fig. 7 Right: the MO-1 7 motor, 24 gear single cell bacteria;
Left: electron imaging highlighting the power train output (7 motors in orange)
(Image Juanfang Ruan, etal 11-2012 Osaka University)[26]

These motors prevent cavitation and improve propeller efficiency using loop feedback sensing, (like an anti-skid brake system on modern vehicles) and incorporate a plethora of other complex bio-mechanism's, including an iron based magnetic direction sensor!*

The motors can be stopped by moving a magnet near them, have forward and reverse gears, and some types spin at speeds up to 100,000 RPM. Think of the intelligence required to create this free-shaft, bio-electric motor, starting out as a glob of proteins capable of replicating in seconds! The micro-tolerances between stationary and moving micro-parts are technically perfect, providing the exact spacing required for water lubrication of the spinning parts. How can one expect the accidents of evolution to invent such a perfect machine? These motors are so tiny they weren't discovered until computer imaging advanced to the present state. Of late, millions are being expended world-wide in efforts to unravel the mysteries of these devices, but alas, man may only observe and marvel.**

50,000 Attempts and Still No Evolution!

As E. coli are said to be among the earliest life forms, yet contain such marvelous and complex motors, one must ask the question: what pre-dated them? Where are their intermediate forms of development, and how was undirected, mindless chemistry responsible for their origin? For those of rea-son, such evidence points to only one option—a powerful and all knowing Creator God.

The subject of a 30 year 50,000 generation study at the University of Michigan, our featured E. coli bacteria were exposed to every conceivable environment in controlled laboratory conditions, this in effort to fast-track and hopefully observe "evolutionary" change. The results? The bacteria were found to resist any biological change whatsoever, the "evolution" discovered totaled a tiny (and previously verified) minor change in diet, and finally—size! This research, which was crafted to prove and study mutational change, essentially *falsified evolution theory*, yet little has been mentioned about the true implications of these findings, the director mentioning the "evolution hypothesis." [27]

*Important Motor Videos: https://www.youtube.com/watch?v=kDPcg59AYZ8
https://www.youtube.com/watch?v=iJ1i_vMrlEc#action=share
https://www.youtube.com/watch?v=6JacathQfoI

**For more on the motors:
http://www.genesisalive.com/the-question-of-complexity.html

Fig. 8 The earth, moon, and sun relationship is fantastically complex

Observations of the Heavens

The moon takes exactly 27.3 days to rotate on its axis a single time, exactly the amount of time it takes to orbit earth. This motion also generates a gyroscopic effect, assisting better orbital stability, unique compared to other moons in the solar system. The moon is 400 times smaller and 400 times closer to earth than the sun, allowing for an eclipse to take place. (Note the four *Blood Moons* taking place in 2014 & 2015.) Consider all the possible sizes of these orbs and the spacing required for this phenomenon to occur by chance. Our moon also sits at the perfect distance to properly affect tides;

otherwise, much of earth's habitable and agricultural land area would be awash daily. The resultant ocean currents (caused by lunar tides) maintain the vibrant sea life earth enjoys; otherwise, our beautiful oceans would quickly become giant stagnate ponds. One should never take these factors for granted; they are designed and not accidental.

Is the Solar System Ancient?

Is the solar system ancient? We now know the moon moves away from earth's orbit about one and a half inches per year. Extrapolated mathematically, the moon would have been in closer orbit only millions of years ago. There's no evidence suggesting the moon has been closer by view of descending shorelines (as increased tidal effect caused by a closer moon would create) so the moon's orbital escape is one proof that invalidates the notion that our solar system has been around for great eons of time. Exactly how long ago was the formation of this planet? Many uniform chronometers suggest the earth and planets are young. New data concerning magnetic decay rates among the other planets and earth suggest a young solar system, especially when we consider the magnetic decay of Mercury, whose magnetic field 1/2 life has been found to be less than 500 years! This measurement has been confirmed by multiple space probe flybys, and was predicted by scientist Dr. Russ Humphreys,[28] who used the Bible as a basis for his calculations. Earth's magnetic field is also decaying at such a high rate that life could not exist in today's form only 20,000 years past.[29][30] Earth's decay and 1/2 life (a mere 1400 years*) is so dramatic that aviation maps must be updated every 90 days, this to keep aircraft compasses in synchronization with earth's fast decaying magnetic field! This fact has lately created some concern in government science circles. (See quote in Appendix XIX about this topic.)

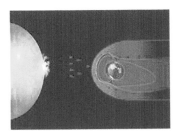 

Fig. 9 Earth's magnetic field protects us, but is running down
at an alarming rate.[27] We should never take such protection for granted.

Note that all other planets in our solar system are uninhabitable; the life sustaining capability of earth is a unique phenomenon. Consider the mineral resources found on earth that make life simpler and more enjoyable on this planet, mentioned early in Genesis in a positive sense.

We must also acknowledge that only *trace* amounts of harmful elements exist on earth (like uranium or arsenic), which in quantity would contaminate the planet. Rationally speaking, earth represents a coordinated set of creative acts and not accidental products of time and chance processes.

*Dr. Thomas Barnes, past Professor of Physics at The University of Texas at El Paso, noted that between 1835 and 1965, geophysicists made some 26 measurements of the magnetic dipole moment of the earth's magnetic field. When plotted against time these data points modeled a decay curve which Barnes used to calculate a "half-life" of earths field of only 1,400 years. On this basis he concluded that the earth's magnetic field was less than 10,000 years old.[31]

When we observe our perfectly synchronized solar system of sun, earth and moon, we see these working together, not apart, in providing earth with a livable range of temperatures, wind, tides, protective atmosphere and liquid water. The only reasonable conclusion is that a Super Intelligence formed our wonderful little corner of the galaxy to contain life and not accidents! In summary, the logical conclusion is that these orbs are the handiwork of an intelligence larger and more powerful than we can imagine. It is after this understanding, our ancestors coined the word God or *Mighty One!*

Most astronomers agree that our universe is run with phenomenal mathematical precision, something no accident can produce through randomness. So when man looks out at the stars, he sees only magnificent power and fantastic images of artistic beauty, not random, order-less matter somehow floating in space. These bodies proclaim as the Bible states, "The Heavens declare the Glory of God" (Psalm 19:1) and nothing less. Astronomers tell us no matter which direction the Hubble telescope is pointed, it appears the galaxies are moving *away* from us on all quarters, according to the "Red Shift" signature. This fact has perplexed scientists for years, befouling many theories about the origin of the universe—but not the biblical one! See more in Appendix XIX.

The Atmosphere

Designed to protect us from the sun's harmful rays and maintain life giving air, earth's atmosphere also provides a reflector of light; otherwise, our globe would be shrouded in the lunar darkness of the moon. Meteorite showers would be deadly if not for our atmosphere constantly protecting us from their bombardments like a shield from a science fiction movie. Consider also the fact that *if* our solar system were billions of years old, these meteorites and comets should have expired long ago, since their life cycles are found to be quite short.[32] Since there are no new sources of these projectiles, could they be fallout from the original creative work of Providence, like batter around the parameter of a mixing bowl? Many qualified scientists suggest so. (See Appendix XIX.) In summary of these evidences, we find the Bible speaks a most accurate description of origins, expounded in these simple yet profound passages in the first verses of Genesis:

In the beginning God created the heaven and the earth... And the Spirit of God moved upon the face of the waters. And God said, Let there be light, and there was light. And God saw the light, that it was good (Genesis 1:1-4 KJV).

From these words we understand that the universe, solar system, and earth were formed by Creation. *Bara* in the Hebrew means God manifested an entity from a non-entity. He then combined light (energy) and water, the Bible tells us, creating earth (or *eth* in Hebrew, meaning "substance"). Note the word "light" in Hebrew actually relates to *fire,* meaning *all energy* with caloric value and not just light photons. So within the passages *"In the beginning God created the heaven and the earth"* and *"Let there be light!"* we find the two most up to date and valid statements concerning origins ever written!

"There is but one climate known to the ancient fossil world as revealed by the plants and animals entombed in the rocks, the climate was a mantle of Spring-Like Loveliness which seems to have prevailed continuously over the whole globe" **Prof Alfred Wallace**

Fig. 10 We live in a masterpiece of God's handiwork, not a field of accidents.

Energy Balance, Matter and the Universe
—the Four Physical Forces and Creation:

1. Gravitational Force
2. Electromagnetic Force
3. Strong Nuclear Force
4. Weak Nuclear Force

Physicists understand that all matter exhibits energy and nuclear balance. For example, if the forces of gravity were slightly smaller, supernova explosions would blow apart our galaxy piece by piece in short order.

At the atomic (atom) level, specific boundaries in nuclear force must be maintained. If the particle attraction level is too low, most all the elements known on the periodic chart would come apart, leaving only hydrogen to maintain its substance. If the nuclear energy force is too high, hydrogen would cease to exist and there would be no water.

Blue Stars: Stars generate energy by the process of nuclear fusion. A star like the sun has enough hydrogen fuel to keep it burning for billions of years. But that's not the case with blue stars. Blue stars are larger than our sun and approximately 200,000 times brighter, expending fuel much faster, and thus cannot last billions of years. Based on their known brightness, most blue stars cannot last more than one million years before running out of fuel—a problem for a long-age universe.

Privileged Species, for a most informative video on this subject:
https://www.youtube.com/watch?v=VoI2ms5UHWg

Blue Stars:
http://www.icr.org/article/blue-stars-confirm-recent-creation/

[1] http://www.evolutionnews.org/2013/12/genome_composes080111.html

[2] http://www.forerunner.com/forerunner/X0714_Lucy_fails_test.html. See also Lubenow, Marvin *Bones of Contention* Baker Books 2004 p. 60, 66

[3] *Scientific American* vol. 311 iss. 3 2014 http://www.scientificamerican.com/article/tiny-genetic-differences-between-humans-and-other-primates-pervade-the-genome/

[4] Institute for Creation Research Paper www.icr.org/article/evaluating-human-chimp-dna-myth-new/ Link: Evaluating the Human-Chimp DNA Myth—New Research Data Also see: www.bio-complexity.org/ojs/index.php/main/article/view/BIO-C.2011.1 Dr. Ann Gauger

[5] Jeanson, Nathaniel T. Acts & Facts Vol. 43 N. 12 De. 2014 www.ICR.org

[6] www.scientificamerican.com/article/human-chimp-gene-gap-wide/ Dec. 2006

[7] Francis Collins, *The Language of God* (New York: Free Press, 2006), 127–28.

[8] Gauger, Ann; Axe, Douglas; Luskin, Casey *Science and Human Origins* Disc Inst Press. p. 86

[9] Gauger, Ann; Axe, Douglas; Luskin, Casey *Science and Human Origins* Disc Inst Press. p. 88

[10] Sternberg Shapiro, "How Repeated Retroelements Format Genome Function," 108–16 cited in 9.

[11] Nature 447 (2007): 799–816. www.ncbi.nlm.nih.gov/pmc/articles/PMC2212820/ pdf/ nihms27513.pdf

[12] Rick Weiss, "Intricate Toiling Found in Nooks of DNA." *Washington Post* June 14, 2007

[13] Wells, Jonathan, *The Myth of Junk DNA* Discovery Institute Press, Seattle WA (2012): citing Laura Poliseno, etal "A coding-independent function of gene and pseudogene mRNAs regulates tumour biology," Nature 465 (2010): 1033–1038.

[14] ibid 10. Luis M. Mendes Soares & Juan Valcárcel, "The expanding transcriptome: the genome as the 'Book of Sand.'" *EMBO Journal* 25 (2006): 923–931. Available online with registration (2011) at http://www.nature.com/emboj/journal/v25/n5/full/7601023a.html

[15] ibid 10. Piero Carninci, Jun Yasuda & Yoshihide Hayashizaki, "Multifaceted Mammalian Transcriptome," Current Opinion in Cell Biology 20 (2008): 274–280.

[16] Gauger, Ann; Axe, Douglas; Luskin, Casey *Science and Human Origins* Disc Inst Press. p. 89

[17] Casey Luskin, *Science and Human Origins* p. 98

[18] The ENCODE Project Consortium. 2012. An integrated encyclopedia of DNA elements in the human genome. Nature. 489 (7414): 57-74

[19] *Acts & Facts*, Institute for Creation Research, Vol 43. 9 (Sept, 2014): 11 www.icr.org/i/pdf/af/af1409.pdf

[20] PNAS paper announcement: (2014): 111 (8) 2864-2865; February 14, 2014

[21] Gauger, Ann; Axe, Douglas; Luskin, Casey *Science and Human Origins* (2012-06-14): 105

[22] Ibid 18. H. A. Erlich et al., "HLA Sequence Polymorphism and the Origin of Humans," *Science* 274 (1996) 1554.

[23] Darrel Falk, "BioLogos 'Christianity Today' Editorial," June 6, 2011, http://biologos.org/blog/biologos-and-the-june-2011-christianity-today-editorial

[24] Gauger, Ann; Axe, Douglas; Luskin, Casey *Science and Human Origins* Disc Inst Press p. 112

[25] Gauger, Ann; Axe, Douglas; Luskin, Casey *Science and Human Origins* Disc Inst Press p. 117

[26] Juanfan Ruan etal, http://www.osaka-u.ac.jp/en/news/ResearchRelease/2012/11/20121127_1 downloaded 5-2015

[27] U of Michigan E. coli study exposed: http://www.noahcode.org/evolution-falsified-i.html

[28] Gauger, Ann; Axe, Douglas; Luskin, Casey *Science and Human Origins* Disc Inst Press p. 120

[29] Dr. Russ Humphreys accurately predicted the magnetism of the outer planets including Mercury in 1983, later confirmed by three space probes. Complete explanation is found in Appendix XV.

[30] Snelling, Andrew http://creation.mobi/the-earths-magnetic-field-and-the-age-of-the-earth

[31] Barnes, T.G., 1971. Decay of the earth's magnetic moment and the geochronological implications. *Creation Research Society Quarterly* 8(1):24–29

[32] CMI - creation.com/mobi cratering

2

First Earth—a World Like No Other

Fig. 11 The Magnificent *First Earth*

Over the centuries, scientists have found much evidence of the entire earth being a temperate and lush place in times past. Tropical forests and fruit trees thrived in what is now barren Siberia. Remains of redwood trees up to ten feet in diameter are found in both the Arctic and Antarctica, and fauna thrived by the millions in what is now Arctic wasteland. This was the *First Earth* that the Bible refers to, an entirely different place than today. Even the nutritional system for man and animals was different, being entirely vegetarian. According to the biblical account, God Himself declared that world to be *very good* (Genesis 1:31). These words express the concept that the First Earth and life therein were created *"as good as could be"* as translated from the original Hebrew text. So what was it like living on earth in those times, and what happened that changed it all?

As the Creator wanted nothing to do with bloodshed, concerning the food chain the Bible tells us: *"I have given you every herb bearing seed which is upon the face of the entire earth and every fruit bearing tree, for your meat"* (Genesis 1:29). This means God's original intent was that there was to be *no* bloodshed on earth. There was little fear of humans among the wild animals the text suggests; wonder, kindness and harmony filled this masterpiece called *earth!*

The Bible teaches that the First Earth was watered using a radically different hydrological system than today. As best as can be determined from the ancient writings, the method consisted of a network of underground aquifers and spring sourced rivers. Also mentioned is a morning and evening dew [that]: *"watered the surface of the entire earth"* (Genesis 2:6), eliminating the need for rain. It's probable storms were few in number and less severe in those times, though the Bible clearly states seasons existed. There is also much evidence that large forests and lush savannahs existed further north and south of their limits today. Examining the flora and fauna found in the fossil record, we see excellent markers defining the isothermal and humidity lines of the past. Trees, plants, snails and smaller animals cannot survive in certain environments, and being unable to migrate, may be mapped, helping us understand the life and climate of the *First Earth* compared to recent times.

Axel Heiberg Island and the Environment of First Earth

Alex Heiberg Island is located in the high Canadian Arctic. Here we find the remains of ancient redwood forests near the pole, their blackened stumps and petrified trunks up to 10 feet in diameter scattered across the now barren landscape. Looking at the fossils here, scientists have found that an amazing variety of warm water life existed in the former times—freshwater turtles, crocodiles, ferns, flowering plants, even rhinoceros—along with the remains of huge forests that once thrived at 82^0 N. latitude! Research scientist Hope Jahren of Johns Hopkins University commented about the past environment at Heilberg, stating: "I've always been enraptured with the idea that the earth can change so dramatically," observing how surprising it is to imagine that earth was so radically different in those times, containing such prolific life at those high latitudes.[1] Tree ring studies indicate no evidence of snowfall during the winters at Alex Heiberg, not even a frost, but a consistently mild environment with temperatures never dropping below 55^0 Fahrenheit, where arctic winters of minus 50^0 F temperatures rage today! Scientists speculate the average humidity was probably around 65-70%, and according to isotope analysis of wood samples, the temperature never dropped below 14^0 Celsius or 57^0 Fahrenheit. And note that this is only a few hundred miles from the North Pole itself! Near identical forests and fauna are found in Antarctica, including large animals such as dinosaurs and again, the redwood trees!

Addressing these conditions, Prof. Alfred Wallace, in his volume *Geo-graphical Distribution of Animals,* comments assertively on the climate of this early earth: "There is but one climate known to the ancient fossil world as revealed by the plants and animals entombed in the rocks, and the climate was a mantle of *spring-like loveliness* which seems to have prevailed continuously over the whole globe...that it was so warmed effectively and continuously is a matter of fact" [2] [emphasis added].

There is but one climate known to the ancient fossil world as revealed by the plants and animals entombed in the rocks, and the climate was a mantle of spring-like loveliness which seems to have prevailed continuously over the whole globe.

—Professor Alfred Wallace

More recently, nature writer Quirin Schiermeier observed: "The Arctic Ocean used to be so warm it was practically Mediterranean, an international drilling team has found."[3] Alex Kirby in the BBC article "North Pole 'Was Once Subtropical'"[4] noted that fossilized algae in ice cores "show the sea temperature was once about 20^0C (about 68^0F), instead of the average now of $-1.5C$"(30^0F). These findings further correlate with a University of Colorado paper explaining the discovery of pine needles, these found beneath 10,000 feet of ice in Greenland!

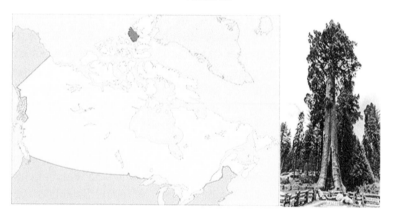

- North Pole

Fig. 12 Alex Heiberg Island, (upper center in red) where redwoods 10 feet in diameter, tropical flora and large mammals once thrived, now a frozen wasteland. A similar ecosystem is found in Antarctica.
(Image Wikipedia 3.0 by Connormah[5])

Fig. 13 Barron Von Wrangell's "Adamovchina Wood" is also heaped high along Siberian North Sea islands, mingled with the carcasses of thousands of mammoth, bison, horse and hippo; forests that once existed where none exist within 1,000+ miles today. They were charred, uprooted and stacked hundreds of feet high as a result of the *Flood*. (Public domain image, Center for Scientific Creation www.creationscience.com)

The Great Forests of the North—Gone Forever

When naturalists from the west ventured into Siberia, they were met with the same evidence of a different earth across those vast quarters. Quoting these first explorers, we are met with telling evidence that another world once existed there, now vanished and replaced with a new one. Baron Von Wrangell, explorer, geographer and leader of the Russian American Company comments on that place: "On the tundra, equally remote from the present line of forest, among the steep sandy banks of the lakes and rivers, are found large birch trees, complete with bark, branches, and roots. At the first glance they appear to have been well preserved by the earth, but on digging them up they are found to be in a thorough state of decay. On being lighted they glow, but never emit a flame; nevertheless, the inhabitants of the neighborhood use them as fuel, and designate these subterranean trees as Adamovchina, or of Adam's time."[6]

Wrangell also found the remains of oxen, sheep, horses, oxen and buffalo on Kootenai and New Siberia Islands, observing that these animals formerly lived there in large numbers. He commented that in the present climate such fauna would be unable to survive, the winters too harsh, nor could they find sufficient nourishment on the present tundra. He concluded these same animals were contemporary with the mammoth, whose remains are found in every part of the island, and deduced a milder climate must have prevailed there in the past, mentioning partially fossilized trees.[7]

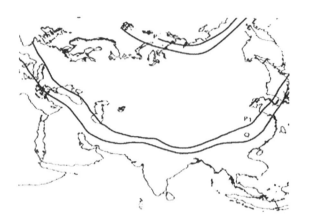

Fig. 14 Pre- and post-flood line of palms across Siberia.
The temperate shift south is notable, showing palms once prolific
along the north Arctic coast following east to Alaska.
(After M. Schwartzbach)

Professor of Geology Martin Schwartbach[8] of the University of Cologne, determined a dramatic southward shift of palm tree growth from the Arctic Ocean southward had occurred (see above map), supportive that the climate was moderate in the past, just as the Bible teaches.

Adolf Erman, in his *Travels in Siberia* (1848) also relates such of this past environment: "It cannot escape notice, that as we go nearer to the coast, the deposits of wood below the earth, and also the deposits of bones which accompany the wood, increase in extent and frequency. Here, beneath the soil of Yakutsk, the trunks of birch trees lie scattered, only singly, but on the other hand they form such great and well-stored strata under the tundras, the Yukagirs there never think of using any other fuel than fossil wood. Thus in New Siberia, on the declivities facing the south lie hills 250 or 300 feet high formed of drift wood, the ancient origin of which, as well as of the fossil wood in the tundras, anterior to the history of the earth in its present state, striking at once even the trees Adamovchina, or Adamic things."[9]

Henry H. Howorth, author of *The Mammoth and the Flood* (1887), spent over a decade in separate expeditions in the Arctic and comments here on the findings of Finnish explorer Adolf Nordenskjold, first to sail the entire north coast of Russia aboard the *Vega* in 1878: "Speaking of the Yenissei tundra, in summer are completely free of snow, but at a limited depth from the surface the ground is continually frozen." He adds that in it mammoth remains are found, along with them masses of old driftwood originating from the "Mammoth Period," known by the Siberian natives under the distinctive name of "Noah's Wood."[10]

Well-known French scientist and naturalist Louis Figurer writes of this environment in his volume *The World Before the Deluge* (1872), telling us: "It is a remarkable circumstance that conditions of equable and warm climate, combined with humidity, do not seem to have been limited to any one part of the globe, but the temperature of the whole seems to have been nearly the same in very different latitudes. From the equatorial regions up to Melville Island, in the Arctic Ocean, where in our days eternal frost prevails from Spitsbergen (the most northerly island in Norway) to the center of Africa, the carboniferous flora is identically the same. When nearly the same plants are found in Greenland and Guinea; when the same species, now extinct, are met with of equal development at the equator as at the pole, *we cannot but admit that at this period the temperature of the globe was nearly alike everywhere. What we now call climate was unknown in these geological times. There seems to have been then only one climate over the whole globe*"[11] [emphasis added].

As deducted from the biblical narrative and supported by the observations of these early naturalists, apparently the most beautiful vacation spot on earth today was common in the *First Earth*. The animals were likely not aggressive and food abounded. The mention of disease or sickness is absent in the accounts of early Genesis, and people are recorded to have lived for hundreds of years. (See the Patriarch Age table in Appendix I.) Chemical analysis of fossilized nataloiud shells and the air aperture's of large insects suggest the atmosphere was oxygen rich and ocean chemistry much different than today. This atmosphere was also likely hyperbolic (of higher barometric pressure and oxygen content), supporting much larger life forms. For example, fossil hawk sized insects with tiny breathing holes have been discovered, these creatures being oxygen starved in today's air.[12]

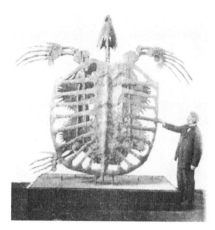

Fig. 15 Animals grew to sizes much larger than today in the First Earth,
this due to a higher oxygen content, lower solar radiation and as
Josephus tells us, better quality food

Hugh Falconer, British naturalist of the 19th century and noted paleon-tologist, is credited with discovering the tortoise *Colossochelys Atlas* in India, its shell measuring 15 x 20 feet in size. The Bible teaches those people also lived for hundreds of years, in the case of Methuselah, 969 (Noah's grandfather) and over 950 for Noah himself!

The Good Life or "Golden Age"

One could enjoy this "good as could be" life that included sunrise and sunsets that were likely color enriched by the moisture laden air (the "evening and morning dew"), possibly creating glorious rays of soothing light at those times. At the higher latitudes, you could travel and enjoy a cool summer retreat, observing the prolific wildlife and scenery. William Winston in his "A New Theory of the Earth" (1737) and much closer to the ancient writers than we, noted that this time was called "The Golden Age" by historians, that the air was much purer, agriculture more productive, and people healthier. (Opt. cited p. 256, 7)

Geologist George McCready Price Writes of This Age

George McCready Price states, "It would be quite useless to go through the whole fossiliferous series in order, for there is not a single system which does not have coral limestone or other evidence of a mild climate way up north, most systems having such rock in the lands which skirt the very pole itself. The limestone and coal beds of the carboniferous period are the nearest known rocks to the North Pole. They crop out all around the polar basis; and from the dip of these beds, they must underlie the polar sea itself…they uniformly testify that a warm climate has in former times prevailed over the whole globe."[13]

Past Harvard professor of Geology Dr. James Dwight Dana writes: "The coral reefs of the Oolite in England consist of corals of the same group with the reef-making species of the existing tropics." From this fact Dana argues that the mean temperature of the waters of those high latitudes must have been approximately "69 degrees F,"[14] a fact confirmed of late.

One concept suggests that the warm ocean currents were distributed more evenly and the land masses warmed by them, similar to the actions of the Gulf Stream and Japanese Current today. (See Fig. 16.) There is strong evidence that North America had a similar Gulf Stream transecting north and south, this from Texas north through central Canada, creating a circulation path for warm currents moving thermal energy from the warmer equatorial oceans toward the pole. Add to this the higher moisture content of the atmosphere and we may be close to the answer.

Atlantis, Josephus, and the Deep Ocean Beaches

According to William Whiston, quoting Josephus, states tradition among the ancient historians tell us that Atlantis was not a city but a *continent,* larger than Africa and Asia. Josephus further mentions: "At the Deluge, God changed the Continent into *Sea.*" Noting the findings of the 1949 exploration project dubbed "Atlantis," researchers located all kinds of formations known to the terrestrial beneath the waves, even sand beaches, now covered in thou-sands of feet of water in deeply entombed silence. The lead scientist on the project, Maurice Ewing of Columbia University, reported on these deep ocean beaches: "One was the discovery of a prehistoric beach sand… brought up in one case from a depth of two and the other nearly three and one half miles, far from any place where beaches exist today." Ewing goes on in the report to state:

Either the land must have sunk two to three miles, or the sea once must have been two or three miles lower than now. Either conclusion is startling. —Prof. Maurice Ewing, 1949

Note that sand is produced by wave action pulverizing sandstone or other rock to tiny bits. Ewing continues, "Either the land must have sunk two to three miles, or the sea once must have been two or three miles lower than now. Either conclusion is startling. If the sea was once two miles lower, where could all the extra water have gone?" Ocean bottoms are typically made up of a fine silt or ooze that accumulates over the centuries. Sand occurs on sea coasts, not ocean bottoms over 1000 miles offshore as in the case of these finds.[15]

Harvard Professor Reginald Daly, geologist of the same place, claimed since the 1920's that "a recent worldwide sinking of ocean level [occurred] about 3500 years ago" (Daly, *Our Mobile Earth,* 1926, pp. 177-179). Note that according to Velikovsky, Professor Philip H. Kuenen of Leyden University confirmed Daly's findings, mentioning: "the time can be fixed at roughly 3000 to 3500 years ago" (aligning with the biblical Flood date) and further. "In thirty-odd years following Daly's first paper, many further instances have been recorded by a number of investigators the world over, so that this recent shift is now well established" (*Marine Geology,* 1950, p. 538). Researchers in unity mention an ash layer in the ocean depths, these covering hundreds of thousands of square miles of seafloor suggesting a cosmic origin. Their deduction related to the high concentration of nickel and manganese associated with them, hinting at some sort of aerial initiated catastrophe. (Note that mammoth tusks mined in Siberia have been found to be peppered with nickel projectiles, an element often associated meteorites.)

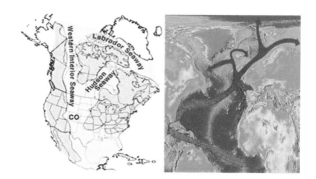

Fig. 16 Possible North American seaway (left) vs today's Gulf Stream
(Images Wikipedia commons lic. 2.0)

The Gulf Stream is approximately 60 miles wide and nearly 4,000 miles long. It moves northward at about 6 miles per hour, its massive heat caloric value warming 1/4 of earth's northern latitudes. The same may be said of the Japanese Current of the Pacific. The North American Seaway pictured LH (thought to exist in the past) likely had the same effect, moving warm water toward the polar zone of First Earth.

The Eastern Gulf Stream represents an excellent example of this concept. Sixty miles wide and more than 4,000 miles long, this moving body of warm water from the equator moves its heat caloric content northward, creating the mild winter climates of Britain and Europe. For example in southern England (the same latitude as north central Canada), the winters are mild with little ice and snow, allowing vegetables to thrive in long growing seasons. According to one source: "The noticeable effect of the Gulf Stream and the strong westerly winds on Europe occurs along the Norwegian coast. Northern parts of Norway lie close to the Arctic, most of which is covered with ice and snow in winter, however, almost all of Norway's coast remains free of ice and snow throughout the year. Weather systems warmed by the Gulf Stream also affect Northern Europe, warming the climate behind the Scandinavian mountains."[16] On the other hand at the same latitude in central Canada (for example at Edmonton, Alberta) the temperature could be minus 50 degrees below zero, over *one hundred degrees* cooler than in Wales the same day of the year!

On the Pacific coast, the Japanese Current has the same influence on the climate of coastal British Columbia and Alaska, influencing their moderate winter seasons and maintaining important Northern ports, like that at Valdez, Alaska ice free. Deducting from the large marine reptile fossils found north and south in the central United States running north through Canada, scientists think a "seaway" once existed there, which could have contained a stream as described, dramatically influencing the climate of the entire region. We can assume God may have repeated this design for other parts of earth as well, a piece of the larger puzzle helping us to understand this past climate. At any rate, these together preclude accidents responsible for their origin but point to a wise Creator acting upon earth's form for our good. Without the extremes of today's weather systems, the oceans could have been calm enough to sail thousands of miles by wind and current power using small craft without worry. Words fail to describe what God calls *"very good"* in that pristine first world. We may only speculate the conditions of those times and see this as God's perfect gift to all mankind. Knowing this, what signatory event could have caused the radical departure from the world that then was, to now?

Another possibility that contributed to this mild climate is the "canopy theory." This concept suggests that the earth was originally surrounded by an additional atmospheric layer and/or integrated as part of a general air mixture but lost in the flood event. Such would have acted to filter harmful rays and worked to trap and/or reduce the oxygen escape rate, creating a hyperbolic (oxygenated) effect. Our current oxygen mixture in the atmosphere is approximately 18%, but in those times it could have been much higher (although too high a percentage of oxygen creates an ignition fire hazard). Considering the additional world-wide growing area creating more oxygen, one may better understand why earth's atmosphere would have been far better than today's.

Such a canopy is also thought to have trapped heat nearer the surface, causing a "greenhouse effect." Speaking to the effect of moisturized atmosphere upon the earth, in the book *The Genesis Flood* (1961), Morris and Whitcomb quote Harold K. Blum who tells us: "Absorption of the outgoing radiation is largely due to water vapor, just as the glass of a greenhouse tends to raise the temperature of the interior, the water vapor tends to raise that of the earth's surface below it."[17]

Recent NASA satellite data confirmed this finding: "Using recent NASA satellite data, researchers have estimated more precisely than ever the heat-trapping effect of water in the air, validating the role of the gas as a critical component of climate change."[18]

In consideration of the biblical statement *"but a mist went up from the earth and watered the whole face of the ground"* (Genesis 2:6), we have another clue based upon known observations, helping us to understand the environmental conditions of those times. The narrative proceeds to describe the spring head of the four rivers of Eden, and the magnificent beauty of the Garden. It seems clear that this wonderful climate was not limited to Eden but prevailed globally before the Flood.

Relating to the index foliage at the high latitudes of this age, Scottish Professor James Geikie in his *Historical Geology* tells us: "There grew in Switzerland at this time a most luxuriant vegetation, embracing many forms now only met with in warm latitudes such as palms, cinnamon trees, etc., along with which were associated many species of maple, plane-trees, cypresses, sarsaparilla, etc. Altogether, nearly 500 species of plants have been found in the Upper Molasse, and more than 800 insects. It is certainly wonderful that...a climate existed within the arctic regions so mild and genial as to nourish there beeches, oaks, planes, poplars, walnuts, limes, magnolias, hazel, holly, blackthorn, log wood, hawthorn, ivy, vines, and many evergreens, besides numerous conifers, among which was the Sequoia, allied to the gigantic Wellingtonia (Sequoia) of California. This ancient vegetation has been traced up to within eleven degrees of the pole, and there can be no doubt that the trees actually grew where they are found, for their roots are [found] penetrating the ancient soil."[19]

This striking discovery proves that in the days when the mammoths and rhinoceroses lived in northern Siberia, these desolate islands were covered with great forests, and bore a luxuriant vegetation.
—Immanuel Velkovski, *Earth in Upheaval 1955*

The Polar Savannah

A number of early observers attest to the fact that these upper latitudes contained a startling plethora of fauna and flora now left in a frozen state, mingled with logs and sands. The existence of this drift in the highest latitudes of Siberia up to the New Siberia Islands suggest huge forests and savanna existed in those places, even to the pole itself, later destroyed by some cataclysm and deluged, stacking the carcasses of a myriad of large quadrupeds in heaps mingled with tree trunks stacked hundreds of feet high, even creating islands in some places. Citing Whitley in the 1910 volume of the *Journal of the Philosophical Society of Great Britain*, Velikovsky in his classic work *Earth in Upheaval* (1955)[20] tells us: "This striking discovery proves that in the days when the mammoths and rhinoceroses lived in northern Siberia, these desolate islands were covered with great forests, and bore a luxuriant vegetation." Such evidence leaves little doubt that the polar regions experienced moderate climates in those times (and likely dry land existed at the North Pole), leaving open the possibility that the lands could have been as mild as the African Savannah and just as populated.

Note also that shell fossils and flora found in Europe suggest that the Mediterranean and interior Europe experienced much milder summer seasons, including lower humidity (an uncomfortable factor in those places today). The fossil life forms of the past, though unable to tolerate living in these locations today, were found thriving there in the past.

The Biblical Model Better Explains These Observations

A *"very good"* earth suggests you could live comfortably in most places lightly attired (as Adam and Eve first demonstrated), play in the warm water, and enjoy the oxygen rich air and better food (as Josephus tells us). One could find a cool drink from spring sourced streams originating from the massive underground aquifers, these that cycled and purified the waters. The "Hydroplate Theory" as put forward by Dr. Walt Brown[21] suggests these aquifers were "pumped" by lunar action that slightly flexed the earth's crust each six hours, pushing and pulling the water throughout earth in pump fashion. This process would displace and cycle the water through huge interconnected caverns beneath the earth's crust (empty caverns not an uncommon feature found around the earth today, now unused). Late research[22] has determined through tree matter analysis that the water supporting some northern fossil tree life had a higher oxygen[18] content, potentially explained by water traveling for some distances across (or under) ground, as this isotope is rare in today's hydrological system of evaporation and rainfall.

The Antediluvian Calendar Was 360 Days

Interestingly, it seems the post-flood ancients did all possible to maintain a 360 day year divided by the 30 day months of the lunar cycle, today out of synchronization with the old. This is true of the Egyptian, Greek, Persian, Latin and Chaldean Empires, suggesting that the calendar of the antediluvians was composed of 12 each 30 day months, and some later event threw the cycle off. (Note also that the calendar reigns of the pre-flood kings unearthed in the cuneiform reflect that the lunar and solar cycles formerly matched.) It seems the calendar of Adam was five days shorter than ours, tremendously impacting earth's solar cycle and hence the climate of the First Earth compared to today.

Whiston tells us: "At the time of Ofiris and Typhoon (Noah)…at about the time of the Deluge, there happened such an alteration both in the month and the year, that the moon lost a 70th part of each day and the Sun *gained* it; whereby the Lunar Year became above 5 days shorter and the Solar Year 5 days longer, wherefore since the solar is now more than 365 days and the Lunar more than 355."[23] His summary explanation: our planet was nearly obliterated by a foreign body, namely a *comet*. His findings were supported by the most conservative mathematicians of the day including Newton; more of his hypothesis will be presented later in Chapter 4.

People were caught by surprise in the Flood, assuming all would go on as it had been and taking life for granted. The Bible records another series of earth shaking events will come upon the earth (see Matthew 24, Acts 2 and Revelation 6), where man will face a final judgment. The lesson? We should never take life on this living planet for granted.

As Revelation 6:12-17 from the Bible reads:

> *I looked when He opened the sixth seal, and behold, there was a great earthquake; and the sun became black as sackcloth of hair, and the moon became like blood. And the stars of heaven fell to the earth, as a fig tree drops its late figs when it is shaken by a mighty wind. Then the sky receded as a scroll when it is rolled up, and every*

mountain and island was moved out of its place. And the kings of the earth, the great men, the rich men, the commanders, the mighty men, every slave and every free man, hid themselves in the caves and in the rocks of the mountains, and said to the mountains and rocks, "Fall on us and hide us from the face of Him who sits on the throne and from the wrath of the Lamb! For the great day of His wrath has come, and who is able to stand?"

Along with this impressive and much more prolific earth, God also gave a special and significant union to His crowning achievement creation of man, that of love and marriage, the greatest and most important gift of all. In concluding these descriptions, such was this place God made for the first couple and their offspring, *created* to share and enjoy. People are *the central* reason why this Paradise and Eden were formed, but as always, living in this place came with reasonable boundaries. These were soon broken, and in measures, this wonderful Eden *lost*.

[1] http: //news.nationalgeographic.com/news/2002/03/0326_020326_TVredwoods.html
[2] Alfred, Russell W, *The Geographical Distribution of Animals*, Harper and Brothers 1876 vol. 1
Schiermeier, Quirin (2004), "North Pole Once Enjoyed Mediterranean Climate" http://www.nature.com/news/2004/040906/full/040906-8.html.
Kirby, Alex (2004) "North Pole 'was once subtropical,'" BBC News http://news.bbc.co.uk/1/hi/sci/tech/3631764.stm.
[5]http://commons.wikimedia.org/wiki/File:Axel_Heiberg_Island,_Canada.svg#/media/File:Axel_Heib erg_Island,_Canada.svg
[6] Wrangell, *Journey Along the Northern Coastline of Siberia and the Arctic Ocean* Id. 129.
[7] ibid, Wrangell 124
[8] Schwarzbach, Martin *Das Klima der Vorzeit* 1974 Stuttgart p. 210
[9] Erman, Adolf, *Travels in Siberia* 1848 vol. ii p. 379
[10] *Voyage of the Vega*, I p.380, 381, from Howorth, *The Mammoth and the Flood*, 1887
[11] As quoted from *Moses and Geology, or The Harmony of the Bible with Science*, p. 166.
[12] http://news.sciencemag.org/2012/06/where-have-hawk-sized-insects-gone
[13] Price, George M. *The New Geology*, pp. 652 ff.
[14] Dana *Manual of Geology*, p. 793
[15] As cited from Velikovsky, Immanuel (2012-12-01). *Earth in Upheaval* 1955 (Kindle Locations 1904-1915). Paradigma Ltd. Kindle Edition 2012 . M. Ewing: »New Discoveries on the Mid- Atlantic Ridge, *National Geographic Magazine*, Vol. XCVI, No. 5 (November 1949). Used by permission
[16]Gulf Stream - Wikipedia: *Localized Effects*
[17] Morris & Whitcomb *The Genesis Flood* P&R press 1961 p. 253 citing Harold K. Blum *Time's Arrow and Evolution*, Princeton University Press, 1957 p. 57
[18]http://www.nasa.gov/topics/earth/features/vapor_warming.html
[19]Geikie, James *Historical Geology* W &R Chambers pub. 1876 p. 76, 99,100
[20] Velikovsky, Immanuel *Earth in Upheaval* 1955 p. 23 used by permission
[21] Brown, Walter, Hydroplate theory http://www.creationscience.com/onlinebook/
[22] Ibid 1
[23] Whiston, William *The New Theory of the Earth* 1737 p. 180. Whiston was contemporary of Newton

3

Why the Flood Event?

Fig. 17 The Ark

The world we live in today is a post-flood world; its most magnificent beauty only an image of what God created in the beginning. As the entire universe, solar system and earth were created ultimately for people to live in and enjoy, the first inhabitants were asked by God to obey certain simple rules. But that was not all; the consequences for disobedience of these were clearly spelled out.

We all know the story of the Fall, where the chief of rebels, a being called Satan, enticed Adam and Eve into rebellion. His first recorded words were a lie: "You shall not surely die," and secondly, deception: "For God knows that in the day you eat of it your eyes will be opened and you will be like God" (Genesis 3:4-5). Lies and deception are the mark of this being; his cunning treachery follow throughout the centuries to this very day. Jesus

Christ called him the "father of lies" (John 8:44), always promising the fabulous but delivering death and suffering instead. We know the consequences of this failure by the first couple were fantastic. God introduced the sentence: death, weeds in the fields, pain in childbirth and many other negative changes that altered the earth and all life. Lost forever was the intended lifestyle God planned for them in the First Earth. He had warned them yet they failed. This was the first of their woes; more were to come as man spiraled further away from God. The message: obedience is not optional if blessing and protection is desired.

Now, rather than enjoy the Garden and wildlife God placed for their sustenance and enjoyment, they were sent out of the place made specifically as a wonderful gift! Instead, they toiled in steady effort and saw death introduced. Possibly God determined that man had too much free time on his hands, so He created more difficult work to keep him focused. Death of our body may seem a harsh sentence, but God intended that with this hard sacrifice, man could return repentant into the next life by the Spirit, their sin atoned for. We serve a Holy God; rebellion, lies and sin are abhorrent to Him. Satan is His opposite; he practices all three at will and advocates the same. We must beware of him:

Be sober, be vigilant; because your adversary the devil, as a roaring lion, walks about, seeking whom he may devour: whom resist steadfast in the faith, knowing that the same afflictions are accomplished in your brethren that are in the world. But the God of all grace, who hath called us unto his eternal glory by Christ Jesus, after that you have suffered a while, make you perfect, establish, strengthen, settle you (1 Peter 5:8-10 KJV).

Subsequent to the Fall, animals were killed and sacrificed (Genesis 4:4), this a degradation from the original earth that was designed with a food cycle *without* bloodshed. What a disaster! Now Adam and Eve had to watch the creatures they adored and loved needlessly perish. In spite of all this failure and sad consequence, we see the Creator working with the free-will and faults of man, still hoping, nurturing and comforting. Then we have the first terrible crime: Cain murdering his brother Abel, even after God Himself had visited and gently counseled the man to beware, warning him: "Sin is crouching at your door" (Genesis 4:7). But still Cain strikes out, killing his brother in a fit of bitterness and rage. God attempted to correct and encourage Cain, but the man was not in control of his emotions, nor would he consider the good counsels of the God who created him! Though Cain had direct communication with the Lord Himself (something every person on the planet would now relish), yet Cain *still* rebelled and failed, no different than his mother and father before him. The unthinkable had happened in the first family! How did the parents take the news? Sin has horrible consequences; let us be grateful for the work of Christ in our spouses and children and the hope we have in Him, an option then not available to Adam and Eve's family. The first funeral must have been a somber awakening; we can be sure God was there as He has been to a million since.

Those Nations Were Beloved by God

For a time things were looking up. "Adam knew his wife and she bore a son and named him Seth" who had a son named Enosh, living 905 years (Genesis 5:6,11). "Then men began to call on the name of the Lord" (Genesis 4:25-26). This was the high point for the Adam family; surely they were overjoyed to see the light of goodness return to their broken home through Seth after the Cain/Abel disaster. Of this period Josephus tells us: "for those nations were beloved of God..." (*Antiquities of the Jews,* Chapter 3).

In time, man continued to decline, and the spirit of rejection multiplied with the help of the rebellious angels, eventually closing off the communion between God and most of humanity. May we always seek to keep our spirit in communion with our Maker, learning the lesson of Cain who stopped the ears of his heart and caused such needless loss, grief and the utter heartbreak in the first family. Unfortunately, rejection of God didn't end with Cain's actions—sin kept spreading and evil kept on its dark march.

The Nephilim or Giants

Years pass after the Fall and first murder, and we find man continues in rebellion. He lives on in defiance to the basic moral principles God set out, and wickedness becomes widespread. The narrative changes and reveals an amazing image of these times past:

> *There were giants on the earth in those days, and also afterward, when the sons of God came in to the daughters of men and they bore children to them. Those were the mighty men who were of old, men of renown* (Genesis 6:4).

So here in the Genesis account, we're given a glimpse of a society unlike anything imaginable today. Giants are mentioned; the shadows of the Greek gods come to life. *Nephilim* the beings were called. Martin Luther translates this word: "those who fall upon others, brigands, thugs, tyrants." The original meaning of the word actually relates to a total of seven different types of Nephilim according to Adam Clarke (a recognized 19th century theologian who studied with the rabbis). We are to understand these "Sons of God" were immortal beings, but far from "good" sons. The text suggests there was first a rebellion in the high realms, hinted by the acts they committed: the taking of the *"fair daughters of man"* without marriage, thereby breaking God's law. We have these beings misusing their power and corrupting the earth, their core motivation being that of *lust*. So after the invasion of earth by this rebellious lot, we find earth's population further corrupted. Were they originally tasked with the protection of human kind? We don't know, but the scene rapidly transforms:

Then the Lord saw that the wickedness of man was great in the earth, and that every intent of the thoughts of his heart was only evil continually. And the Lord was sorry that He had made man on the earth, and He was grieved in His heart. So the Lord said, "I will destroy man whom I have created from the face of the earth....for I am sorry that I have made them." But Noah found grace in the eyes of the Lord (Genesis 6:5-8).

God was pushed too far and a decision was made. He speaks to Noah (through an angel) and reveals what's about to happen—judgment by *water*. One by one they had compromised: man by man, couple by couple, then family by family. At some point they crossed the line of no return. Collectively, society had reached a state where people's hearts embraced evil thoughts *every waking moment* the Bible tells us, noting that even by their *thoughts* God was repulsed.

The sin of lust slowly creeps in and takes over a soul, followed by the cover-ups and lies. Is man on the threshold of the same end for the same reasons today? Eventually, such sin displaces a person's God-given *conscience*, the truth too shameful to admit, then even God's entreaties, like that to Cain, go unheeded. The enemy *perfectly* understands how to drag man into this hole, and he *perfectly* understands where it leads—straight to hell itself, a place where his only solace will be the satisfaction gained from how many he tricked and took with him!

The sins of that world infiltrated cities, states, provinces, and finally *nations*, and where did it all lead? God now decreed the complete annihilation of them *all!* History teaches us that other societies have gone down this path.

God judged them in the past, their experience documented over and over in the Bible to teach us. Where is society heading today? What's happening to our families, governments and nation? God is not one to tolerate sin. Sin is the Almighty's opposite.

The Bible teaches that God dwells in unapproachable light. He is pure; He is holy. He is saddened and abhorred by the rejection of His commandments. On the other hand, God is full of mercy and justice. He gives second, third and more chances in order to redirect us. He provides warnings as He did for Cain. He sends messengers pleading with us to flee from sin. This we should never forget: don't lose connection with God but always read His Word, worship, pray and be ever mindful to protect your conscience and sensitivity to His Spirit! Eventually, like any father who has lost control of his children, God was forced to give man over to his own unfettered desires.

Looking ahead after the Flood, we have speaking to this object the record of Abraham and the three angels en route to Sodom as recorded in Genesis 19. In this conversation, we learn much of God's mercy and by what premise He judges people and even cities concerning this matter. In graphic form, we receive our answer in these passages:

> *The Lord said, "Because the outcry against Sodom and Gomorrah is great, and because their sin is very grave, I will go down now and see whether they have done altogether according to the outcry against it that has come to Me; and if not, I will know." Then the men turned away from there and went toward Sodom, but Abraham still stood before the Lord. And Abraham came near and said, "Would You also destroy the righteous with the wicked?"* (Genesis 18:20-23)

In the end, we find the mind of God on the matter—because there was *one* righteous within the city, He would not destroy it! The record finds such a one, Abram's nephew Lot who was physically dragged out by the angels in the end, showing us how far God is willing to go to save His people. Further, in 2 Peter 2 we have a direct correlation between this event and the Flood, Peter stating:

> *For if God did not spare the angels who sinned, but cast them down to hell and delivered them into chains of darkness, to be reserved for judgment; and did not spare the ancient world, but saved Noah, one of eight people, a preacher of righteousness, bringing in the flood on the world of the ungodly; and turning the cities of Sodom*

and Gomorrah into ashes, condemned them to destruction, making them an example to those who afterward would live ungodly; and delivered righteous Lot, who was oppressed by the filthy conduct of the wicked,...then the Lord knows how to rescue the godly from trials and to hold the unrighteous for punishment on the day of judgment. This is especially true of those who follow the corrupt desire of the flesh (2 Peter 2: 5-10 NIV).

As God so horribly detests sin, He now plans to destroy not a city but the *entire planet* to preserve one man—Noah! Peter warns of a second and final judgment of the earth by *fire*, including the judgment of all individuals including the fallen angels, as the Bible tells us here. Returning to the narrative, we now read:

The earth also was corrupt before God, and the earth was filled with violence. So God looked upon the earth, and indeed it was corrupt; for all flesh had corrupted their way on the earth (Genesis 6:11-13).

Not only had the earth unraveled morally, but it was *filling* with *violence*, the word translated *rabbah* meaning the violence was *multiplying*. The intent of the passage suggesting the vortex of sin was compounding, spreading and engulfing the entire planet.

Sadly, now we have God referring to His adored human creation as *"all flesh."* Gone are the endearing words of a loving God, the wonderful creation of *First Earth* nearly lost; at risk now was all creation, including man! The Father had provided every gift and blessing imaginable and a final 100 years of preaching by Noah, only to watch it all ruined. How sad the state of mankind! The evil one was seemingly victorious at this juncture, save for one little problem—Noah and his family.

Extra biblical texts, such as the Books of Enoch, record that murder, rape and war were raging across the planet at this time. These passages mention that a type of class warfare existed between the angel/human half-breed offspring and those of Adam's descendants. The holy angels report the outcry of the innocents to heaven, calling for justice under the terrible persecutions. We can imagine people in many places were reduced to hiding and subsisting in the wilds, constantly under threat by those of this super race. We don't know for sure, but looking back at the Romans and their coliseum slaughters, those events may provide a clue as to what evil the people suffered under. According to the Book of Enoch, these sick beings were apparently worse than the Romans and even Hitler. Evil changes little. Satan detests God's people and pursues them incessantly.

The Book of Enoch records that the rebel angels brought with them the "deep knowledge of heaven." The text suggests the beings were teaching unethical procedures and possibly engaging in genetic engineering. In the Book of Enoch we find reference in chapter 1:7 stating they were committing: *"sins against birds, beasts and reptiles,"* and the *"cutting of roots."* Could this passage mean that they had broken into the genetic code? Many observers think so. We do find the remains of oddly proportioned human heads and unsightly reptiles and fish around the globe, suggesting such. If they had been modifying the DNA and engineering mutants, we can be assured such prodigy would not have been allowed on the Ark, so they would have perished in the Flood with their masters, and their "root" destroyed. Consider the possibility that the genetic diseases of today are but leftovers of the evil tampering from the past, carried across the Flood boundary. Note that more than one tyrant has experimented along these lines in known history—the telltale work of evil beings.

It's also possible that advancements in weaponry took place, whereby the planet could be contaminated permanently. Here is corrupted humanity at stage *Five*. We must ask ourselves, is mankind in our time acting better? Consider the genocide that occurred in WWI and II and lately on the African continent, the physical and chemical abortions afflicting millions, and the weapons of mass destruction (WMD) brandished across our planet, heartlessly deployed against civilians. (Such was the case recently in the Mideast.) One must wonder, what impact does the sum of these represent to heaven compared to Noah's day? Adding the general moral sins of earth in its present state, it's reasonable to suggest our generation is most certainly at stage four, and likely touching stage five, *the final stage triggering the end of mankind's existence.*

4

Pre-Flood Civilizations

Fig. 18 The massive stones of Baalbek (Ralph Ellis Photo GNU 1.3)

The great stones of Baalbek in Lebanon. An unfinished stone sits in place at the original quarry. This block weighs an estimated 1200 tons; no means are known to cut or transport such a monolith today.

Technology of the Ancients

To suggest the civilizations of those ages were backward and without technology is completely in error. Considering life spans ranged in multiple hundreds of years, the transfer of information from one generation to another would have been astounding. Knowing what man can achieve today in fifty or sixty years of productive creation, think of the knowledge potential of people who lived five, six or even nine hundred years! The notion "If it's ancient, it must be primitive" is a misnomer regarding our thinking of these past civilizations. Teachings that have flooded our screens suggesting early man as club welding "cavemen" are not at all what honest archeology unearths at the dig sites. In the scheme of biblical history, man started at the very top mentally, socially and spiritually. The Bible teaches that as part of Judgment, men will "flee to the caves" (Isaiah 2:21). The biblical narrative found in early Genesis is clear: Adam's descendants mined and refined gold, copper, iron and precious stones; the Bible records Cain even built a city. Music and art were developed. In this light, what evidence have we to help better understand the civilizations and capabilities of these past ancients? We will now depart from the biblical narrative and pursue a small portion of uncensored ancient history for that discussion.

Batteries, Lighting and Baalbek

The crafted blocks found at Baalbek *(see pic on previous page)* are not the work of any known race of antiquity. It seems that some unknown civilization started construction here and was interrupted. No one understands what methods were used to create or move these monoliths, the largest known on earth, as no technology exists today to build or transport such monstrous stones. Deep within the ruins of the Middle East, more amazing technological finds have been uncovered. One such find was batteries, on display at the Bagdad Museum for years and well documented. These devices used lead and zinc arranged in exactly the same manner batteries are constructed today, the only item missing to activate them was an electrolyte (vinegar would be sufficient), and current will flow. This experiment was accomplished successfully using one of these artifacts! Underground lighting? Ancient Egyptian reliefs show royalty using exactly that.[1] In addition, a small, toy sized airplane was recovered. When the discovering party realized the relic appeared to be more than just a plaything, aerodynamic tests were performed on the object and the airfoils were found to be perfect for its design. The model appeared to better represent a miniature of an actual aircraft than a toy. One plate uncovered did show full-sized aircraft of modern appearance.

At Baalbek, researchers maintain that these large stones were part of an older city site, under construction when work abruptly ceased for some unknown reason. Later civilizations added to the ruined site and named it Heliopolis, or "City of the Sun"; the city also aligned with the Great Pyramid. Arabic legends hold that the original city was built by "giants," or Titans.[2] (See Appendix II.) Researchers note the stones at Baalbek are similar in construction[3] to those found in Japan, Bolivia and Peru. Engineers visiting these sites located remains of partly completed building stones in intermediate stages of construction, some showing fine cuts in boulders of many tons, sliced through like butter on blind tangents, suggesting the use of cutting methods unknown today. Others appear to have been molten in place, fitted together without the use of mortar. Corridors and step heights at some sites suggest the inhabitants were oddly tall, adding confirmation that giants occupied the land in those times. Noting that these sites are often separated by thousands of miles, they exhibit similar construction techniques, causing some to suggest these sites were visited by air and constructed by *aliens*. A more tenable theory is these were built by the offspring of a super-race just prior to the Flood.

In summary, when we look at such evidence across the globe, one must admit an entirely different picture of ancient civilization unfolds. Could it be that these great structures were the work of the fallen angels and/or their offspring using high technology? Did their elaborate and complicated construction projects simultaneously and instantly cease when the Flood occurred? In many instances, such a possibility is not out of the question.

Fig. 19 The Great Pyramid of Giza

The Great Pyramid, the oldest yet most architecturally perfect building on earth, a "mystery."

Which building is the largest and most architecturally sound in the world? The Great Pyramid of Giza, which is also the oldest building on earth! Historians note other structures nearby are but mere imitations, a poor image of this work. This structure is composed of approximately 2.3 million limestone and granite blocks, none of which weigh less than two tons and some as much as seventy. The base of the pyramid covers some 568,500 square feet, the length of each side about 754 feet and height nearly 450 feet. With the capstone, the structure would reach 480 feet (the "rejected" capstone, displayed in a nearby museum, was never installed). The polished casing stones that formerly lined the outer surface were removed years ago, thought to be used for the building of Cairo. There were 144,000 of these plates; this is no coincidence with the mystery of the 144,000 in the book of Revelation. The builders are said to have been masters of mathematics, engineering, astronomy and physics. The accuracy of the structure is phenomenal, and it's aligned perfectly with the cardinal points. The foundation consists of 13 acres yet has only settled about one inch over thousands of years. The pyramid engineers also created ball and socket corners, protecting the structure from earthquakes, technically impossible today. There are concaves on each face of the pyramid, creating eight faces, not four. Scholars still ponder its mysteries.[4]

Allen Austin in his recent volume, *The Middle of the Earth, Genesis in Egypt** (2012) tells us that the Great Pyramid at Giza is also aligned perfectly with the constellation Orion, proposing this heavenly sign as the dual man-women constellation of the night sky. Austin points out that Adam (read as Atum in the hieroglyphics) included the women Eve taken from man's rib, a union perfectly depicted in the earliest hieroglyphic images. Austin suggests their original and true meanings have been corrupted by modern Egyptologists, asserting that many of the images depict spiritual connotations that relate directly to those of the Bible and date back to the time of Adam himself!*

Author Note: The Constellation Orion has been the focus of both Scripture and science for centuries, invoking the thought that it may be the natural center of the Universe. See https://www.youtube.com/watch?v=oS0cnoePJOw

*See video set *The Middle of the Earth* by Allen Austin:
The Middle of the Earth 2/4 - YouTube
https://www.youtube.com/watch?v=g1q0Km13ZTM

An amazing video concerning the theory of Orion's biblical importance by Dr. Robert Gentry: Robert Gentry—- The Center of the Universe Part 1 - YouTube
https://www.youtube.com/watch?v=oS0cnoePJOw

Modern secular historians purport the concept that if an article or building is unexplainable through the modernist's lens, they assign them to be a "mystery." To this end, archeologists have coined a new term in which to describe such anomalies, based on acronym: OOPArts, or "Out-Of-Place Artifacts, and why? Such findings confound the preconceived notion: "If it's ancient, it must be primitive" concept, so advanced by modernist conceptions based on the false evolutionary trajectory of man's development, not God's. (See chart end of this chapter.)

Other unexplained artifacts include deeply covered human remains and tools, metal, wood and other obviously manmade objects, engraved or formed by human hands, yet found deeply buried in the earth. Also documented are deeply buried walls, dolls, steel balls, extrusions, writing and idols. One such item was extracted by chance in a well drilling operation, and dubbed the "Nampa Idol."[5] (See image Appendix V.) This small figure was found over 300 feet deep in water deposited sandstones beneath a 15 foot thick lava flow. The find was witnessed and documented in an accurate well log, showing the object's precise depth and geologic position in the strata. Due to its small size, it was captured in the 6 inch well casing and pumped to the surface mostly intact.

Other finds include footwear imprinted in rock dated hundreds of millions years old in Nevada and Utah, these in the layers certified by expert geologists[6], other artifacts were discovered: a ceramic ladle was found in coal[7] and other metal or stone utensils in deep layers. These were coined a "mystery," "non-site" or "freak of nature," all in order to be excused and left undocumented by the establishment science community. Tools, art and other articles have been found in deep quarries in both Pennsylvania and France, exposed in cuts to the shock of the workers when unearthed. Many of these individual items were rushed to universities for examination, where they were promptly characterized as oddities and dismissed with the wave of a hand and no further comment.

The reference geologic strata of many such finds often range in order of millions of years (according to evolution standards), this in direct opposition to origins accounts based on the scheme of "modern" geology. This system of time reference is based upon the Geologic Column, using a scale dependent on the *presupposition* that evolution is true, the animals found in each layer purported to have sequentially evolved in an upward scheme one more complex than the last in time. Accepting relics as mentioned would controvert this model and upturn the basis of a thousand mistaken books and as many PhDs, all conferred on the basis of false evolutionary presumptions that persist today.

A large section in the Appendix is devoted to exposing the mistaken notion of the Geologic Column, which better documents the sequence of destructive mechanisms operating in the *flood year* than evolution's supposed 500 millions. On the other hand, these finds as a group fit well into the biblical model of origins and the true history of man, better explaining these unexplained structures which show our technology quite limited compared to what likely existed in the past. Many of these locations contain blocks so large none can conceive the method of transport between quarry and construction site, yet amazingly professors are quick to assure students of their "educated" opposition to the biblical narrative and explanations, claiming such as "religious" and "myths," yet have no better explanation to offer but the "mysterious" to explain these sites!

Puma Punku, Tell Tale of Technology Lost

Fig. 20 The methods and means of stone cutting at Puma
have never been understood nor duplicated.
(Image Wikipedia commons 2.0)

Pumu Punku, a city site in Bolivia, perplexing to modernists who reject the concept that the ancients were advanced. In this place, apparently still under construction when destroyed, the stone shaping methods and means surpass many known for sheer size, detail and complexity.

At this writing, an intense research project is underway incorporating the latest spectral analysis methodology to determine how these Lego-like blocks were sliced from granite at Puma Punku. According to the first Europeans who visited there 400 years past, when inquiring locally about the method by which these massive stones were made and moved, the following narrative was recorded as their answer:

A story was told by the local Aymara Indians to a Spanish traveller who visited Tiahuanaco shortly after the conquest, spoke of the city's original foundation in the age of Chamac Pacha, or First Creation, long before the coming of the Incas. Its earliest inhabitants, they said, possessed supernatural powers, for which they were able miraculously to lift stones of off the ground, which ...were carried [from the mountain quarries] through the air to the sound of a trumpet. [8]

Was Puma Punku, like Baalbek, a pre-flood city under construction and subsequently interrupted and destroyed by water? Maybe yes, maybe no. Are these findings consistent with the Genesis account? *Absolutely yes.* One thing is universally understood—no one knows what technology was used to cut or move these stones. So the question remains, had these people achieved technology beyond our realm of knowledge? Based on the evidence, it seems so. No one can connect these sites with other cultures near them on the same continents today. They seem better understood as the remains of cities destroyed in the Flood catastrophe.

Fig. 21 The Antikythera Device, calculating planetary
elliptical movements at the time of Christ

Technology from the Stars, the Greek Antikythera Mechanism[9]

This technology was discovered in 1903 by sponge divers working an ancient Greek shipwreck dating to the time of Christ. After modern analysis this device has been found to be unimaginably accurate in predicting lunar, solar and planetary movements. The instrument also calculates "rhythms of transition"—the always changing *elliptical* orbits of planets which consume *decades* to complete their changing circuits, incorporating mathematics thought not to exist until the 15th century. Close analysis determined the unit was accurate out to 76 years and possibly further, some saying as much as 600 years! Only recently did researchers discover the unit is based on the Babylonian "A" astronomical system, which pushed the original assigned origin date rearward to 3500 BC (near the time of Adam). No such chronometer like this existed until the computer age—those being much larger and requiring external power to operate.

In times past, the Church has been wrongly accused of deducting from the *Bible* that the world is flat, a myth perpetrated by skeptics over the years. Silly images of ships sailing over the edge of a flat earth were conveniently associated with the Bible and made public. Such assertions are patently false and were never derived from the Scriptures. The Bible does mention the "Circle of the Earth" (Isaiah 40:22), suggesting a globular concept of earth, long before western civilization confirmed it. In fact, the word *globes* is the Italian derivative of "circle" and actually comes from the original Bible text!

Further confounding the ancient/primitive notion, we have the Antikythera device, capable of determining *longitude* according to naval researchers. In recent history, longitude (the lines of degrees vertically running from pole to pole) was undeterminable, a system not available until the 18th century to fix them. With this capability, this device predates our so called "advanced" technology of Western Civilization by thousands of years![10]

In 2014, a host of researchers and a small army of divers headed to the Greek island site, their task: finding the remaining pieces of the Antikythera, searching for more of its capability and knowledge of the ancients not thought so primitive anymore! Moreover, the existence of such a device suggests its designers lived hundreds of years in order to design and test such a device that operates across centuries. If this is the case, the device supports the authenticity of the age of people given in Genesis 5! (See table in Appendix I.) Concerning such technology lost, King Solomon addressed this general topic in the Scriptures:

> *There is nothing new under the sun. Is there anything of which it may be said, "See, this is new"? It has already been in ancient times before us* (Eccl. 1:10).

Solomon understood that previous civilizations had advanced technology prior even to his times. In the humanist view, these advances are impossible; in their understanding man was simply a dumb brute just evolving from apes in the mistaken theme of upward complexity from the cave, but in the biblical model of history, these "mysteries" and technology like the Antikythera fit quite well.

The Two Pillars of Seth

Turning to the records of the Jews written long before our current Bible was assembled, could God have communicated with pre-flood man warning of the coming judgments as the Bible does for us today? Was it possible that Noah had warning of a pending disaster? To answer this question, we have the record of Josephus, a Jewish solider/scholar turned historian by order of the Romans after the conquest of Israel in AD 70. According to his account (quoting Enoch), God informed Adam the world would be subject to two later judgments, one by water and another by fire. As such, we have in the historical record the mention of the Two Pillars of Seth. In the works of Josephus, he refers back to the ancient writings of Enoch, mentioning the record stating that inscribed on the two were the history and advances of the pre-flood ancients before the flood itself.

The narrative tells of huge structures made not by the Egyptians, but by these people of Seth, constructing one pyramid of stone and another of brick, that word used to describe the "pillars." The one was specifically designed to survive a deluge; the other of brick to protect the information if judgment came by fire. Quoting Josephus:

> *And that their inventions might not be lost before they were sufficiently known, upon Adam's prediction that the world was to be destroyed at one time by the force of fire, and at another time by the violence and quantity of water, they made two pillars, the one of brick, the other of stone: they inscribed their discoveries on them both, that in case the pillar of brick should be destroyed by the flood, the pillar of stone might remain, and exhibit those discoveries to mankind; and also inform them that there was another pillar of brick erected by them. Now this remains in the land of Siriad to this day* (Josephus 1:2:3:70:71).

So Noah had not only the spoken tradition of the coming judgments of both water and fire, but he and his family knew also the testimony *inscribed* on these two mighty towers, built by the hands of his own ancestors! Considering this, we can better understand Noah's instant reception to the call of God concerning the Flood. To Noah, the written prophecy of a thousand years in the form of the Pillars of Seth was simply a confirmation of the larger matter. All the inhabitants of earth had this same warning yet apparently mocked it. Today we have the testimony of the Bible, foretelling the end-time events spoken of by Christ as recorded for 2000 years just as trustworthy and equally so ignored!

Fig. 22 The Pillars of Seth could have appeared as these:
written on them was the wisdom of the Ancients of Noah's day,
including warnings of the coming Flood and Fire judgments.

Notice Josephus mentions their whereabouts: *"This remains in the land of Siriad to this day."* Josephus is not alone in the mention of these Pillars of Seth, but also Plato, the Coptic records of Masoudi, and others. Oxford Astronomer John Greaves records: "Surid [Seth], one of the kings of Egypt *before the flood*, built two great pyramids." In this account the Great Pyramid is referred to as "the Eastern Pyramid." The record states: *"...In the Eastern Pyramid [the Great Pyramid] were inscribed the heavenly spheres and figures representing the stars and planets...."* Further, Austin in *Genesis in Egypt* tells us, "The manuscript of Makrizi gives a similar account stating: *"The first [the Great] Pyramid was especially dedicated to history and astronomy; the second to medical knowledge."* [11]

Scripture tells us Moses was educated in the accumulated wisdom since the Flood time, assembling the same for us in Genesis:

And Moses was instructed in all the wisdom of the Egyptians (Acts 7:22).

Now consider this biblical pronouncement from God through Isaiah concerning Egypt and a pillar: "In that day there shall be an altar to the lord, in the midst of the land of Egypt, and a pillar at the border thereof to the Lord. And it shall be for a sign and for a witness unto the Lord of Hosts in the land of Egypt" (Isaiah 19:19-20).

So here we have another astounding possibility, that in the rewriting of history by the secular Egyptologists and others, concealed is the fact that the Great Pyramid of Giza was actually built by Seth, Prince of Adam, as a sepulcher for his father as directed by God! Not only this, but was designed to survive the Flood (as Josephus tells us,) and is indeed one of the two Pillars of Seth! Noting the size and design of this structure, such a theory is quite tenable. Consider also that Methuselah himself was associated with the construction of these pillars; so here we have in the flesh a witness to these facts in Grandfather Methuselah, since he passed just prior to the onset of the Flood. So in Methuselah we have one who lived all through this period, and further, during the construction of the Ark itself! (See chart of Patriarch ages in Appendix I.) We may imagine the wise old sage of 900 years, standing by at the construction site as any grandfather would do, cheering on his grandson and great grandsons before the first drop of rain fell!

Fig. 23 Gobekli Tepe stands in the way of the foundation
of modern archaeology, said to "change everything."
(Image Wikipedia commons 2.0)

Turkey's Gobekli Tepe Structure, Upending Historical Archaeology

In 1994, archaeologist Klaus Schmidt of the German Archaeological Institute was credited in making one of the most startling archaeological discoveries in our generation: the *Gobekli Tepe* structure in central Turkey. Here were found massive carved stones 19 feet high, thought to be about 11,000 years old using Carbon-14 dating techniques. (Authors note: see critique of these dating systems in Appendix XIII & XIX, relating to the filtering effect of C-14 and UV intrusion of First Earth's atmosphere and higher earth magnetic field, providing a resultant *appearance of age.*) One Smithsonian reporter states the pillars were "crafted and arranged by prehistoric people

51

who had not yet developed metal tools or even pottery." In contradiction, other experts interviewed assert the inhabitants used "advanced technology" in their stone cutting of images, that were "precisely engraved" on the pillars! Schmidt does admit the monuments could not have been built by ragged bands of hunter-gatherers.

The scientists interviewed consider the site key to the emergence of settled communities that surrounded the temple 10,000 years ago, a contradiction in stone to stories found in the modern literature on this topic. For decades, public school texts have portrayed "early man" as cave dwelling, backward oafs, grunting their way through daily life with club in hand. Here at Göbekli, we have the earliest buildings known (so claimed), and nearby was found a graven image of a well-dressed man carrying fruit and produce, suggesting this culture was agriculturally based, *not* hunter-gatherers! In close observation the image has six fingers, suggesting it was patterned after the giants described in 2 Samuel 21:20 where battles were fought against the sons of Anak such as Goliath. In reality, Gobekli Tepe well represents a city of the first chapters of Genesis, showing man at the top of development as the Bible has claimed for thousands of years, as with Cain building a city! (See Genesis 4:17.)

Schmidt concludes, "Though I stood among the looming megaliths eager to take in their meaning, they didn't speak to me. They were utterly foreign, placed there by people who saw the world in a way I will never comprehend."[12] It is sad that these professionals refuse to consider a biblical model in which the evidence fits so well. The H2 documentary* commentator Andrew Collins seems to get surprisingly close to the biblical account in the narrative, but stops short, referring to C-14 dating as an excuse to pre-date Göbekli Tepe before the biblical creation date of 4000 BC. Collins states:

We have here what contradicts a normal understanding of the evolution of civilizations. Göbekli Tepe is regarded as an archaeological discovery of the greatest importance, since it could profoundly change the understanding of a crucial stage in the development of human society. —Andrew Collins

Echoing this remark, Ian Huddler of Stanford comments: "Göbekli Tepe changes everything."[13] In 2006, South African expert in palaeolithic art David Lewis Williams called Gobekli Tepe "the most important archaeological dig anywhere in the world, yet few believe the textbooks will integrate this revelation."

Note these structures were completely covered in a layer of water deposited cobbles and silts, obviously not carried in by wind or erosion as this hill is nearly 3,000 feet above sea level! In close photographic inspection of the till, they seem consistent with the geologic deposition surrounding area for many miles, and in the opinion of the author, consisting of water laid deposits. It seems the entire region had been below water since Gobekli was constructed, a fact the commentators ignored, expounding on the possibility that meteor strikes causing tidal waves and earthquakes were responsible for its end, graphically depicted in the H2 video. Other experts attempt to excuse the flood deposits, surmising the inhabitants neatly backfilled the site themselves!

In a final shocker, reporters were informed that human remains were found "around the site." Collins then suggesting the site a funerary: "This is because human remains have been found outside the perimeter of the site, suggesting that humans may have been buried or left in open burial niches outside, to be eaten by animals." Another report confirmed human skeletons were found there (no mention of such in the H2 clip), the explanation given that people had brought in corpses of relatives and propped them up between the pillars! The excuse given was that Gobekli was a "funeral shrine" of some sort, related to the death of the "hunters." What was not mentioned is the fact that celestial sighting apertures are installed at Gobekli, not exactly a place where stargazers would assemble along with the uncovered deceased.[14]

In consideration of this evidence, what would one expect to find if the roofs were falling in from an earthquake? Rule number one, exit the buildings and find a safe archway, exactly the position these remains were apparently found. Family *bury* their dead in the cultures surrounding this site, so the funeral home story is hardly tenable. Archaeologists seem obsessed at the mention and re-mention of "hunter gatherers" when they speak of Gobekli, dogmatically following textbook archaeology in spite of the evidence before their very eyes! We would expect the human remains would elevate the significance of the site tremendously, but these seem rarely mentioned. I suggest the researchers wish to deflect the truth of the matter, that is, Gobekli strongly supports the Flood and the Book of Genesis; but no one dare suggest so or risk wholesale excommunication from institutional archaeology. Collins does take the honest route in the H2 film narrative as far as the general public can tolerate, his day job safely outside the realm of "institutional science." In Collins' fine book, *Gobekli Tepe—Genesis of the Gods* (Bear and Co. 2014), he shows the aforementioned statues of human figures from the period (well dressed, holding fruits and vegetables) dating back to

9000 BC! This date would place the image as pre-flood, Collins attributing the work to "The Watchers of the Book of Enoch" (Opt. cited reference, plate 23). So much for the "hunter-gatherer" theory!

The Yonaguni Monument

Following another lesser known yet significant find, we come to the Yonaguni Underwater Monument in Japan. This underwater superstructure was discovered in 1987 by professional tour diver Kihachiro Aratake, a director of the Yonaguni-Cho Tourism Agency, while out scouting for new tour locations. Diving off his boat, he suddenly encountered several massive stone underwater structures. Approaching closer, he could see that the colossal edifice was actually a sunken arrangement of monolithic blocks stretching hundreds of feet across. After encircling the monument several times and taking photographs, he then rose to the surface with the exciting report and images that shocked the world.

Figure 24 Yonaguni Monument underwater building site
(Image credit J. Patocal[15])

The next day, his photographs and story appeared in Japan's largest newspapers and shortly thereafter a group of scientists was organized and sent in to investigate. They soon identified a number of other formations in the area, which sparked instant controversy and attracted crowds of diving archaeologists, media and curious nonprofessionals, *none* of whom were able to ascertain its origin. Could Yonaguni possibly date back to an entirely different and profoundly older time? Initial dates of origin were posted as pre-historical or nearly 10,000 BC; later efforts (not listing the methods) changed the date to 2500 BC, though experts have nothing to reference the site to culturally. Historians suggest the structures could be the ruins of Mu, the fabled Pacific civilization rumored to have vanished beneath the waves like Atlantis of lore. Similar to Puma Punku, the inhabitants also vanished from history, the construction methods of Yonaguni unknown. Another mystery for some but potential flood evidence for others.

In the documentary video referenced,* an interesting treatise of several such findings in the Middle East are covered, including highlights of both the Gobekli Tepe and Yonaguni sites. The existence of the Yonaguni structure is so confounding to modernist interpretations that they refuse to consider its man-made origins, suggesting the monoliths the work of natural wave action or *"freaks of nature."*

What Triggered the Flood? "The Comet" Theory

In 1737 William Whiston penned his classic, *A New Theory of the Earth*, proposing that a comet was responsible for the deluge. Whiston claimed this comet made cyclic revolutions along its circuit each 575 years since the creation date of approximately 4000 BC. Then on the seventh round, the comet made too close a pass by earth. According to Whiston's hypothesis, in this round (he claims aligning perfectly with the date of the Flood, the 17th day of the second month after the autumnal equinox of 2349 BC), its course passed within 10,000 miles of earth, that is, between the earth and moon. Since the comet's mass was 6 times the diameter of the luminary, it caused disastrous results on earth.

Whiston cites collaborating observations by the Chinese and others, going back through the years 1767, 1193 and 618BC, including that of Caesar's Comet of 44 BC, along with verified observations of AD 531, AD 1106 and AD 1680. The last pass caught the attention of none other than those masters of astronomy and mathematics Newton and Halley, who could not dismiss this possibility.** It seems their observations vary from that of modern astronomers who doubt this comet's existence, or acknowledging the historical record exists. They claim the sightings are from other independent ice travelers, not possibly from the most important comet ever to pass our planet!

In truth Newton himself was a strong proponent of creation, the Bible, and a youthful solar system (<10,000 years). Always ready to defend his origins position, he likely of contrary philosophy compared to his modern counterparts. A day is coming when the truth shall be known.

Dr. John Keill (1671–1721) was a mathematician and important disciple of Isaac Newton. He studied under the esteemed David Gregory with distinctions in physics and mathematics. He lectured extensively at Oxford, helping students understand difficult Newtonian concepts. Concerning Whiston's the-ory, Dr. Keill was initially skeptical, but later switched. Keill's comments:

"I cannot but acknowledge, that the Author of the New Theory of the Earth, has made greater Discoveries, and proceeded on more Philosophical Principles, than all the Theorists before him have done. In his Theory there are some very strange coincidences, which make it indeed probable, that a Comet at the Time of the Deluge passed by the Earth. It is surprising to observe the exact Correspondence between the Lunar and Solar Year, upon the Supposition of a Circular Orbit, in which the Earth moved before the Deluge. It cannot but raise Admiration in us, when we consider, that the Earth at the Time of the Deluge was in its Perihelion, which would be the necessary ef-fect of a Comet that passed by at that Time, in drawing it from a Circular to an Elliptical Orbit. This, together with the Consideration that the moon was exactly in such a Place of its Orbit at that Time, as equally attracted with the Earth, when the Comet passed by, seems to be a very convincing Argument that a Comet really came very near, and passed by the Earth, on the Day the Deluge began." (Opt. cited ref. P. 441)

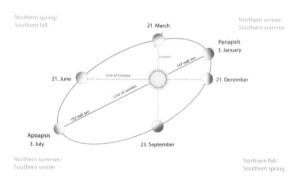

Fig. 25 The new elliptical orbit of earth, thought to have elongated by action of the passing comet of late November or early December 2349 BC, also altering earth's calendar. After Whiston, 1736. (Image Wikipedia commons GNU lic 1.2[16])

As a final note, it should be mentioned that Immanuel Velikovsky, author of those two works that shook the intellectual world in 1950 and 1955—*Worlds in Collision* and *Earth in Upheaval*—was inspired by Whiston's volume to pen them.

In honest evaluation of these discoveries (including Whiston's hypothesis), science is faced straight-on with more evidence affirming the relevance of the literal Flood account, challenging modern origins interpretations. In truth, none of these discoveries are a mystery to one who holds the Bible truthful and a reliable source of history.

Note: For an excellent overview of archaeology and the Bible:
www.answersingenesis.org/articles/nab/does-archaeology-support-the-bible

Civilizations Lost 2012 History 2 channel video clip Turkey's Buried City Video - Ancient Aliens - HISTORY.com.[17]-http://www.history.com/shows/ancient-aliens/videos/turkeys-buried- city?m=5189719baf036&s=All&f=1&free=false

**See Gibbons—*The Rise and Fall of the Roman Empire*, Chapter 4, also Ramsey & Licht, *The Comet of 44 BC,* Oxford Uni. Press, 1997

[1] http://www.smith.edu/hsc/museum/ancient_inventions/battery2.htm

[2] Landis, Don editor, *The Genius of Ancient Man* Master Books 2013

[3] http://www.aquiziam.com/ancient-technology.html

[4] Adapted from Austin, Allen *The Middle of the Earth: Genesis in Egypt* 2011 used by permission.

[5] Corliss, W.A., Sourcebook project 1990 *Ancient Man, a Handbook of Puzzling Artifacts* p. 384 also *Forbidden Archeology* by Dr. Richard Thompson and Michael A. Cremo, (Torchlight Publishing, 2012) p. 805 used by permission

[6] http://www.cai.org/bible-studies/fossil-artefacts-found-coal

[7] ibid 5. p. 636

[8] David Zink. *The Ancient Stones Speak* 1979. Musson Books.

[9] Ancient Astronomy: Mechanical Inspiration: *Nature News*

[10] http://aaronrother.com/Portfolio/AntikytheraDevice.pdf

[11] *The Middle of the Earth,* Austin, Allen 2012. Also see webpage *The Pyramus of Seth*, by Austin.

[12] *Smithsonian Magazine*, Andrew Curry, November 2008

[13] "History in the Remaking" *Newsweek*. 18 Feb 2010

[14] Collins, Andrew, Gobekli Tepe, Bear & Company 2014 p. 79
For a general reference for Gobekli Tepe see www.electrummagazine.com/2011/10/gobekli-tepes- oldest-temple-in-the-world-an-archaeological-stone-age-site-in-anatolia/ And the above cited volume

[15] J. Patokal http://wikitravel.org/en/User:Jpatokal GNU 1.2

[16] https://commons.wikimedia.org/wiki/User:Gothika GNU 1.2

[17] http://news.nationalgeographic.com/news/2007/09/070919-sunken-city_2.html

The True State of Man

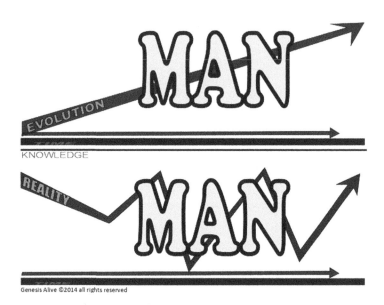

Fig. 26 Man's true historical trajectory of development lower half, the upper, that of evolutionary models, not fact (after Dennis Peterson, *Unlocking the Mysteries of Creation*).

The top half of this graph represents the notion of human progression based on evolution. The lower based on the observation of the true history of man and God's Word. Creation starting on the left being "very good" or "as good as could be" as described in Genesis, along with the first and perfect man, Adam. Time proceeds from left to right as mankind enters into cycles of moral rising and falling as reflected in history, even the history in today's making.

5

The Noahic Covenant

As we continue with the biblical narrative, we now find Noah face to face with God, about to receive one of the most profound messages ever delivered to man:

And God said to Noah, "The end of all flesh has come before Me, for the earth is filled with violence through them; and behold, I will destroy them with the earth. Make yourself an ark of gopherwood; make rooms in the ark, and cover it inside and outside with pitch" (Genesis 6:13-14 NKJV).

In the days of Noah according to the Scriptures and Christ Himself (Matt. 24:37), man was in a moral free fall, utterly descending off the chart. In the mind of God, for a century humanity had been given every opportunity to repent under Noah's preaching, but things had only deteriorated further. We must assume such an extreme measure was equal to the seriousness of the offenses. Humanity seems to have gone into a vortex from which there was no return. God knows all, and seeing that if nothing were done, the entire planet including Noah would be destroyed. So He sent an angel with His decision. Then, in a shocking turn in the relationship between God and man, a new contract was offered on Noah's behalf:

But I will establish My Covenant with you; and you shall go into the ark—you, your sons, your wife, and your sons' wives with you. And of every living thing of all flesh you shall bring two of every sort into the ark, to keep them alive with you; they shall be male and female. Of the birds after their kind, of animals after their kind, and of every creeping thing of the earth after its kind, two of every kind will come to you to keep them alive (Genesis 6:18-20 NKJV).

God now offers something none anticipated: a *covenant*, the first use of this word with over 250 uses to come in the Old Testament alone. The Hebrew word was *berith,* from *bar,* meaning *to purify and cleanse, or purification.* As God is pure and dwells in unapproachable light, direct connection with sinful man first required an act of purification, even if spoken into existence by God Himself! This is truly a wonderful thing, and each time we take communion we can remember the sacrament not only as a renewing of our covenant with Christ, but in the same instance providing cleansing just as God communed one-on-one and cleansed Noah! In the New Testament, we observe a reoccurrence of this very same act, this in the moment Christ initiates the first Holy Communion and takes the bread and the cup, then recites the following:

> *Then He took the cup, and gave thanks, and gave it to them, saying, "Drink from it, all of you. For this is My blood of the new covenant, which is shed for many for the remission of sins"* (Matthew 26:27-28).

After the meal, washing of feet and sacrament given (John 14:31), Jesus states: *"You are already clean because of the word which I have spoken to you"* (John 15:3). Now, as Christ had not yet died on the cross yet here declares the Apostles *"clean,"* we have an interesting doctrinal issue! Further, commentators[1] expound on the word *"many,"* for at this single comment the work of Christ extends to all mankind for *all* ages, not only a single family (as in Noah's case), nor a people (such as the Jew's Mosaic Covenant), but to all who have ever lived! Such is the all-encompassing power of Christ that overshadows the works of Noah in the grand scheme of our great God!

After all is said and done, we have the body of the contract and other stipulations spelled out by God. Up to this time, we know of no other contract God invoked with man since the time of Adam and Eve. Noah understood how quickly that one had spoiled and had no intention of defaulting now. Notice the emphasis was on Noah, the head of household. Fathers take note: to every man as leader of the home here's why the evil one makes him his constant target.

Noah had also watched the lives of other godly ancestors before him as examples. One we know was Enoch, his great, great-grandfather, He was so named *instructor* in the Hebrew, who *"walked with God and God took him"* (Genesis 5:24). Noah's father was Lemech; Methuselah was Noah's grandfather and Enoch's son. It appears this family line was God fearing and blessed, as it says in the Book of Hebrews in the Bible, Enoch was not only pious but *"pleased"* God (Hebrews 11:5). One account credits Enoch as being a pre-flood king who penned 9600 books!

Such is the influence of those who follow the ways of our Lord, their families blessed from generation to generation. This blessing continues forward with godly offspring who flourish in the land, all under the protection and watchful care of the Almighty. Noah determined he was not going to miss this opportunity; no doubt he watched the lives of his successful ancestors and took note. Enoch likely instructed his family well, and besides, there stood the Pillars of Seth as a powerful confirmation. What an amazing family heritage of faith! Beyond the covenant and blessing, we have the main contractual points at hand:

Noah's Responsibilities:

You shall build an Ark to specification. (Genesis 6:14-16)
You shall lodge, care for and feed two of each animal kind,
    plus the extra pairs for domestication.
You have a deadline.

God's Responsibilities:

Noah and family shall receive cleansing from their sins (the "Covenant")
    and a new confederation with God Himself (Genesis 6:18).
He (God) will bless Noah and his children with life. He will sustain
    them through the deluge (now the *only* family with "Covenant"
    on the entire planet!).

Similar to any construction contract today, there was a plan, deadline, materials defined and finish specifications given. As for Noah's part, he exchanged the years of work building the ship and received just payment; the sparing of his life and that of his family, motivation enough to stay on task and finish well! So here we have God appearing (we assume an angelic intercession), laying before Noah the whole plan.

Keeping in mind the potential state of technology of the times, the Ark construction site was likely dramatically different than portrayed in your typical Sunday School class. Noah would employ a full scale mill including the most modern tools available. If that culture had equipment capable of slicing through granite and moving stones of 1200 tons, we may ascertain equipment existed to easily work with wood and metal. (Note the gopherwood tree is known as a cyprus type, or possibly cedar to the ancients.) Assyria (the traditional locale of Noah's habitation) was well timbered with cypress after the flood, and we know from fossils this tree was available before the event, and was a well known ship-building material among the ancients.

We must assume along with Noah's righteousness, he was a man of means. There is a little known phase in Christendom suggested in James 3:15 concerning a man's intelligence and capability, simply stated: "the wisdom that comes down from heaven." According to the rabbis, this "wisdom phase" was first given to Adam in full measure, so can we assume Noah obtained such and conducted business well enough to meet every need to construct the Ark and sustain his family. Such wisdom is imparted by God as a *blessing* for man's good and ultimate prosperity. Job had such wisdom, as did Solomon, "the wisest man on earth." As this vessel was the first of its kind in the world, mastering its construction would no doubt require a sound and creative mind. God picked Noah on purpose, and like Jesus, he likely had a woodworking background. Noah must have been a determined man of good constitution; setting out on a boat building project of this magnitude at the age of 500 took significant fortitude. Along with leadership, he also held the responsibilities of preacher, husband and father.

In a very real way, this endeavor would bless Noah as he watched his sons grow to maturity and become more and more expert in their trades. No doubt each had their gifting in working with wood, metal, interpreting plans, or maybe administration and logistics. The patience required to maintain a steady pace on a job like this would be Noah's ultimate test of leadership and endurance. The task would require a man of inspiration in such an under-taking with there being times of frustration and disappointment along the way. Any contractor will tell you that tackling a project never before done always has its challenges and setbacks. These would build character into the sons of Noah, all mankind benefiting once they landed and set out to lead earth's next population. With Noah as leader and a strong faith in God, every-thing possible was provided for them to succeed.

Noah's wife had the task of keeping the domestic responsibilities in order. We know there were eight people in this program. Like Eve, she would be mentoring the mothers and children of the next generation that would populate the *entire world*. Looking around at the state of things morally, Mrs. Noah must maintain a perfect example for the other women to follow. First and foremost on her mind was making sure the sins of the past would *not* be carried to the next generation. We can be sure her depth of commitment to God and faith would attain new and deeper levels in this experience. We don't have her name directly in the Scriptures, but some of the rabbis refer to her as Naamah, daughter of Zilla. She vanished from view once we exit Genesis yet was named a hundred times in the Flood stories that would follow her. Mention of her character in those accounts was all positive; she was noted in history as the good grandmother. Looking past the Flood, she did well, and we may be thankful for her part in sustaining our lives and training up the next generation of women who would birth mankind.

The Gospel Covenant

Stepping away from the chronological narrative, let us consider the broader picture. Now in the present arrangement, we find an image of the contract Christ makes with humanity, yet in Noah's case not just to *one family* but to the *entire human race*. Under this *New Covenant* in Christ, none are required to work for decades, endure the embarrassing ridicule of a mocking society, and finally endure a 365 day cruise with thousands of animals, snakes and bugs, all in a vessel with a single porthole! These same elements—baptism by water, submission to authority, obedience and *covenant*—precisely image the relationship Christ would offer mankind 2,000 years distant. It now has a powerful effect for all to embrace today and further at a far, far lower cost!

This act of fellowship would not be the only reward God planned for Noah; there would be more to come in due time. Noah understood the consequences of failure. He still felt the harsh effects of the Fall a thousand years distant, and failure now was not an option to him. He had heard about the spoiled Garden existence and resultant consequences; there would be no listening to distracting voices now. He was doubly confirmed as he watched the world around him completely unravel. Keeping all this in mind, Noah listened carefully and acted accordingly; there would be no excuses, no counter. He understood the gravity of the situation and the opportunity to accomplish something great on mankind's behalf—our behalf! It was a great juncture between God and man, and Noah decided to look up, obey God and go to work.

The Obedience of One Saves the Earth

It's amazing how obedience can influence the mind of our holy God. Every father, mother and child should take notice: if you wish the same protection, covenant and blessing Noah obtained, follow his example in faithfulness. In reality, every human being on earth is invited to exercise the influence Noah had with God, all this through Jesus Christ! In a later time, we can recall God's interaction with Moses, presenting him with a new set of rules written in His own hand in the form of the Ten Commandments, promising love and blessing to those who worship and obey, but destruction to those who disregard His ordinances. Where the Pillars of Seth made with human hands failed, these words of God have remained vital to this day. May we learn their lesson and obtain their amazing promises!

Fig. 27 The Covenant between God and man
was proposed to Noah and continues to bless us today.

I, the LORD *your God, am a jealous God, punishing the children for the sin of the parents to the third and fourth generation of those who hate me, but showing love to a thousand generations of those who love me and keep my commandments* (Exodus 20:5-6).

---

[1] See *Adam Clarke's Commentary* p. 254-6

6
The Gathering

Fig. 28 Loading Day (Image Wikipedia commons, Edward Hicks)

The wolf also shall dwell with the lamb, and the leopard shall lie down with the kid; and the calf and the young lion and the fatling together; and a little child shall lead them (Isaiah 11:6).

The Ark was finally completed after years of difficult toil and hardship. The entire family was anticipating the arrival of the animals. All were uncertain how the boarding arrangements would work out. In the final days of high expectation and with patience nearly expired, someone heard a noise. First, a head sticks out the edge of the clearing, then another. The dogs begin to bark and the timid visitors pull back in an instant and were gone. A few minutes later they reappear, acting odd, one of the party picking up on their strange behavior thinks perhaps, "Those deer would never come this close in daylight; I wonder what's going on?" Their behavior gets the attention of the others and all stop to watch. "Could this be the beginning of it?" someone asks, setting down their load. More animals of various kinds appear, then more yet, lining the edges of the clearing, looking and bobbing their heads, waiting for some sign: is it life or death? Both sides freeze…and for a few moments time seems to stop; then it dawns on them all—we have to make this work. The deer move closer, ears go up then down, waiting for some signal of acceptance on the human side. The animals sense it before the people and move closer.

The women back away from the ramp in order to calm them, then more wildlife appear, now coming in twos, and so it begins. The lower deck is designed for the larger animals, stalls segregated from natural adversaries. There's little time to hem and haw about this they think; you can see the urgency on the faces of the animals, and so they bravely move up the gangway. Nothing can prepare a person for such an experience; not since the beginning of time has such an event taken place. Shivers run down their backs and tears flow freely; even the most resolute barely holding back from breaking down. A spirit of accomplishment exhilarates them now, the thrill and joy sweeping every heart. After all these years, faith *is* becoming sight; they had trusted God and Noah's word; and now, *all* are being rewarded beyond comprehension!

Each had given their lives for this very moment in history, having no idea how it would all play out, hoping against hope. All the embarrassment and talk, the mocking and snickering they had endured for years, all came together in this moment. A hush settled upon them, this is real they thought, and only God could accomplish such a wonderful miracle! "Thank the Lords" were rising to heaven as they labored; praises and songs come forth from the women! They had little time to celebrate, the task before them uncertain yet immense. All understood it's going to be a busy few days here at Ark Park, the reality of the coming calamity setting in. What Noah warned them about sobers them now. This flood thing is really going down, and earth is going to be swept of all life!

There's a louder noise away off in the clearing, and the brush is moving. The animals in line freeze and stare back. Something larger and more terrifying emerges into view and a commotion breaks out, the back line scatters and snarls are exchanged; but after a time and reassurances by the handlers, the other creatures settle down and the lines reform. It seems the reptiles are arriving, immature youth maybe but striking with their colorful shimmering coats none the less! The men take a breath thinking this could go south fast; God wasn't joking, He said all and He meant *all*. The crew is deeply struck with the reality of it now. Around them a busy scene is unfolding, the air and ground crowding with the fullness of God's creation coming just to see them, depending on *them*! Their initial joys transform to a state of apprehension and seriousness combined. The importance of the task is finally striking home as the once empty halls of the vessel are starting to fill with these new tenants. How are we going to handle these toothed babies? "Please help us, Lord" prayers go up!

The men jockey into position, seeing who has the courage to handle the situation. They've never been this close to these guys before, maybe once in a zoo somewhere with heavy wire between. Large or small those are really big teeth, and they hoped mommas didn't come along to see their babies off! They took a breath and reasoned, "God got us this far; He will work this out too." More prayers ascend and they move cautiously around the creatures. Then one of the braver more experienced women steps forward. The animals sense a lack of threat with her and a calm cattle-like submission begins to settle among them. The men think to themselves *"She can have that job"* and move back. Up and down the line order prevails, the ramp now cleared; but the boys have trouble hiding the quiver in their voices. The animals allow a large birth around the reptiles, maybe some being adversaries, so at least the people weren't alone in their concerns!

Dinosaurs, Space and the Ark

The issue of dinosaurs and the Ark has raised questions for many years. Since the first fossil discovery of large bodied reptiles in the 1800s, dinosaurs have now been found buried in heaps world-wide. The perplexing question remains, did dinosaurs load on the Ark? The straightforward answer must be *yes,* some did; the second, but how? Dinosaurs lived "millions" of years ago it's claimed, so which account is true? And so the controversy begins. To put this subject in contrast, note that dinosaur, like animals, are clearly mentioned in the Scriptures, as in Job 40:15-19 (NKJV):

> *Look now at the behemoth, which I made along with you; he eats grass like an ox. See now, his strength is in his hips, and his power is in his stomach muscles. He moves his tail like a cedar; the sinews of his thighs are tightly knit. His bones are like beams of bronze, His ribs like bars of iron. He is the **first** of the ways of God; Only He who made him can bring near His sword* (emphasis added).

67

Notice the first verse: "*Look now at the behemoth, which I made along with you...He moves his tail like a cedar...*" (verse 15,18). In this passage we have God proudly displaying a *behemoth*, exhibit number *one* in His dis-course with Job, happily describing His creation! This being God's *first*, not second choice demonstrating God's creative power in the humbling of Job. The second phrase: "*which I made along with you.*" In this verse reflect back to Genesis 1:26 "and God made the beast" on day six, the same day He made Adam, thus collaborating the two accounts. "*He moves his tale like a cedar.*" Cedar trunks obviously have more girth than an elephant's tail, so God is talking about another kind of animal. Next: "*He is the first of the ways of God.*" (vs. 19). This passage suggests the animal described is among the largest. What should we take away from this serious God-to-Job discourse?That the Lord is *very* interested in dinosaurs, and note, Job lived *after* the Flood.

Have Dinosaurs Lived in Recent History?

We have many historical accounts of dinosaurs living in the ages after the Ark landed. For centuries, mariners recorded encountering "sea mon-sters" and placed images of them on their charts. Across China, we have documented sightings, paintings and carved images of these creatures (China having the most prolific number of fossil sites known). There are even re-ports that one of the dynasties maintained a huge lizard in chains and put on display at special celebrations. One widely published account was that of Gilgamesh[1] from Babylonia, who journeyed into the wilderness and killed one of the creatures, returning with its head. We also have accounts of me-dieval times with knights going off to slay their dragons, suggestive of reality documented in word and image.

As Alexander the Great traveled across India, it's recorded that the lo-cals directed the captain's attention to a cave where was noted the sighting of a giant lizard, the natives begging the chieftain not to slay it.[2] Based on a number of historical accounts, it seems that it was sporting to hunt these an-imals in earlier times, reducing their number. As such, back in Noah's day, dinosaurs may have been contained to isolated areas due to hunting pressure and reduced habitat. If man had the technology to shape and move stones weighing hundreds of tons, it's not improbable to imagine the ancients pos-sessed weapons capable of bringing down such creatures, even for sport.

Fig. 29 Dinosaurs were reported by eye witnesses
as beautiful animals. (Image © Roman Mordashev)

Many other written and visual accounts exist around the world of such sightings, images and encounters with the creatures we call dinosaurs. In the swamps of the Congo, Papua New Guinea and Cameroon, locals treat their existence as commonplace and have names for multiple varieties. When shown images of different species of reptiles and mammals from around the world, they shake their heads at images of fauna such as bears, elk or moose, but when it comes to dinosaurs they casually pick out species they have personally observed, know by track or have acquaintance of those who have seen these creatures firsthand.[3]

Sightings in England

In 336 BC it was recorded that King Morvidus was swallowed by a Belua, as described by historian Geoffrey of Monmouth. Dozens of these creatures were observed and documented, stating they devoured both man and beast. Migrations of flying reptiles were consistently recorded between the years AD 1170 – AD 1532, where folks could determine the approach of foul weather by observing the creature's flight before the storms.[4] Bill Cooper in his volume *After the Flood* (1995) documents over 120 locations in England alone that recorded sightings and slayings of a variety of these animals. Some were noted as troubling to fowl and rabbits.[5] Other eyewitness accounts noted these creatures having a beautiful coat of jewel-like skin that shimmered in the sunlight, not unlike many smaller lizards today. We should keep in mind that in the initial creation, these animals could have been without fear of man or even friendly, noting that the largest of horses and even elephants are known to be kindhearted, gentle and of a submissive manner.

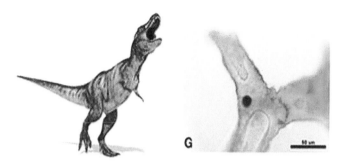

Fig. 30 Soft tissue finds are quite common among pre-historic reptiles, yet publicity of such is limited to a few newspaper articles.

A further enigma exists in the case of Tyrannosaurus Rex, icon of the movie "Jurassic Park." Parts of this creature have now been found in soft tissue.[6] When scientists unpacked fossilized bones extracted from a find in Montana, they were shocked to discover intact red blood cells in the dry bones. This find has created no small stir among public science institutions, who have taught for over 100 years that dinosaurs are millions of years old. Such findings as these are assigned to the realm of "mysteries," as these institutions have no intention of correcting their million year timelines. Of late, more deep tissue has been unearthed from T-Rex, including large portions of cartilage matter still elastic to the touch.[7][8] How can discoveries like these be reconciled with current dogma as taught in the Geologic Column? Each fits well within the story of Noah and the Bible but wreak havoc in evolutionary camps. They are now working to deflect the issue of soft tissue by effecting silence on the matter, hoping evidence like these finds will somehow go away if ignored long enough.

Taken together, such reports cannot be ignored. Only with the advent of the internet do we have these discoveries on display for fair and open consideration, along with their obvious corroboration with the biblical account.

"Living Fossils"

Other creatures long thought extinct "millions" of years ago but found alive today include the Coelacanth fish, said to have lived over 300 million years ago, thought to have gone extinct with the dinosaurs 70 million years past, as dated by none other than the Geologic Column! In the 1930s, these fish started showing up on fisherman's lines, and to date, hundreds have been caught and photographed. There are many more examples similar to the Coelacanth, showing that the vastness of the ocean could produce even more contradictions for evolution. It seems that no evidence, no matter how convincing will be allowed to challenge their precious theories! Institutional science claim themselves as "scientific" while proclaiming those of the faith or of the Intelligent Design community are pseudo-scientific, which is ridiculous in light of these facts.

General Questions Relating to Practical Matters and the Flood

Considering the environment of the current, post-flood earth, that of a cooler, more temperature divergent and sparsely vegetated landscape and oxygen depleted atmosphere, it's easy to imagine such conditions had a stunting effect on all life including the growth of dinosaurs. Such factors also lead to lower reproduction rates. Biologists tell us lizards keep growing until death. The First Earth with its oxygen rich atmosphere, amazing foliage and life sustaining characteristics seem ideal to allow these animals to attain the sizes observed in the fossil record. In the post-flood age, that of a completely different environment (now supporting human life spans of less than 100 years, e.g. with higher UV radiation, etc.), one can easily deduct why animals and plant life would be much smaller compared to their predecessors we find entombed in the Flood strata.

Extinction is a common factor affecting many species, caused by change of habitat and/or hunting etc., which likely contributed to the general reduction of the post flood dinosaur populations. Hundreds and even thousands of other species are known to have become extinct in current experience; these factors together well explain the dinosaur's general absence in the present and cannot be dismissed. We have the dinosaurs in the fossil record that preserves their past for us, but in no way does their presence in that state contradict the biblical narrative. Such point to a common watery disaster, a wholesale wiping of the dinosaurs and so many other species off the planet.

Fossil Deposits of Dinosaurs

Dinosaurs are found in thousands of locations around the world in one specific condition: buried in *water deposited* sediments turned to stone. This method of preservation is without question and provides ample support to the authenticity of the Flood account itself. One cannot separate these animals from this method of preservation and their destruction. The given purpose of the Flood was to end all life and save a few, dinosaurs included. As such, we find them in densely packed graveyards of water deposited strata, which supports our Flood narrative. Dinosaurs are found in association with many other species of sea, air and terrestrial wildlife including birds, cockles, mammals, beaver, insects, snakes and a myriad of other creatures—these typically not reported in literature nor displayed in the museum exhibits. Sadly, these facts have been left out of the textbooks; today's dogma wrongly influencing the thinking of the masses. (This subject is more thoroughly expanded upon in the "Fossils" section in Appendix VII - X.)

Links: http://www.noahcode.org/dinosaurs.html

The Question of the Ark's Livable Space

Ark Size[1]	547ft X 91ft X 55ft
Capacity[2]	81,062 tons burden/2.68 million cubic feet
Time at Sea[3]	365 Days
Initial Flood	190 days
Subsiding Phase	165 days
Bulk Capacity - Train Cars	450 box cars[4]
Crew	8
Cargo	Approximately 35,000[5]

Fig. 31 Table of Ark Specifications, original work of Genesis Alive research (Note an additional 10 days were spent in the subsiding phase apparently for ground drying)
1. Based on a cubit equaling 21" from Greaves, *Clarke's Commentary* p. 70 1832 Note that the pre-flood inhabitant cubit could have been much larger, see Cumberland's weights and measures p. 34
2. Dr. John Arbuthnot, noted British 17th century mathematician
3. Adam Clarke in *Clarke's Commentary* 1832 p. 77 (view freely in Google Play; Adam Clarke Bible)
4. CSX Railroad *"Railroad Equipment"* www.CSX.com (5238 feet³ 50 foot box car)
5. Morris & Whitcomb *The Genesis Flood* Pres & Reformed Pub. 1961 p. 69

The Ark had space to contain a total capacity of 450 rail cars or approximately 3 million cubic feet in volume. Using the dimensions related in the Bible, the Ark is calculated to carry over 80,000 *tons* burden. By comparison, the passenger ship *United States* is approximately 55,000 tons burden or 30% less than the Ark. Today's supercruise ships are approximately 100,000 tons, designed to carry approximately 9,000 people, cargo and fuel for weeks in travel comfort.

Among the reptiles, mammals and birds, experts have calculated less than 20,000 basic species were needed to preserve life in the new world,[9] the Ark having ample of space for them all. The "kind" groups could easily broaden to the number of species we see today, yet would require little of the available space on the Ark. When challenged about this fact, critics fail to come up with the math or science to back up their criticisms.[10] Additionally, it only makes sense that God would have prompted only healthy juveniles (especially of the larger species) to board, economizing the needed volume and feed required. As it was God Himself who provided Noah with the plans for the vessel, we can be assured the Ark had all the space required. Once settled, a state of hibernation likely prevailed upon them (as designed by their Creator in the first place), having the net effect of reducing the needed food and water supplies generally, saving even more space. So answers the volume and food questions concerning these practical matters.

Age of Mountain Ranges

Another logical question arises: How were the high mountains covered with water? Interestingly enough, even contemporary geology tells us earth's mountain ranges are relatively young, less than 5 million years old, a number only 2 million (in the evolutionary time measurement), a fraction of earth's commonly advertised age of *billions*.[11] Relative to the large time scale of the evolutionist, such figures represent only a tiny movement on their 4.5 billion earth-age clock. Another issue challenging long-age cosmologies comes from known erosion rates. One scientist calculated that at the present erosion rates, all the mountains of the world would be worn flat in less than 10 million years![12 13] This figure has been echoed by a wide array of geologists, and along with the shocking revelation that most all of earth's mountain ranges are infants geologically speaking, seems logically conflicting.[14 15] (Of course these ages are based upon the reckoning of the Geologic Column, an untouchable idol in itself, a subject expounded upon in Appendix XII.)

Relating to mathematics and geologic origins, a certain professor took a class on a coastal field trip. Upon arrival to said locale, the instructor announced that the age of these beach deposits was approximately 2 million years old. One student with a reasonable ability to calculate in his feet, commented if this was so, the coastline should now be in Idaho, 400 miles east! To the logical person, geology must align with mathematics, physics and reason. Often these are to be checked at the door versus some theory, this in order to save the coveted chart of geology and/or evolutionary thought. So in the Deluge event, the evidence is everywhere that many ranges were formed catastrophically, their movement occurring rapidly. Consider the upper layer of Mt. Everest is known to consist of *sea floor*, this determined by the aquatic creatures buried in her summit. Geologists admit the Himalaya uplifted recently and rapidly within the time of man's existence, yet date her summit to be some 600 million years old! (See images of several mountains compared to age-layers in the latter part of Appendix XII.)

73

Sea Mounds, Trenches and Abundant Geologic Work

We now understand more about the great sea troughs, extending deeper than the mountains high. The sum of these two features accounting for any water lacking to deluge earth's surface. Dr. John Morris, senior geologist at Institute for Creation Research states: "The key is to remember that the Flood didn't have to cover the present Earth, but it did have to cover the pre-Flood Earth, and the Bible teaches that the Flood fully restructured the earth." As the Bible records: *"The world that then was, being overflowed with water, perished"* (2 Peter 3:6). It's gone forever. The earth of today was radically altered by that global event. The Flood accomplished *abundant* geologic work [Note: as previously mentioned, it's said that the ocean floor contains thousands of volcanoes, including underwater beaches and other features thousands of feet below the surface (see the 1949 report of the Atlantis Project[16], eroding sediments here, re-depositing them there, pushing up continents, elevating plateaus, denuding terrains, etc. Mt. Everest and the Himalayan range, along with the Alps, the Rockies, the Appalachians, the Andes and most of the world's other mountains are composed of ocean-bottom sediments, full of marine fossils laid down by the Flood. These rock layers cover an extensive area, including much of Asia. They give every indication of resulting from cataclysmic water processes. These are the kinds of deposits we would expect to result from the worldwide, world-destroying Flood of Noah's day."[17]

Polar Ice Caps Absent

Knowing that the pre-flood world likely had no polar ice, these melted would add an estimated 220 feet to the world's oceans.[18] The Bible speaks to these boundaries directly:

> *You fixed the earth on its foundations never to be moved. You covered it with the deep like a garment; the waters stood above the mountains. At your rebuke they fled; at the sound of your thunder they rushed away, flowing over hills, pouring into valleys, down to the place you had fixed for them. You determined a boundary they could not cross; they were never to cover the earth again* (Psalm 104:5-9).

Notice the sequence of events this passage portrays: first, God *"covered it...like a garment, the waters stood above the Mountains."* This suggests the initial actions, then a period of *stasis* as mentioned in Genesis 8 (to be discussed in detail later). Secondly, the waters *"rushed away, flowing over hills"* down to the place where God *"had fixed"* for them. Note carefully the words used to describe the final flood actions— *"rushed, flowing, pouring."* Is not the surface features of our planet best explained in this manner? In the view of the author, a pilot for over 40 years and working beneath the earth's surface for over 20, he proclaims that these words from the Psalms expressly and perfectly describe earth's primary feature forming events since creation. These *true* sequence of events form the basis of *true geology.*

From the earliest days, the old masters understood these objects. Scottish Professor Geikie, reflecting on mountain building, tells us: "Thus, the student learns that some of the most marked features of the globe's surface are of comparatively modern date. For neither the Alps nor the Himalaya had any existence before Eocene times…the sea flowed over the sites of these mountain ranges, and over the areas where in subsequent ages the Pyrenees and the Carpathians made their appearance. In short, it becomes evident that, during the deposition of the Eocene strata, Europe existed as an archipel-ago—the sea then covering large areas which are now dry land."[19]

Local Flood Arguments

If the Flood were merely local, there would have been no requirement to construct an ark 500 feet long as directed by God. Such a notion defies the entire premise of the narrative. God could have simply instructed Noah to remove himself to a higher place and prepare a covering, the animals following! No, if the Bible were so far mistaken, who could rely on it or any other portion as truth? (See Appendix XIII showing sandstone deposits like the Tapeat's covering millions of square miles, hardly a remnant of a "local" flood.)

Water—Was There Enough for a World-Encompassing Flood?

The earth today is about 70% covered with water, totaling some 140 million square miles in surface area. In contrast, the earth has only about 57.2 million square miles of land surface, and only a fraction of that able to support life. Scientists tell us that if the underwater canyons of the current sea floor were level, the volume displacement onto the continents would engulf the earth to a depth of 8,000 feet! Now assuming these underwater features are mostly catastrophic in origin (which their appearance and geology strongly suggest), they are a result of the tectonic movements caused by the Flood itself. These factors are considerable.

New Subsurface Water Reservoirs Found

In 2014, scientists reported that they had discovered a huge deposit of water holding mineral called ringwoodite below the earth's crust, said to hold enough water equivalent to *three* of earth's oceans by the researchers. A temperature of 2000^0 F. was determined.

Northwestern University lead scientist Steven Jacobsen and seismologist Brandon Schmandt of the University of New Mexico have confirmed this reservoir's massive size, shedding new light on the origin of earth's water. "It's good evidence the Earth's water came from within," said Jacobson. The water is contained in a mineral called ringwoodite, a blue rock that lies 400 miles (700 kilometers) underground in the mantle—the layer between earth's surface and its core. The discovery was based on data captured using nearly 2,000 seismometers. "We should be grateful for this deep reservoir. If it wasn't there, it would be on the surface of the Earth, and *mountain tops would be the only land poking out.*" Jacobson commented.[20]

The researchers mentioned the probability that this water could easily be converted and sent to the surface if it had an escape path. As amazing as this find is, it shows us how new evidence dashes the old argument regarding the *lack of water.*

The Smaller Species

With the dinosaurs and larger mammals dealt with and settled, we have the smaller species to consider, each no less important to God. This included but was not limited to: mice and rats, skunks, mink, otter, fisher, marten and wolverine, along with every other mammal, reptile, bird and insect known to live at the time that God wanted preserved. One can only imagine how the accommodations were worked out. Envision weasels and cats on one end, mice and rats the other. Birds birthed on the upper levels away from natural predators. We may surmise the annoying squawking, calling and chirping fits that erupted night and day at the start, their calls erupting at one end of the boat and circling back again to the start. At first, the comedy of it all must have been hilarious; think of the echoes orchestrated by the unruly personalities, unable to resist the temptation to be the loudest, start up a round of calling to disturb the calm at will. Such likely started with the monkeys on the second floor, then the apes chimed in and so it went; in short order the entire vessel was quaking with the sounds of entire class and subclasses of every mammal, bird and reptile on earth, including the elephants!

Each couple likely got a shift watching over things we can only surmise, emerging blurry eyed at the end. The newness wore off fast one would think, each couple becoming acquainted with their wards and vice versa. We can imagine this was part of God's plan to have them become familiar with their passengers in the days before the calamity. Many last minute changes were likely required to get this great menagerie situated and settled. It would take time for this diverse group to become accustomed to their new home and company. The Ark was truly a world-class zoo!

[1] http://www.answersingenesis.org/articles/nab/what-happened-to-the-dinosaurs
[2] Aelianus, Claudius, On Animals, Book #XV, Chapter 19-23, c.210-230
[3] http://creation.com/mokele-mbembe-a-living-dinosaur (accounts from Cameroon, the Congo and Papa New Guinea)
[4] Bill Cooper, *After the Flood*, New Wine Press 2005, p. 142
[5] Cooper, *After the Flood*, New Wine Press 2005, p. 143-4
[6] http://www.ksl.com/?nid=1012&sid=22746901
[7] http://creation.com/still-soft-and-stretchy
[8] www.msnbc.msn.com/id/7285683/
[9] Morris, Whitcomb *The Genesis Flood*, 1961 p. 68 quoting Ernest Myer
[10] Safariti, John *Refuting Evolution,* Creation Pub 2005 p. 42
[11] Morris, John D. *The Global Flood*, 2012 Institute for Creation Research Pub p. 79
[12] Roth, A.A., *Origins—Linking Science and Scripture*, Review and Herald, Hagerstown, MD, p. 263 1998
[13] Schumm, S., Disparity Between Present Rates of Denudation and Orogeny, *U.S. Geological Survey Professional Paper 454*, 1963
[14] *The Origin of Mountains*, Cliff Ollier and Colin Pain, Rouledge Press, London 2000
[15] Morris, John D. *The Global Flood*, Master Books 2012
16 New Discoveries on the Mid-Atlantic Ridge«, *National Geographic Magazine*, (November 1949) and Patterson *Scientific American* August 1950.
17http://www.icr.org/article/did-noahs-flood-cover-himalayan-mountains/
[18] http://science.howstuffworks.com/environmental/earth/geophysics/question473.htm
[19] Geikie, James *Historical Geology* 1876 p. 74
20http://www.newscientist.com/article/dn25723-massive-ocean-discovered-towards-earths-core.html#.U7UtXkAXJsP

7

The Door Is Shut on Man

Fig. 32 "So those that entered, male and female of all flesh,
went in as God had commanded him; and the Lord shut him in" (Genesis 7:16).

Noah checks off the calendar. Outside, the air feels different and the sky hazy. The animals have quieted down and many are entering hibernation, waking only occasionally for food and water. The forest around the ark is now strangely quiet, signifying the local animals have moved out. The sky has an eerie look to it. Noah goes off alone to pray and seek God's direction. "It's been a while since I've heard from God," he thinks. "We must be getting close. I trust you, Lord, but things are really getting odd around here."

At God's direction, the crew camps inside the Ark for a few days with the ramp open. From outside they could hear an occasional call or jeer from onlookers as time went by. One may envision the headlines flashing around the globe, and the gathering of spectators and onlookers that came out to see for themselves. A huge craft full of animals would doubtless create a huge sensation; the local hotels full. Once they loaded, one can suppose campsites started to spring up with the people waiting to see Noah fail and the authorities breaking up such religious nonsense before it got out of hand.

Some visitors likely did everything possible to stir up the animals, trying to get their attention for fun, throwing rocks and the like, keeping the authorities busy. We assume the occupants looked out with concern occasionally to see their neighbors and friends, ones they grew up with or even close family. Noah's lucky prediction of the animals coming must have made some think twice about his sermons, wizardry to the extreme they thought.

Flood Zero Hour

The sympathetic intellectual, the priest and the drunkard were there, philosophizing why such backward fundamentalists should be allowed such freedoms in these progressive times. Laws should be made against such grandstanding, children could be wrongly influenced by these crazies. People were meandering around and about, gawking at the whole affair. Others were waiting for something to happen, as Christ relates: *"Just as in the days of Noah, they were eating and drinking and giving in marriage"* (Luke 17:26). They had rationalized themselves out of connection with God, completely filling themselves with the things of the world. They had missed the entire point: God had created everything for them in holiness and goodness, yet they had utterly forgotten Him. Noah's heart undoubtedly broke; for a hundred years he had tried to reason with them, for a thousand more the Towers of Seth stood tall in confirmation of the Flood's inevitability, just like the Scriptures today warn mankind of the next judgment.

The mysterious animal migration had likely got some people thinking, but either way it mattered little now, the time to repent was in its final countdown. All of us must stop and ask ourselves the same question today: is earth again in the final countdown? Are we out of touch with God? What are you thinking about every waking moment? Would God be pleased with your thoughts, or have you become just as blinded as those outside the Ark that day? Last the Bible tells us: "Then the Lord shut them in" (Genesis 7:16). The word translated *God* now changes again; this time it's *Lord* or *Provider*—the Giver of bread, the Giver of life. God decreed He would destroy Earth in Genesis 6:3; in 7:1 Noah is instructed to board; and finally in 7:16 God closes the door. How sad was the Provider, now forced to move against His own creation! The Lord, their *Father,* forced to wipe away His *own* formed in love and joyful expectation, now forced to turn away from His own creation!

79

wished them to take the higher road! But alas, the children followed their fathers in sin until the cycle was unbreakable, and here they were.

What began so adoring when the angels shouted for joy "in the beginning" is about to end. The time since the declaration of doom a hundred years before has now expired. It was His judgment and *His* hand that closed the door; Noah could only stand back in awe and watch by hand unseen the great ramp tightly close and the Ark's interior grow dark. Judgment is God's business. Oh people of earth today, don't miss the acceptance, grace and provision God has made for us thats available in Christ right now! Learn from the past mistakes before it's too late!

Noah's Last Known Sermons

Accounts found outside the biblical text capture these scenes as the destruction unfolded. The author cannot confirm these as valid but cannot discount them based on the framework the Bible records for us. The Scriptures tells us Noah was a preacher of righteousness. Though not recorded specifically, we can assume his exhortations were passionate and serious, having the pulpit of the world and apparently, the very last voice for God in that place. Every good pastor feels a sense of responsibility for their people but just think of the responsibility knowing that your words and reasoning represent the last hope for the entire world! We can be assured God used the words of Noah, just as those of every honest pastor who pleads for reason before it's too late. A few lines are recorded here for the reader's consideration:

"Men sated with faithlessness, smitten with a great madness, what you did will not escape the notice of God, for He knows all things, the immortal Savior, who oversees everything, who commanded me to announce to you, so that you may not be destroyed by your hearts. Be sober, cut off evils, and stop fighting violently with each other, having a bloodthirsty heart, drenching much earth with human blood. Mortals, stand in awe of the exceedingly great, fearless heavenly Creator, imperishable God, who inhabits the vault of heaven. And entreat Him, all of you, for He is good for life, cities, and the whole world, four-footed animals and birds. So that He will be gracious to all. For the time will come when the whole immense world of men perishing by waters will wail with a dread refrain. Suddenly you will find the air in confusion and the wrath of the great God will come upon you from heaven. It will truly come to pass that the immortal Savior will cast forth upon men...unless you propitiate God and repent as from now, and no longer anyone do anything ill-tempered or evil, lawlessly against one another but be guarded in holy life." When they heard him they sneered at him, each one calling him demented, a man gone mad.

Then Noah Cried Out

"O very wretched, evil-hearted fickle men abandoning modesty, desiring shamelessness, tyrants in fickleness and violent sinners, liars, sated with faithlessness, evildoers, truthful in nothing, adulterers, ingenious at pouring out slander, not fearing the anger of the most high God, you who were preserved till the fifth generation to make retribution. You do not bewail each other, cruel ones, but laugh. You will laugh with a bitter smile when this comes to pass I say, the terrible and strange water of God. Whenever the abominable race disappears, root and all in a single night, and the earth-shaking land-quaker will scatter cities complete with their inhabitants and the hiding places of the earth and will undo walls, then also the entire world of innumerable men will die. But as for me, how much will I lament, how much will I weep in my wooden house, how many tears will I mingle with the waves? For if this water commanded by God comes on, earth will swim, mountains will swim, even the sky will swim. All will be water and all things will perish in water."

Final Refrain—Noah Enters the Ark

"But when he had spoken these things in vain to a lawless generation the Most High appeared. He again cried out and spoke. 'Now the time is at hand, Noah, (to say all in turn), to do to the immense world everything which on that day I promised and indicated to you, as much as the myriad evils generations did previously, on account of a faithless people.[1]

"And all the people shall fear...and trembling and great fear shall seize them to the extremities of the earth. And high mountains shall be shaken and shall fall and be dissolved and the mountains shall flow down, "to slip through, to leak, to fall away like water" and be turned into side channels, and shall melt like wax before a flame. And the earth will be rent with a splitting and a crackling, and everything on the earth will be destroyed.[2]

"And when He gives forth his voice against you, will ye not be shaken and affrighted by the mighty sound? And the whole earth shall be shaken, and trembling, and thrown into confusion...And the heaven and its lights be shaken and trembling, [and] all the sons of the earth."[3]

1. The Sibylline Oracles Book 1: Noah bidden prepare for the Flood
2. Gizeh 1:5-7 3. 1Enoch (Black) 102:1-3

8

The Waiting Is Over—It Begins

Figure 33 "The Fountains of the Great Deep Burst Forth" (Genesis 7:11)

Then the Lord said to Noah, "Come into the ark, you and all your household, because I have seen that you are righteous before Me in this generation, for after seven more days I will cause it to rain on the earth forty days and forty nights, and I will destroy from the face of the earth all living things that I have made." And Noah did according to all that the Lord commanded him (Genesis 7:1-6 NKJV).

A certain prophet was warned three times by an Eagle that a deluge was coming, but each time the warning went unheeded. He told the man that the entire Gila Valley was to be flooded but still no heed. Then there was a peel of thunder and an awful crash, and a green mound of water raised itself over the plain. It seemed to stand upright for a second and cut by lightning. It rose and fell on the prophet's hut. When morning broke there was nothing left alive but one man, Szenkha, who saved himself by floating on a ball of resin. Then the waters fell. —Pima native flood account, Appendix II

82

G od gives Noah His highest thanks and appreciation for all he has done, showing the world that faith and obedience truly has its rewards. Few people ever lived to receive such kind and thoughtful words from God himself. Then the unimaginable begins:

At the Beginning of the Flood

The Bible says the first event was not rain, but the *"Fountains of the great deep burst forth"* (Gen. 7:11). This passage suggests more of a volcanic event preceded the Flood than water from the sky. Likely the massive aquifer system around the globe shattered, portions blowing into the atmosphere. Observing the mid-ocean rifts and the parallel surge lines near them, it's evident that a rapid separation of the crust occurred sometime in the past and was as suddenly halted. Then we have the moist pre-flood atmosphere itself, participating in the watering of the earth's surface in the cycles of dew before the Flood. If we launch water, dust aerosols and strata skyward, it only makes sense that the atmospheric layers would have been disrupted and adversely affected, maybe condensing the moisture into rain. We must also take into account that if the aquifers were emptied, the void would cause the continents to drop in a general displacement. We have leftovers in the form of caverns around the world to support the aquifer concept. The earthquakes and Krakatoa-sized volcanic actions would likely level every standing man-made structure on the planet in hours, leaving nowhere for the populous to escape the coming storms. Now that earth may be viewed from space, we can imagine how the continental plates folded and rippled, resulting in the ridge patterns exhibited in mountain ranges world-wide.

The Hebrew word *Mabbul* translated "Flood," is used only for the waters of the Noahic Flood in scripture, never to be uttered again by God, except as quoted in Psalms 29:10 referring to the same terrible event. Its meaning more profound than simply high water, the root suggests a liquid mixing of earth by force!

Reality Sets In

Family and friends were likely outside trying to talk sense into the soon-to-be mariners, the crowd stirring and getting impatient. Then all at once something strange happened. They watched the loading door on the Ark slowly close, as if by some unseen hand. Startled, Noah and his family stood back in safety and watched. The final countdown has now expired, the mocking expressions on the faces in the crowd now changed. "Maybe there is something to this," they thought. At first people were startled. Once the entry closed and nothing more happened, people looked around at each other for assurance and the jeering started again. Some in the crowd may have started throwing things or worse. "Nice trick, Noah" was likely shouted, "You almost got us, ha," but the laughter faded when they heard the distant rumble of thunder and felt the earth move at first just slightly, but the second jolt was real!

Now the shouting and mocking suddenly ceased, the carnival atmosphere over. They fell silent now, listening, looking up and around. Then another major jolt hit and the mocking turned to shouts and screams. Many panicked and stampeded for their homes, some stayed fast thinking to ride it out, while still others thought, "Noah is a good guy, he will relent and let us aboard." When their entreaties failed, they resorted to crying out in panic, pleading for help. Admitting their error too late, they begged Noah to just allow the children aboard. Then the pounding and ramming came. We can be sure every method of entreaty and treachery was deployed to gain entrance, but none worked. No one could be trusted. Noah understood that God's command was God's command. We can surmise Noah's heart broke a thousand times with every plea. He may have been tough but he was still human.

The quakes hit again, and again, now so severe none could stand. They crawled now, at a loss for what to do next. That's when the first drops began to fall. Looking up, they saw the sky turning jet black across the northern horizon, the first storm of many was moving rapidly toward them, engulfing the land with no method of escape. (This noted from the recorded observations of the Chinese flood record.) The sun dimmed. The thunder and lightning increased in intensity, possibly the first major storm in earth's history, a thou-sand times worse than anything they had ever before experienced. The thoughts of the spectators turned to all those years Noah had warned them. "He was right all along," they thought to themselves, "but now it's too late!" Some thought of the sacred writings on the Towers of Seth, warning this would happen, but oh, if they would have only listened! Some reasoned it's all just a coincidence, thinking the quaking and storms would pass and life would return to normal in a few days. Others may have tried to go back and make it right with Noah. But that's not how it works once judgment com-mences; relationship with the Almighty is a condition of the heart, and God knows the *heart*. His decrees are immutable—look what happened to Adam and Eve in the garden, they were never allowed a second chance to return!

Fig. 34 The world was engulfed in volcanic activity.

Thoughts on Known Geologic Activity and the Flood

The Columbia lava flows exceed 90,000 square miles in the Northwest United States, the second largest known. This flow contains multiple layers to depths of 5,000 feet, mostly formed beneath water.

The atmosphere of the entire planet would have been greatly altered by this single event, and according to the Scriptures, events like this were occurring simultaneously across the globe.

Many geologists insist the process of mountain building is a slow one, but others differ,[1] noting the subduction zones are catastrophic, active and generally volcanic. The evidence points to a *past* catastrophic origin of the mountain ranges, example number one being Mount Everest, whose buttresses are sea-floor packed with marine fossils. (See Appendix XII.) Other well known mountains show the same, such as Mount McKinley, North America's highest peak, being a thrust feature resulting from the Pacific plate subducting beneath the North American plate by force, a force not in action today. Earth is the only planet in the solar system with these plates.

The Hebrew word used for flood, being *Mabbul*: to mix, mingle, confound or confuse, has an interesting usage here, found nowhere else in Scripture save reference to this single event. As the many layers of sediments around the earth are water transported and deposited, this word better and more completely describes the Flood.

Fig. 35 Liquefaction acting on foundations had global implications
during the Flood (1964 Niigata, Japan damage—public domain image)

In modern geologic terms, a process called *liquefaction* helps us better understand an important destabilization process that likely occurred at the Flood onset. Liquefaction is generally associated with quicksand and earthquakes, and as shown in the image, this process transforms ground normally capable of supporting buildings into a viscous and pliable material, playing a major role in the initial breakdown and subsequent sorting of the sediments in the Flood. With much of the earth's surface in this state, understanding how the crust became imbedded with the dead plants and animals caused by the Flood becomes more apparent. The expansion and contraction of surface material as earthquake waves transit an area will literally pump ground water vertically, permeating the surface with water. Add the flood waters described in the Bible, and we can imagine how entire formations were transformed into moving bodies of heavy silt/slurry flowing across the planet, capable of attaining high speeds and sorting into layers.

Another geologic phenomena called *turbidity current* exactly describes such moving layers, indicated by the sorting of the fossil material within. As defined by NOAA:

> *Turbidity currents can be set into motion when mud and sand on the continental shelf are loosened by earthquakes, collapsing slopes, and other geological disturbances. The turbid water then rushes downward like an avalanche, picking up sediment and increasing in speed as it flows. Turbidity currents can change the physical shape of the sea floor by eroding large areas and creating underwater canyons.* [2]

One such turbidity called the *Tyee* formation in Oregon is over 10,000 feet thick and left a remnant at 4,000 feet above sea level! (See Appendix XIII.) Another, the Morrison, is a massive fossil bearing layer located between Colorado and Utah covering 600,000 square miles, containing aquatic fossils mixed with dinosaurs. The westward exposure is viewable at Dinosaur National Park near Vernal, Utah. The worldwide presence of assorted fossils and sedimentary layers running miles deep helps us better appreciate the magnitude of the Flood. As most fossils are found within such geologic structures, this explains why we rarely observe fossils and strata forming on any such scale today. For example, the Karoo deposit in South Africa is known to run miles deep and covers over 200,000 square *miles,* containing *billions* of fossils. Reliable sources report there are currently *one million*[3] separate fossil deposits known in the world today, widely separated geographically. Taken together, such a volume of evidence cannot be explained away as minor or a result of local events; they tell a story, the story of the Flood.

The Destruction of Civilization Likely Occurred in the First Hours

The hyper-speed release of water into the earth's atmosphere likely destroyed the structure maintaining the hyperbolic atmosphere of the First Earth. Now this too was gone, the life enriching environment of earth damaged beyond repair. The unfolding series of earthquakes, tsunamis, volcanic action, typhoons, falling ash and rain combined created an unimaginable calamity on earth. Every structure more than a few meters high was leveled, save a few. The human population could not escape; they had ignored and mocked God despite Noah's many years of nonstop preaching in full view of the Ark. They and all animal life not aboard horribly and completely perished within the Flood year, most in the first few days, many in the first hours.

The Continents Are Broken
and the Plates Are Moving!

Fig. 36 The action of Subduction, where the Pacific Ocean Plate was driven
under the North American Continental Plate *rapidly* as the mid-ocean rifts became active,
likely subducting and recycling many pre-flood civilizations into *magma*. (see also Fig. 39)

As the First Earth is being destroyed and the crustal plates start moving, cities are buried and sucked below the crust, being dissolved into magma and thrust back to the surface. The drawing above depicts subduction whereby unimaginable forces press on adjacent plates, one descending below the other. The evidence is compelling showing these features were catastrophically formed not by a slow inch-by-inch process as suggested in today's geology textbooks but by forces exerted and measured in days. The aquifer system is now shattered, continental plates are moving and new mountain ranges are forming. The old order is passing away and the new emerging, only a shadow of its glorious past, and only an image of what God had called *"very good"* in the beginning.

Further commenting on the West Coast subduction and its effects, Dr. G. Frederick Wright, in his *Man and the Glacial Period* tells us: "The connection of lava-flows on the Pacific Coast with the Glacial Period is unquestionably close. For some reason which we do not understand, the vast accumulation of ice in North America is correlated with enormous eruptions of lava west of the Rockies. The extent of outflow of lava west of the Rockies is almost beyond comprehension. Literally hundreds of thousands of square miles have been covered by them to a depth—in many places—of thousands of feet. Here again we find volcanoes exerting their influence at the higher levels in the strata; but in the Rockies it is more as if the tired earth, in its last throes, had belched forth these enormous emanations of lava, as it were, in its dying effort. So from the lowest to the highest layers of the earth's crust we find that volcanoes and volcanic products have been in the main causes (if not the entire cause) of stratification. The volcanic mud of the Old Red Sandstone (England), the Argillaceous material of the oil-shales of the carboniferous, the lavas of the Tertiary, the pumice of the Atlantic Ocean, the loess—ubiquitous and most superficial—all these are of un-doubted volcanic origin." [4] (Such catastrophic events and their relation to glaciation are further detailed in Appendix XVI.)

The Bible describes the initial events in detail, as in Genesis 7:19 which states: *"The waters prevailed upon the earth."* Our English translation does little justice to the original meaning of "prevailed," the word actually meaning: *"overwhelmingly mighty."* No part of the earth's surface was left unaffected. The volcanic activity alone would have been enormous, dwarfing any known in history.

As the undersea plates separated and expanded as the fountains released, we know the Pacific Plate and others around the world subducted into adjacent structures. The Pacific Plate is known to have been driven beneath the North American Continental plate catastrophically. This resulted in numerous volcanoes when its material came in contact with the hot outer mantle, then turned magma and rose, creating the Cascades and other ranges, including the still active Aleutians and the Alaska Range and many others around the globe. The volcanoes active today, as noted in the May 1980 Mt. St. Helens eruption, give us a glimpse of the active past. The Pacific zone subduction remains unstable, referred to as the *"Ring of Fire,"* an active series of volcanic vents that encompass the entire Pacific Rim. The same may be said of many portions of the mid-ocean Atlantic rifts and subduction zones around the earth; they are the tell-tale remnants of the Flood catastrophe, not the slow work of eons past. We need to keep in mind the relative thickness of the earth's crust in the eyes of God—the flood effecting a mere 6 miles of the earth's crustal thickness across an 8,000 mile diameter sphere. In relation to the globe, this figure equals only a tiny percentage of the total relative thickness. In perspective, a pencil line on paper would not have the definition to locate Mt. Everest to the eye of the reader if drawn across the entire Asian continent coast to coast.

World Class Scientist Dr. John Baumgartner
Speaks out on the Continental Plates

Dr. John Baumgartner is a geophysicist employed at the Los Alamos National Laboratory in New Mexico. His work involves complex analysis and computer modeling of the structure of the earth's interior as related to tectonic activity. He has also been a strong detractor of the concept of the Geologic Column, arguing that many segments of the column are missing entirely. In 1997, *US News & World Report* interviewed Baumgartner, publishing a four page report concerning his work on plate tectonics. Dr. Baumgartner has developed a computer modeling program called *Terra*, whereby he successfully modeled the process of earthquakes, volcanoes and the movement of the earth's continental plates for study and predictive analysis. Gerald Schubert of University of California states of Baumgartner's work: "Baumgartner is a world class scientist."

There is compelling evidence from the fossil-bearing sediments on the continents that the breakup occurred during the time these sediments were being deposited. We are convinced that this "continental sprint" as it's been called, was during the time of the Flood, and part of the mechanism for it. — Dr. John Baumgartner

The *US News* article reports: "Baumgartner created *Terra* expressly to prove that the story of Noah and the Flood of Noah in Genesis 7:18 happened exactly as the Bible tells it...his numerical code [Terra] actually proves the Bible is correct." Creation Ministries International lately interviewed Baumgartner,[5] quoted here from an article providing an overview of his work and findings relating to the Noahic Flood and movements of the earth's crust.

"I believe there is now overwhelming evidence in favor of continental break-up and large-scale plate tectonic activity. The acceptance of these concepts is an amazing example of a scientific revolution, which occurred roughly between 1960 and 1970. However, this revolution did not go far enough, because the earth science community neglected and suppressed the evidence for Catastrophism— large-scale, rapid change—throughout the geological record. So the timescale the uniformitarian scientists today are using is dramatically too long. The strong weight of evidence is that there was a massive catastrophe, corresponding to the Genesis Flood, which involved large and rapid continental movements. My conclusion is that the only mechanism capable of producing that scale of catastrophe and not wrecking the planet in the process had to be internal to the earth. I am persuaded it involved rapid subduction (sinking) of the pre-flood ocean floor, pulling the 'plates' apart at the beginning of the Flood, and was probably associated with the breaking up of the 'fountains of the great deep' described in Scripture."

Magnetic Reversals Found
in the Ocean Rifts and Mountains

Fig. 37 Steen's Mountain in Oregon, where magnetic reversals were found to have occurred in *hours*, not thousands of years. (Image by author)

The rapidity and large amplitude of geomagnetic variation that we infer from [flow B51 Steen's Mtn.], even when regarded as an impulse during a polarity transition, truly strains the imagination.
—Coe and Prevot report[6]

Other evidence of a past rapid movement of the undersea plates comes in the form of the telltale physical and *magnetic signatures* found on the undersea rifts. Scientists have known for years that the structure of these "mid-ocean rifts" contain features of past events. Not only are there signs of rapid spreading as Dr. Baumgartner points out, but further, we find magnetic markers showing that the magnetic poles were reversing their north and south directions during this period. These polar "markers" show up in the parallel bands of magma (molten rock), expanding away from the mid-ocean rifts, suggesting a rapid pumping action occurred (possibly by lunar/tidal action peaking each 6 hours), forcing the floor apart and under the continents. This phenomenon helps to explain the folding features and mountain building events we see across the world today. We know these occurred sometime after creation and before now, the only known intervening episode being the Great Deluge as recorded in the Bible.

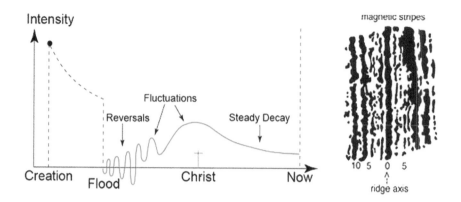

Fig. 38 The graph on the left theorizes the rapid reversals that occurred during the flood year. Right hand, actual magnetic shift plots found adjacent to the mid-ocean rifts (Graph courtesy Creation Ministries International www.creation.com)

When the center of these undersea rifts were drilled downward, scientists found the reversals frozen down their length,[7] captured in time once the magma cools, locking the compass switches in the rocks.* Clearly, much geologic activity was happening worldwide in the Flood period. Evolutionists attempt to assign these intervals with great ages, such as 40,000-700,000 years. This notion came under great scrutiny of late when samples from the Columbia flows in the scarp faces of Steen's Mountain in Oregon (where the exposure formation edges can be sampled) shocked the science world[8] as to their rapid reversals, suggested by the researchers themselves, could be measured in *hours!*

This period [of 15 days] is undoubtedly an overestimate...Nonetheless, even this conservative figure of 15 days corresponds to an astonishingly rapid rate of variation of the geomagnetic field direction of 3° per day." — Coe and Prevot[9]

As a final note, Dr. Russ Humphreys[10] predicted (preceding the discovery in Oregon) that if sometime in the future such a finding (that is, rapid reversals) were detected in the rocks, such evidence would provide significant support of his theories. With the Steen's find, one could then connect seafloor events to rapid magnetic change sequences elsewhere, a correlation of a global event.

*Author note: Dr. Russ Humphreys reported that of 200,000 such core samples taken, fully half or 100,000 show reversals around the earth.

The mid-ocean ridges or rifts are undersea chains that make up the boundary between seafloor plates. It's clear these inter-planes are in stasis today, but like a missing bridge on a highway, they tell a story.

Understanding the expansion/subduction process, where seafloor "spreading" makes contact and dives under a continental plate (see next figure), some expansion process from the ocean floor center must have affected the entire action, originating from the center "rifts." Seafloor Spreading occurs when all these processes—subduction, rift pushing and spreading—act together. Massive earthquakes are generated and magnetic direction potentially shifts; then magma erupting from the rifts is affected by the earth's magnetic field and the iron particles within align with the North/South lines of force while the flows are still hot. When the mass cools below the Curie temperature of 1000^0 F,[11] the polar direction becomes locked in position and can be measured. When it's sampled, the scientist carefully indexes the extracted core to determine its polarity relative to magnetic North. To determine the underwater parallel ridge compass directions, crews tow a sensor along the sea bottom and the sensing equipment collects the data.

Dr. Baumgartner continues on earth physics: "From an estimate of the viscosity of the outer core, where the currents associated with the earth's magnetism exist, there is no reason why the magnetic field can't reverse rapidly. Moreover, there is field evidence that it *has* reversed rapidly, within weeks. In addition, drilling the seafloor has shown that, regardless of the overall direction of the magnetism detected from the surface, the magnetic direction within a drill core frequently varies widely. This is less consistent with slow spreading than with a rapid welling up of new magma during a period of rapid reversals. The magma in contact with the surface will reflect the direction at that time, but by the time the deeper magma cools a few weeks later, the direction has switched again—and so on for deeper levels."

When correlating the three indicators: a) core drilling the sea rift centers and finding back-to-back reversals, b) observing the same "flips" pushed out along the undersea parallel ridges, and c) the rapid reversals noted in the Steen's Mountain find, we find that together they constitute powerful evidence all are related to a single event. Further, as the magma was pushing up and spread the seafloors (the author believes that lunar cycles were involved, hence a pulsing action creating a line of magma apparent on the seafloor), the plate movements affected the magnetic reversals by unbalancing the "parasitic" magnetism interaction between the plates, subducting material and earth's general magnetic signature. Finally, the hard data from the Steen's provides correlating results from a time perspective, providing the smoking gun evidence that the entire globe was involved in these processes. Subduction on Oregon's west coast also triggered the Columbia Flows of recent and vigorous appearance.

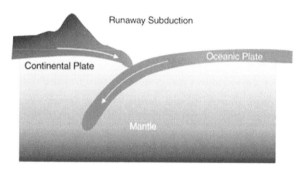

Fig. 39 Runaway Subduction or CPT; where the weight of the sinking material accelerates the spreading process through gravitational pull (Image courtesy Creation Ministries International www.creation.com)

Catastrophic Plate Tectonics or "CPT" is a new theory that explains the process of subduction, which once begun, could accelerate rapidly. (See image above.) In this model, gravity acts on the dropping or "plunging" crust material (sea floor in this instance), pulling the entire mass downward and assisting the sea-floor "spreading" process. This model suggests a global tectonic event powered by the gravitational pull of the sea floor(s) at the continental boundaries as they plunged into the earth's mantle. The CPT model demonstrates that the plates moved quickly during the Flood catastrophe, not at rates of centimeters per year as currently proposed by uniformity, but at *meters per second* rates. The CPT model more readily explains many of the earth's features including mountain folding, these being pushed (in accordion fashion) rapidly as a result of plate collision.[12] It's a well-known fact that the near vertical fault lines along the subduction planes are a major source of earthquake activity today, a remnant of much more such activity in the past. In Oregon, accretion lines may be viewed along Highway 20 some 20 miles inland, suggestive of a very active process now frozen in stone, with no sign of movement today. Above them the Oregon "Coast Range" was formed, this by the action of subduction, and their peaks found containing marine fossils.

Understanding that God is the Grand Master of physics, mathematics and all science, we see He had other plans for mankind and Noah, who somehow rode out this storm holding out in some eddy the Lord Provider arranged for His precious cargo of eight plus passengers.[13] So in this treatise, we have very strong support in the earth sciences of *rapid* tectonic activity, fully aligned with the record of Scripture, which also contain a witnessed and documented account. Such an account may not be discounted as scientific evidence, silencing the argument stating the Bible is confined to the realm of religion alone.

We now turn to other catastrophic events occurring on the earth's surface, while our crew of eight and passengers were riding out the storm of the millennium, huddling in the safety of the Ark.

Catastrophes that Evidence the Power of the Flood

Fig. 40 Mountain Folding, erroneously described to students of geology as uplifts, better understood as compression folds (Image Canada Dept. of GeoScience, Ottawa - From *In the Beginning,* Center for Scientific Creation[14])

To better understand the general catastrophe at hand, we must turn to the descriptions of past catastrophes to place in perspective what may have occurred in these first days of destruction on earth. Quoting George Macready Price concerning the general distribution of volcanic action:

In the rocks of all parts of the world, ancient displacements have been detected, with throws of vertical range measuring from 200 to 2,000 feet; and if these were suddenly brought about, as all analysis seems to indicate, there must have, at some time in the past, been earthquakes of indescribable violence.[15]

Fig. 41 The Lisbon earthquake of 1755 (image Wikipedia commons 2.0)

Famed Austrian geologist Edward Suess observed: "The earthquakes of the present day are certainly but a *faint reminiscence* [emphasis mine] of those telluric movements to which the structure of almost every mountain range bears witness. Numerous examples of great mountain chains suggest by their structure the possibility, and in certain cases the probability, of occasional intervention in the course of great geological processes of episodic disturbances of such indescribable and overpowering violence that the imagination refuses to follow the understanding and to complete the picture of which the outlines are furnished by observation of facts. Such catastrophes have not occurred since the existence of man, at least not since the time of written records."[16]

The Mississippi Earthquake of 1811

As examples of the known power of earthquakes, we first have the record of the "Great Earthquake in the West," taking place in November through February of 1811-12, around the Mississippi. This quake caused a substantial loss of life and destroyed the town of New Madrid, Missouri, along with many surrounding homes and structures. Tremors continued for weeks, culminating in January and February 1812. The event affected a region along the Mississippi for some 300 miles between the mouth of the Ohio and St. Francis rivers. Heavy shocks reached as far as the mountains of Tennessee, Pittsburgh and the Atlantic coast. Shock after shock hit New

Madrid, destroying the town and portions of the country.

An eyewitness account written by Eliza Bryan records: "On the 16th of December, 1811, about two o'clock, a.m., we were visited by a violent shock of an earthquake, accompanied by a very awful noise resembling loud but distant thunder, but more hoarse and vibrating, which was followed in a few minutes by the complete saturation of the atmosphere, with sulphurous vapor, causing total darkness. The screams of the affrighted inhabitants running to and fro, not knowing where to go, or what to do—the cries of the fowls and beasts of every species the cracking of trees falling, and the roaring of the Mississippi the current of which was retrograde for a few minutes, owing as is supposed, to an interruption in its bed formed a scene truly horrible."[17]

The Mississippi water changed color to a reddish murk, mud being thrown up from its course. Large fissures violently opened and snapped closed, throwing up sand, coal and mud, shooting water jets when the fissure closed again. The air became filled with heavy vapors of a purplish tinge. The Mississippi reversed course for a day, turning back overnight just as violently, its waters roaring and destroying everything in its path. Square miles of forests were swallowed up in this process, hills vanished and new lakes formed in their place, the largest being the 18,000 acre Reelfoot Lake that exists to this day, caused when the Mississippi back flowed into a swamp!

Huge fissures opened, swallowing everything in their path and closed again in moments, exposing deep sections of strata, including fossil bones of pre-historic animals such as ichthyosaurs and mammoths. Graves were opened and scattered. Black oily water emerged up to the belly of a horse in some areas. Forests and other property dropped up to one hundred feet with the resultant broken features. Considering the Noahic flood, we may multiply the magnitude of these events by many times, providing a grim picture of the scenes as they unfolded at the time of the great Flood. Pondering the thought if such a thing happened today, how would people react? Would they consider what happened in Noah's time and reflect upon eternity?

The 1835 Concepción Earthquake

On February 20, 1835 Concepcion, Chile, was struck by an earthquake that destroyed 33% of the kiln-dried brick buildings, 71% of the mud-brick buildings and 95% of stone-built types. A tidal wave generated by the quake was known to have crossed the ocean to the Society and Navigator Islands, three and four thousand miles away, causing severe damage. Concerning the power of this earthquake, observing French geologist d'Orbigny made the comment: "After having seen at Callao in Peru the ravages which a sweeping earthquake may make, I am justified in believing that the upheaval of the Andes would suffice to destroy at one stroke by a movement of water all the terrestrial fauna of the *globe*" [emphasis mine]. In recent times, an 8.8 magnitude again struck the city of Concepción in February 2010, killing over 500 people and injuring thousands nationwide. Geologists concluded that the city had been displaced roughly three meters in this quake. The zone is near a subduction of the Pacific and Continental plate in Chili.

Tidal, Storm Surge and Tsunami Power

To briefly discus the power of water in catastrophic storm conditions, we have the many eyewitness records of history to teach us. Tsunamis can have wavelengths ranging from 10 to 500 km and wave periods of up to an hour. As a result of their long wavelengths, tsunamis act as shallow-water waves. A wave becomes a shallow-water wave when the wavelength is very large compared to the water depth. In deep ocean, the typical water depth is around 4000 meters, in such a tsunami may attain speeds of 200 m/s, or more than 500 miles per hour (700 km/h)!"[18] This formula for disaster played out May 22, 1960, when a Chilean earthquake reached a Rector Scale magnitude of 9.5 (the strongest ever recorded).

This quake sent out a series of fatal tidal waves up to 50 feet high, striking the US coasts from California to Alaska and wreaking havoc across the Pacific. Traveling at speeds of over 500 miles per hour, the wave slammed into the Pacific islands including Hawaii and resumed west to impact the shores of New Zealand, Australia, the Philippines and all the way north to Japan. Thousands of miles from its source, the waves still maintained heights of 30 feet (10 meters) at these amazing speeds! The losses to human life were enormous, with an estimated 5,700 killed, inflicting 800 million dollars in damage.[19]

Fig. 42 Damage to Hilo, Hawaii, caused by the Great Chilean Earthquake May 20, 1960. The tidal wave crossed the Pacific Ocean at speeds nearing 500 *miles per hour;* contour lines indicate distance traveled in one hour. (Images NASA & Wikipedia Comm. 2.0)

The Chilean event was eclipsed in destructive power when on December 26, 2004, the great *Indian Ocean tsunami* struck. This tsunami was caused by an 800 mile long undersea rupture of the "Ring of Fire" mega-thrust, approximately 100 miles north of Simelule Island, Sumatra. Creating a 9.2 magnitude earthquake equivalent to the explosion of 23,000 Hiroshima-sized atomic bombs, the event caught thousands completely off guard on a Sunday. There was no time for alarms to sound due to the close proximity of the epicenter near these densely populated areas. The human toll was enormous, the waves striking the low lying districts of a number of larger cities and villages. This calamity marks the most devastating catastrophe known in modern history, reportedly killing nearly 230,000 people.[20]

Indian Ocean Tsunami—Casualty and Cost Statistics

Human deaths: 226,000 dead, including 166,000 in Indonesia, 38,000 in Sri Lanka, 16,000 in India, 5,300 in Thailand and 5,000 foreign tourists Number of people injured: Over 500,000

Number of people affected: Up to 5 million people lost homes or access to food and water

Number of children affected: 30% of the casualties are children, and 1.5 million have been wounded, displaced or lost families[21]

Known Destructive Power of Storm Waves

As noted in the book, *The Genesis Flood* by Morris and Whitcomb (1961), the breakwater complex near Wick, Scotland, for years challenged man's best efforts to contain the tremendous power of wave action from storms. Reinforced with a structure of 1,350 tons (that failed in the great Storm of 1872), the same engineer watched in horror as his invention was removed like a play-toy directly from the very channel it was to protect. Not to be outdone, the monolith was doubled in size to 2,600 tons and subsequently treated likewise in a storm that followed soon after construction! In France at the port of Cherbourg, a significant storm struck the massive riprap breakwater, tossing its material made up of 2-1/2 ton stones over a 20 foot high seawall like so many basketballs and removing concrete blocks weighing over 120,000 pounds more than 50 feet.[22]

The destructive power of water is multifaceted and well understood. We can see when these physics are applied to any material including steel or stone; no destructive capability is impossible for this liquid to undertake.

Volcanism and Krakatoa

In the most dramatic event ever witnessed by modern man, we have the 1883 eruption of Krakatoa. Preceded by months of huge plumes of steam and ash, earthquakes and nightly glowing flows, the locals on the neighboring islands enjoyed the show in celebrations; but that would soon end.

On Monday morning, August 27, 1883, several explosions took place, signaling that this was the big day. In the mightiest set of eruptions known to modern man, the entire island exploded, annihilating 2/3rds of its mass and ejecting 5 cubic miles of earth skyward. The major explosion was heard 2,000 miles away in Perth, Australia, and 3,000 miles distant in Mauritius, four hours after the occurrence. It is estimated that the explosion carried the force equivalent of 13,000 Hiroshima nuclear bombs and was 4 times the power of the largest hydrogen bomb ever detonated. Ash was propelled 50 miles high, ascending as a dark cloud into the atmos-phere, completely obscuring the sun over a vast area and finally encircling the earth. Debris of many tons was ejected for miles. Overall, the world's temperatures plunged nearly 1.2 degrees Centigrade on average, disrupting weather patterns for five years. The pressure wave was recorded across the globe and continued to register for days. The initial August 27th explosion reported to have reverberated around the earth seven times. It was said that anyone within ten miles of the site went deaf from the concussion alone, if they even survived. Tsunamis up to one hundred feet high were generated, destroying over 160 towns and villages and reportedly killing nearly 36,000 people (later counts brought this number closer to 120,000). Ships were carried inland, one for over a mile and a half. In the year following, groups of human remains were reported afloat on the Indian Ocean, laying on rafts of volcanic pumice and washing ashore as far away as East Africa.

Fig. 43 A satellite view of earth during hurricane season
(Image by NASA)

Tornados, Typhoons and Hurricanes

The largest tornados may stretch more than two miles across and stay on the ground for dozens of miles, attaining wind speeds of more than 300 miles per hour, high enough to drive 2x4 lumber through oak trees. Stories from the early West document the uplifting and removal of people, wagons and livestock and depositing them miles away. Also associated with tornados is a terrible roar, along with peals of lightning and thunder. Few buildings are safe in the path of a tornado. In the cataclysm of the deluge and complete disruption of earth's atmosphere, tornados likely appeared for the first time in history. As a terrible reminder of the fury such a storm can inflict, we have the additional destructive power of the typhoon, such as Typhoon Hayian, designated a *Super Typhoon*, possibly the most powerful one ever recorded by man. Hayian struck the Philippines on November 8, 2013, killing 20,000 and displacing over 600,000, inflicting widespread damage across the entire country at the estimated cost of 2 trillion dollars. Tornado like events are mentioned in Job, described as a "whirlwind."

God Himself comments as follows:

Then the LORD answered Job out of the whirlwind, and said:
"Who is this who darkens counsel By words without
knowledge?Now prepare yourself like a man;
I will question you, and you shall answer Me.
Where were you when I laid the foundations of the earth?
Tell Me, if you have understanding.
"Who determined its measurements?
Or who shut in the sea with doors,
When it burst forth and issued from the womb;
When I made the clouds its garment,
And thick darkness its swaddling band;
When I fixed My limit for it,
And set bars and doors;
When I said, 'This far you may come,
but no farther, here your proud waves must stop!'

"Have you commanded the morning since your days began, And
caused the dawn to know its place,
That it might take hold of the ends of the earth,
And the wicked be shaken out of it?
It takes on form like clay under a seal,
And stands out like a garment.

"From the wicked their light is withheld,
And the upraised arm is broken.
Can you lift up your voice to the clouds,
That an abundance of water may cover you?
Can you send out lightnings, that they may go,

"And say to you, 'Here we are!'?
Who has put wisdom in the mind?
Or who has given understanding to the heart?
Who can number the clouds by wisdom?
Or who can pour out the bottles of heaven..?" (Job 38)

God and His Word are absolutes, they adequate and powerful, containing the full and complete model from which man may study His works, and then with *fear*.

Fig. 44 A tornado making ground contact (image Wikipedia CC 2.0)

Then the LORD answered Job out of the whirlwind, and said: "I will question you, and you shall answer Me!" (Job 38:3)

The Bible tells us the Flood began when *"all the fountains of the great deep bust forth."* The Hebrew definition of all is any, every and *whole*. There is world-wide evidence that eruptions of this magnitude occurred *simultaneously* at the onset of the Flood. To imagine hearing and feeling the successive concussions and earthquakes, the roar of tsunamis, volcanoes, tornados, hurricanes and typhoons spreading across the planet in unison would have been completely terrifying. Add to this was the unstoppable rainfall and flooding. We can be sure many turned their minds to those past appeals made by Noah, now wishing they had responded differently. We leave this for the reader to comprehend, being mindful the objects used by God in this terrible judgment being that of water and *"bursting forth."*

The Opening Events of the Next Judgment

We have in the earth proof after proof and evidence after evidence of this great catastrophe as recorded in Genesis. The Bible tells us there will be another announcement, heralding the coming of *Christ*, this not with the exploding of mountains, hurricanes and rainfall, but with *Peals of Thunder* and the blast of *Mighty Trumpets*. Where before, Christ ascended from earth humbly before a few in a corner, He will then come as King of Kings and Lord of Lords, nobly mounted for all to see and ready for *battle*.

This too will be an event world-encompassing in scope, for the Scriptures declare:

> *As lightning comes from the East and flashes to the West, so also will the coming of the Son of man be!* (Matthew 24:28b)

And further:

> *And I saw heaven opened, and behold a white horse; and He that sat upon him was called Faithful and True, and in righteousness he doth judge and make war...And he hath on his vesture and on his thigh a name written, King of Kings, And Lord of Lords* (Revelation 19:11,16).

Rest assured God will have no less honor for His Son, last seen dying and ignominiously stripped on a tree, now coming in *all honor* and *all power* to set the record straight.

The Succumbing

Unimaginable scenes of struggle occurred in the initial days of the Flood. With the general calamity engulfing the planet, few man-made structures would have survived the first day. The Appendix records instances where remains of man and beast have been unearthed together, many in cave structures strangely sealed in waterborne solutions of lime, gravel and sediment. Some caves show signs of successive backfilling attempts, possibly initiated by those dwelling within, eventually succumbing to the water and the ever-present onslaught of wild animals, painting a grim scene of terrible struggle.

It's difficult to imagine what was happening to these people as the catastrophe unfolded. First, the terrible succession of detonations as the volcanoes erupted and earth's crust fractured on a global scale. Oh, the trembling, explosions, cyclones and ash fall! Everything left alive from the initial eruptions would be heading for any cover to be found, such becoming terrible scenes of hysteria and panic in those first hours and days. Reality would then set in with all the hopelessness, fear and scores of hydrophobic deaths. (One city in Asia being so named.) The populace drowning and fighting for safe refuge; the weeping and cries of the little ones for help. The convergence of fearful animals and people competing for limited space on the high ground and finally, the grim inevitable as each helplessly watched their loved ones slip hopelessly into the waves.

Neither the well financed nor governmental elite were safe—none would escape. As the waters rose and habitable land mass decreased, the struggle for life multiplied, especially on higher ground. (Such is noted in the Fossils section concerning the hippopotamus finds in Italy.) Eventually each would be looking for anything that floated to survive, striking out onto the water itself; and no matter what their craft, eventually succumbing to the waves. The land reptiles would now be perishing and sinking by the thousands, as such found in the lower layers and covered first; this being in a general sense the burial sequence observed in the fossil layers today. Often mammal fossils are found in the higher layers, which once they are drowned, resurface after several day's time (more directly described as "bloating and floating"), possibly mingling among large floating log mats known to exist as part of any major flood.

Such grim descriptions are only mentioned to remind the reader what judgment by a holy God could be like, not that God is evil or unfair. Our God is a holy God, and when man turns his back and mocks Him long enough, His patience expires and inevitably, as a last resort, judgment is decreed.

Fig. 45 The last safe haven on earth

(Image courtesy Creation Ministries International www.creation.com)

The time period from Adam to the Flood was ten generations or 1,600 years, from the Flood to Christ approximately 2,400, and from Christ to the present just over 2,000 years. A day is coming the Bible tells us, when the next end will come. We are likely near that time, the horrific details of the coming judgment found detailed in the Book of Revelation, Matthew and elsewhere in the Scriptures, written for us as a warning in our time. As were the warnings posted on the Towers of Seth, so we read of them in the Bible today, and they will surely come to pass.

[1] *Origin of Mountains*, Edited by Cliff Ollier and Colin Pain Routledge, London 2000

[2] http://oceanservice.noaa.gov/facts/turbidity.html

[3] https://mapsengine.google.com/map/viewer?msa=0&mid=zIY48eTMIq2I.kDMDh0AGlz4c

[4] Journal of the Transactions of the Victoria Institute, LXII, 98 ff.

[5] http://creation.com/probing-the-earths-deep-places Overview of Dr. John Baumgardner

[6] Coe, R.S. and Prévot, M., 1989. Evidence suggesting extremely rapid field variation during a geomagnetic reversal. *Earth and Planetary Science Letter* 92:292–298

[7] J.M. Hall and P.T. Robinson, "Deep crustal drilling in the North Atlantic Ocean," *Science* 204:573–586, 1980

[8] Coe, R.S. and Prévot, M., 1989. Evidence suggesting extremely rapid field variation during a geomagnetic reversal. *Earth and Planetary Science Letter* 296,7

[9] Coe, R.S. and Prévot, M., 1989. Evidence suggesting extremely rapid field variation during a geomagnetic reversal. *Earth and Planetary Science Letter*

[10] Humphreys, D.R., 1986. Reversals of the earth's magnetic field during the Genesis Flood. *Proceedings of the First International Conference on Creationism*, Creation Science Fellowship, Pittsburgh 2:113–126

[11] http://en.wikipedia.org/wiki/Curie_temperature

[12] Austin, S. and 5 others, *Catastrophic plate* tectonics: A global model of earth history; in: Walsh, R., *The Third International Conference on Creationism*, Pittsburgh, Pennsylvania, p. 609–621

[13] http://creation.com/the-earths-magnetic-field-and-the-age-of-the-earth

[14] Center for Scientific Creation, Phoenix, AZ http://creationscience.com/onlinebook/HydroplateOverview4.html [15] Price, *The New Geology*, p. 242

[16] *Face of the Earth*, Suess, Edward I 17 ff., quoted by Price, op. cit., p. 244

[17] Letter of Eliza Bryan as referenced in "Lorenzo Dow's Journal," Published By Joshua Martin, Printed by John B. Wolff, 1849, on pages 344 - 346

[18] http://www.bom.gov.au/tsunami/info/ PP. 5

[19] Cited from Morris & Whitcomb, *The Genesis Flood* 1961, P&R publishing p. 264 quoting *Civil Engineering*, Vol. 30 July 1960 p.88

[20] en.wikipedia.org/wiki/Tsunami - History

[21] www.newscientist.com/article/dn9931-facts-and-figures-asian-tsunami-disaster.html#.U3JYB3YXJsM

[22] Cited from Morris & Whitcomb, *The Genesis Flood* 1961, quoting Bascom, Willard, *Scientific American*, V. 201 Aug 1959

9

The Time of Waiting

ow finally afloat, Noah, family and their reluctant cargo have a storm to ride out; not any storm, but the worst storm in earth's history! Now amidst the terrors of it, we can be sure they wished in their hearts this long expected event had never begun.

As the waters "prevailed" for another 150 days, the good ship held fast, its builders happy for the close attention paid to every plank, rib and fastener they had attached with care. I am sure Noah had to chastise his sons for accuracy and sturdiness more than once in the process of building. Those of us who parent understand. Say as you will, but nothing teaches like experience. We may imagine them thanking their father over and over for those chastisements now, their very lives depending upon their craftsmanship of every frame, bolt and plank. Lesson after lesson in parenting and authority were being taught, these folk the seed of the new human race.

one anticipated the ride that was coming. Their vessel was like little more than a rubber toy floating on a river in high flood stage. But the Ark held fast, and like those on any voyage riding out a terrible storm, we can be assured many a prayer went skyward in those days, each with its unknowns and challenges. Their live cargo could have required constant atten-tion, the day and night watch and repair of leaks, the tension of it all, only to wake to another morning or night (not knowing which) and start all over again for forty days and nights! In such a tempest, one can imagine that in a few days time the entire crew swore off sailing for good, dreaming of the day when they would set foot on dry ground again. They must have listened to Noah's teaching and encouragement and prayed, listened and prayed. After many days, God sent a "warm wind" across the surface and the reced-ing process of the waters began. I can think of no happier folk than these when the storms calmed, waters ceased rising and the sun came out. Soon the tops of mountains came into view!

Scientific Observations

The Bible provides an exact date when the flood began, its duration, observations of events, the termination of the rain and fountains, recession period, dates of sightings, reconnaissance, final resting place and ending date. These are witnessed and documented accounts, and as such fall into the cat-egory of "scientific observation." These no different than say, a geologist's account of the sequence of events recorded before, during, and after the Mt. St. Helens eruption that commenced on May 18, 1980 and forward. Such observations caused the rewriting of feature forming geologic theory set to paper for 100 years prior, heretofore unobserved. To say the Bible is not a book of science, i.e., an honest and accurate observation, is an error. God sets the framework for man to study; science therefore is and was never intended to mock that framework. Man's knowledge is limited; God's is not. As humans we can never be sure we have all the evidence nor certain we interpret the evidence that we have correctly. One piece of controverting evidence can reverse and unravel most any theory at a moment, like at St Helens, but God is never changing. Over and over again critics have put forth theory after theory to "disprove" the Bible and these accounts, and over and over they proved in error and God's Word true.

The Written Record—Where Did It Come From?

Biblical archaeologists tell us that Genesis was originally inscribed on a number of sequentially ordered tablets. The word "to write" in Hebrew ac-tually means to cut in, or dimple stone, in other words, to inscribe as what we know as *cuneiform*. Now that a huge volume of these tablets have been unearthed and translated in the Middle East, an entirely new understanding of the ways and means people did business and communicated in those times has been revealed. After years of study, discoveries in a number of unearthed *tel* dig sites revealed a code used by the scribes, called *"toledot* phrases." Toledot or *doth* differs from *dor* in Hebrew, where *dor* is used over 100 times in Genesis relating to family line and not history. Toledot directly relates to origin, history, history of the rise, or development of a thing, in other words—*history*.

For example, in Genesis 6:8 we read: *"And these are the generations of Noah."* This informs the careful scholar that Noah is the author of this record or "tablet," the toledot phase placed at the *conclusion* of the record, not the beginning. The word *generation* or *teledot* more accurately translates this verse: *"This is **the history** as recorded by Noah"* (emphasis added). The next passage in which we see this statement is in Genesis 10:1, where we read: "And these are the Generations of the Sons of Noah; Shem, Ham and Japheth," or better translated; *"This is **the history** recorded by the Sons of Noah, Shem, Ham and Japheth"* (Genesis 10:1 emphasis added). This indicates that the sons of Noah jointly authored the written record from Genesis 6:8 through 10:1, and sure enough, a triple version of this scroll was translated, covering the space of time from Noah's "the history" in Genesis 6:8 inclusive of the segment of time of their personal experience, including what occurred after Noah's passing.

Most Bible versions can miss the importance of the word meaning and context as used by the ancients, making all the difference in understanding the meaning. This methodology has been determined the standard method of the scribes (a school of professional cuneiform writers) used in constructing a tablet in those times.[1]

Authority of the Toledot

Determining factors relating to the authenticity of historical tablets include three important requisites:

1. The author was living throughout the period in which the tablet records
2. He was a firsthand witness to the events documented
3. The narrative concludes near the end of the author's life

Of the eleven subsections of Genesis (see table), this methodology is exactly replicated in each case, adding strong validity to the fact that Genesis *is* accurate and witnessed history.

True Archeology Aligns with the Biblical Record

The writing and high level of culture is prevalent as deep as archaeologists go and confound the essential basis of evolutionary based history which erroneously insists "If it's old, it must be primitive." This idiom is exactly the *reverse* of what is found in the Tels, where the real evidence exactly *match* the chronology of man's development as found in Genesis. Evidence coming to us such as constructed articles and advanced metallurgy. One analysis at Ur found iron tools used before 2700 BC of bronze alloyed with tin, (a prerequisite of advanced casting) also an image artifact was found consisting of 82.9% copper, 1.33% nickel and .88% antimony—noted as very advanced forging work.

Hence, writing and the development of highly advanced civilization are found at the foundation. Such finds prompted Sir Leonard Woolly to comment in his book *The Sumerians*: "The fourth millennium before Christ saw Sumerian art at its zenith" referencing a time near Adam.

Of late, complete libraries of near flood-time cites have been uncovered, confirming biblical events of patriarchal times including direct references to the Flood. Excavations at Nippur, Ebla,[2]* Mari, and Nuzi have all yielded written confirmation of Old Testament history, dating long before Abraham, a thousand years before writing was in use, according to the modernists! At Mari, the archives contained actual names used in the Bible such as Peleg, Terah, Abram, Jacob, Laban, and others. Multiple tablets (and a prism, see below) have been found containing direct references to Creation and specifically the Flood, mentioning lists of before-flood kings, (such as the 10 mentioned in Genesis 5) written in a form of writing representing the earliest known (pre-canaanite). There are also two more finds, prism WB62 and WB444, recording lists of rulers who reigned "before the Flood," [and] "after the Flood." It seems the deluge was matter-of-fact knowledge near the 2400 BC suggested flood date.

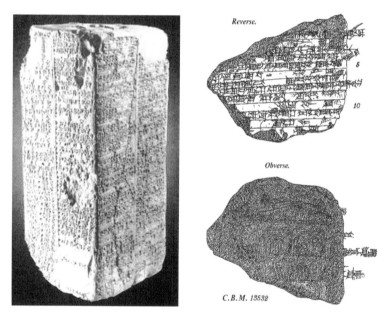

Fig. 46 Prism PR 444, (LH) listing the kings who lived before the Flood and
Tablet CBM 13532, (RH) inscribed w/portions of Genesis Chapter 6 & 7
closely matching our modern Bible & dated to a period soon after the Flood

In a broader perceptive, it's amazing that the Scriptures *do* provide an expanded view Noah could not have seen. Yet the record is found to be trustworthy around the world in the form of fossil remains and a plethora of catastrophically formed features unexplained by any other geologic means. Noah would have never doubted the possibility of such global support of the Flood narrative, as such mattered not to him, he saw it all happen, he was there! Noah's written observations are factual, global in context and confirmed in the realm of geology, paleontology, history and archeology. They have full support in the recorded history of many hundreds of cultures (which opposing secularists attempt to dub "Flood Myths" as summarized in Appendix II) and the fact is, the more archaeologists dig, the more they prove the accuracy of the Bible in all area's relating to the Flood.

Such criticisms are upended by tablet CBM 13532, detailed here and following, this writing considered per-canaanite and this tablet in particular - the oldest writing known, recording none other than the story of the Flood!

Note at Ebla, over 17,000 tablets were unearthed that included dozens of biblical place names and people groups. The tablets also included the creation and flood stories, closely resembling the biblical account in pre-Hebrew syntax. Place names included the five cities on the plain, Jerusalem and Salem dating back to the 3rd millennium BC, or just after the Flood. Word use at Ebla is Semitic: for instance the word "to write" is k-t-b (same as the Hebrew), for "king" is "malikum," and that for "man" is "adamu." See link: http://www.icr.org/article/ebla-its-impact-bible-records/

1	Genesis 1:1	Genesis 2:4	God Himself
2	Genesis 2:4	Genesis 5:1	Adam
3	Genesis 5:1	Genesis 6:9	Noah
4	Genesis 6:9	Genesis 10:1	Shem, Ham & Japheth
5	Genesis 10:1	Genesis 11:10	Shem
6	Genesis 11:10	Genesis 11:27	Terah
7	Genesis 11:27	Genesis 25:19	Isaac
8	Genesis 25:12	Genesis 25:18	Ishmael, through Isaac
9-11	Genesis 25:19	Genesis 37:2	Esau and Jacob

Genesis Tablet connections containing *toledoth phrases* (After Wiseman[3] 1985).

Early Flood Story Tablet Undermines Liberal Criticism

Some Bible critics assert the Genesis Flood account was rewritten after Moses' version, claiming it is actually based on the Epic of Gilgamesh, found in Nineveh in the 1800's and inscribed around 600 BC. (Moses lived at about 1300 BC.) It was determined this version was copied about 300 years after the Flood. "Epic" has similarities but is full of fairy tale-like details few consider true. Upon the weight of the Gilgamesh version modernists wishfully claim that Genesis is merely an imitation. Unknown to most archaeologists, an earlier Flood tablet exists, discovered in the ancient Babylonian city of Nippur in 1890. In 1909 Dr. Hermann Hilprecht translated the text, given catalogue designation CBM 13532. This tablet dates from about 2200 BC or within 100 years of the Flood itself. The similarities between the Genesis record and the Nippur tablet are complelling, as no detail differs from the biblical account. Here in part is a transcript of Hilprecht's translation, reconstructed by Fritz Hommel:

The springs of the deep will I open. A flood will I send which will affect all of mankind at once. But seek thou deliverance before the flood breaks forth, for over all living beings, however many there are, will I bring annihilation, destruction, ruin. Take wood and pitch and build a large ship!...cubits be its complete height...a houseboat shall it be, containing those who preserve their life...with a strong roofing cover it...the ship which thou makest, take into it...the animals of the field, the birds of the air and the reptiles, two of each, instead of (their whole number)....

As a result of this evidence,* Dr. John Morris informs us: "This clear text stands as both a confirmation of Scripture and a condemnation of liberal "scholarship." It so clearly undermines the "critical" view... Professor Hilprecht himself was hardly a defender of Scripture, yet he was a recognized expert in ancient languages. His translation originally caused quite a storm of controversy among academics, for it undercut their position that Genesis carries no authority, but no challenge was ever levied against his translation. Few know of the tablet or of its strong testimony to Scriptural authority."**

*Pinches, G. and F. Hommel. 1910. *The Oldest Library in the World and the New Deluge Tablets.* Expository Times. 21: 369 Source: Dr. Bill Cooper, *The Earliest Flood Tablet,* Pamphlet 382, May 2011, published by the Creation Science Movement, Portsmouth, UK.
**Morris, J. 2011. Genesis, Gilgamesh, and an Early Flood Tablet. *Acts & Facts.* 40 (11): 16. http://www.icr.org/article/genesis-gilgamesh-early-flood-tablet/

Criticism of biblical authenticity peaked in the 1940's but was squelched when a young boy discovered a cave full of earthen jars containing the "Dead Sea Scrolls" in 1947. These were found to include a portion of every Old Testament book except Ruth. One scroll contained a complete copy of Isaiah, matching today's conservative King James Version (as translated from Hebrew) yet buried during the Roman wars 2,000 years prior. Note that one of the major themes of the Book of Isaiah is the return of Israel to its native homeland, which occurred six months after this find in 1948!

Sadly, an entire generation of modern theologians have been wrongly influenced by mistaken secular archaeology, knowing only a part of the story. Critics attempt to explain away these ever so foundational chapters as allegory, myths and/or oral legends, casting a cloud upon passages we now know have been "written in stone." (What did Satan say to Eve: "God did not surely say...") This to the detriment of many who *wrongly* trusted these worldly teachers and books, authored to explain away non-existent "difficulties." But alas, change comes hard, the new evidence is unshakably clear that the trustworthiness of the written words of Genesis as we have them today are true, and we can be assured of one thing, Genesis is *"The History."*

The Early Writers Knew Nothing of Global Geology

Professor John Woodward in his early treatise, "The Natural History of the Earth" (1726) expounds on this fact. Woodward provides us with a very telling account where as the commerce and explorations of the renaissance expanded across the globe, so did understanding of the world-wide implications of the Flood. Setting out from England, France, and all over Europe, these early explorers set foot upon the general scope of earth and came to a general conclusion as summarized in Woodward's comments that: "The fossils and sea shells are found atop the highest mountains and in the deepest mines at every part of the Globe." Further pointing out that neither Moses (the assembler of Genesis) nor Noah could not have had any knowledge of this "Universality of the Deluge," that was so broadly seen in earth's natural history. He mentions their (Moses and Noah's) particular travels took them only as far as "Egypt, Median and Arabia, all of which have few marine bodies [and that Moses as writer] could reasonably infer nothing as to the whole Globe, the Universal overflowing of it, and the destruction of its frame."[4]

Woodward mentions that fossils were of regular occurrence in the mines and wells of England and on the European Continent, many known to be indigenous to remote places. The only explanation for their occurrence was long transport by water. He also noticed that along with the shells were lodged the parts of "land animals, vegetation and even whole trees" in the mines. He goes on to mention the fact that the high latitudes also held out-of-place fossils such as "breadfruit trees, magnolias, ferns, oaks, cinnamon and ginko, now found growing only in south China and India, but reported in fossil from as far away as Antarctica." Woodward clearly understood that a general and uniform destruction by water engulfed the planet, along with an alteration of earth's climate, just as the Scriptures teach.

John Woodward is credited as being among the first to understand and document the general effects of the flood and climate change relating to the fossil record. He saw clearly how each fit into the biblical model and founded the concept of fossil distribution by specific gravity, and sought to describe the physics of the atom. As a long time friend of Isaac Newton, he was buried alongside him at Westminster. We can call him one of the true Fathers of Geology. So within this section of Genesis we have one writer, Noah, and seven witnesses. We can be sure there was not a liar among them, as who would dare tamper with the Word of God after what they had just experienced?

The Abating Water, Feature Forming and Currents

The waters abated as recorded in Genesis 8 and began the process of running off the continents into the new sea basins. The change began with the cessation of the water influx and a dry wind the Bible tells us in Genesis 8:1 and lasted another 150 days. Finally, the Ark set to rest on Ararat, the narrative records, though weeks remained before party and cargo would be able to remove themselves from the vessel. At this point, mountain tops were observed on the horizon (Genesis 8:5), giving hope that the end was finally near. We can assume this was a big day aboard the Ark; maybe singing broke out. If so we can be sure the entire cargo chimed in creating a cheerful din!

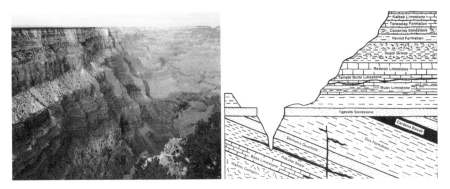

Fig. 47 The Grand Canyon, its layers a testament to the Flood, note the shear of pure Tapeats Sandstone at the Great Unconformity (RH image) and the evidence of rapid erosion (LH image): "And the waters ran continually off the earth for 150 days" (Genesis 8:3).

How does water erode rock? This issue had perplexed geologists for decades, when in 1983 they got their example in the Glen Canyon Dam incident. An excessively large snowpack runoff that year overfilled the reservoir, the fully open dam floodgates unable to compensate for the extra volume of water. Here it was found (a fact which caused a near catastrophic dam failure) that as water passed over the steel bypass valves at a certain velocity, gas bubbles formed, acting as powerful jack hammers capable of eroding feet of hardened metal and/or rock in hours! Geophysicists now have proof positive of how multiplied tons of running water could erode off any rock surface, lava included, in a very short time period.

Genesis 8:5 gives us additional detail, for the text using the word "continually" in English is not the whole and true meaning in the Hebrew. Expanding on the word definition, the translation is better rendered: "going and returning" of the water. This means there must have been tremendous tides running past the grounded ship (and mountain peaks for that matter) day and night, based on the six hour lunar cycle. (Some suggest the currents ran as fast as 80 meters/second).[5] At first, little friction would hold the pow-erful torrents in sway until the general recession exposed the land masses, now unable to restrict the powerful torrents. We can assume the bulge of water would move quickly from one side of the globe to the other, affecting the submerged surface in ways known only to God.

William Kirby of the Royal Society Considered These Effects

Relating to the verse in Genesis 8:,5 we have President William Kirby of the Royal Society considering these effects, noting them as the period when multiple stratifications were rapidly forming across the earth's surface. Such layers are considered the work of great eons of time by the uniformitarian geologist, when actually they are simply explained in this verse. In his Bridgewater Treatise entitled *The History, Habits and Instincts of Animals*, Kirby spoke to this period: "As it appears to me that the scriptural account of the great Cataclysm has not been duly weighed, and its magnitude, duration, momentum, varied agency, and their consequences sufficiently estimated by geologists, I will endeavor as briefly as I can to call to their attention and Christian philosophers generally, to the most striking features exhibited by it..." In the seventh month of the deluge on the seventeenth day of the month, the Ark rested on the mountains of Ararat, from which period the waters returned off the face of the earth "going and returning" as it is in the Hebrew, but rendered in our translation "continu-ally." Almost all ancient versions adhere to the literal sense (going and re-turning), which seems important, for it indicates a *flux and reflux* of the waters, which would affect the deposition of the matters floating upon or suspended in them."[6]

Now considering the great amount of study attributed to stratigraphy since that date, his understanding of the action of waters on sediments have born out. Further, a differential speed between the crust and outer mantle is known to exist (the latter turning at a slower relative speed, slipping on the viscous layer of magma). We may consider this factor also acting between the seafloor and the water, having the same effect of the solid earth rotating at a higher rate than the sea could follow. All these effects combined acted as God determined, and the layers seen today were set down beneath the waves.

Paleo-Current Studies Support the Flood

Using a variety of underwater sensors, scientists are able to predict, with reasonable accuracy, the trends of ocean currents using computer modeling. Similar to a planetarium, these tools are capable to predict what was happening in the oceans in times past. An expert in this field, Professor Art Chadwick,[7] spent many years collecting hundreds of thousands of measurements from over 10,000 locations around the globe. In modeling these so called *paleo-currents*[8] (derived from computer modeling). Chadwick has produced amazing predictive results and may also model past events, even as far back as the Flood period. Surprising to all, these results show a reflection of the biblical narrative specific to that period as set out in Genesis 8. As related in the volume *The Global Flood* by Dr. John Morris, we have the revelation here paraphrased:

Quoting Dr. Chadwick: "We have verified the stable southwesterly [i.e., the currents were from the northeast] pattern of paleo-currents across the Craton [Continental mass] with some variation throughout the Paleozoic. In the Mesozoic the currents exhibit increasing variability and shift from predominantly westerly [i.e., from the east] to predominantly easterly [i.e., from the west]. By mid Cenozoic there is no discernible direction continent-wide pattern, reflecting expected tertiary basinal sedimentation. These patterns and transitions must accompany major changes in global current trends."[9]

In this research we have evidence that a world-wide change in ocean currents *did* occur at the time of the flood, and not only a reversal as Dr. Chadwick mentions, but the *"subsiding"* event was observed in the models, just as mentioned in Genesis 8, when the subsiding phase of the Flood occurred! After the main event in the "Mesozoic" (the geologic time frame where evolutionists believe there was a world-wide catastrophic die-off—e.g. the Flood), and after this the patterns returned to the relative ebb and flow cycle of today.

Not having such complex equipment aboard the Ark, Noah sent out what he did have to reconnoiter the area; two birds—the raven first and finally a dove, which came back empty handed the first flight, then on the second returned with an olive branch. These two, the dove and olive stem, have been the symbols of *peace* ever since.

Fig. 48 Hope: *"In the seventh month, on the seventeenth day of the month, the ark rested upon the mountains of Ararat"* (Genesis 8:4).

Now Noah found the earth around the grounded craft secure, and God granted permission for the crew and cargo to take leave of the vessel.

As recorded for us in these beautiful verses found in Genesis 8, the Bible tells us:

> *But God remembered Noah and all the beasts and all the cattle that were with him in the ark; and God caused a wind to pass over the earth, and the water subsided. Also the fountains of the deep and the floodgates of the sky were closed, and the rain from the sky was restrained; and the water receded steadily from the earth, and at the end of one hundred and fifty days the water decreased.*
>
> *In the seventh month, on the seventeenth day of the month, the ark rested upon the mountains of Ararat. Now it came about in the six hundred and first year, in the first month, on the first of the month, the water was dried up from the earth. Then Noah removed the covering of the ark, and looked, and behold, the surface of the ground was dried up. In the second month, on the twenty-seventh day of the month, the earth was dry* (Genesis 8:1-24 NASV).

Now the great door of judgment opened. Now was seen an entirely transformed and *empty* world, and here we have our eight humans and their lively cargo. The silence outside must have had a moving effect; they now utterly *alone in the world.*

Summary

A few points of summary are in order at this point of the narrative, referencing times and duration of key events:

Genesis 7:11: *In the sixth hundredth year of Noah's life, in the second month, the seventieth day, were all the fountains of the great deep broke up.*

Genesis 7:12 It *rained* for 40 days and 40 nights.

Genesis 7:15 *And the Lord shut them in;* it was God's judgment, only He is completely just and perfect in knowledge to do so, the wildlife within wiser than the people without.

Genesis 7:18 *And the waters prevailed*, and were increased greatly upon the earth, and the Ark went upon the face of the waters. Adding the dates and times recorded, we find the Deluge lasted 365 days, allowing for alternating 30 and 31 day dates of the Hebrew calendar and Whiston's hypothesis.

Genesis 8:2 *The "windows of heaven"* and the *"Fountains of the Great Deep,* stopped."* Also the Bible tells us the rains "restrained." The Ark was grounded. It's significant that some think the New Testament records that Christ rose from the dead on the same exact *day,* thousands of years later, three days after Passover!

Genesis 8:14 *In the 601st year,* second month and 27th day of the month of Noah's life, they opened the portals and coverings to a new earth (extra-biblical accounts state that as Noah stepped out of the ark, a scene of death and horror awaited him, that of drowned "men and horses" seen at every turn).

The flood was over at last. A year had passed—365 days had gone by, using the Jewish calendar to count off the epoch event. The Judgment ended and mankind receives a second chance. How will he do?

10

The Epoch Ends; Life Restarts on Earth

Fig. 49 When they stepped off the Ark, they gave thanks,
approximately 2348 BC

*Then God spoke to Noah, saying, go out of the ark, you and
your wife and your sons and your sons' wives with you. Bring out
with you every living thing of all flesh that is with you, birds and
animals and every creeping thing that creeps on the earth, that
they may breed abundantly on the earth, and be fruitful and
multiply on the earth. And Noah built an altar unto the Lord; and
took of every clean beast, and of every clean fowl, and offered
burnt offerings on the altar* (Genesis 8).

They finally landed. There was never a happier lot in all history than
this crew and cargo. One can imagine the joyful calls and whinnies
of the creatures that came forth from the vessel now, more than any
other before or since in history we can be sure! I suppose there was a near
stampede for the door when it opened and the interior flooded with light and

fresh air! The sounds, sun and breeze would be enough to stir the entire craft. The human cargo had little time to formally celebrate now; the happy work began. It was a great day for all of them, and truthfully, for all mankind. All the earth should celebrate this most wonderful day in history, and actually we do so unknowingly, as this date is suggested to be the same as Christ's resurrection day!

Interesting that the word *families* is used to describe the groups of animals in the narrative, further indicating God took notice of their biologic divisions. God also directed Noah to take three pair plus one of the domestic animals and fowl, assuring a pair for each couple, these needed as they started their new lives in this world. In a way, having the spares aboard may have assured the party that God would carry them through. They must have received the best of care.

So we have the image of a grand celebration of worship, gratefulness and thanksgiving. Many a tear flowed. Out of their precious domesticated animals they offered a seventh, constituting a *seventh of everything they possessed in this new world!* Their sacrifice was a supreme act of trust, for likely they had depleted much of the remaining food stores on the Ark. May we learn by their example that our ultimate dependence is upon God and act in that same faith. God has His ways; tithing is a pure and simple act of faith and reminder of our dependency. It is hard to show me a tithing household who is without, but notice a hundred who neglect this practice and wonder why they are often in need.

They were grateful to the One who inspired Noah to build the vessel and provide such a mighty deliverance while they witnessed the full destruction of an evil world right before their eyes. Their absolute trust and faith were now acted out by giving back, their precious mite seemed little compared to what they were given. Then came the bonuses, God being moved to do even more:

And the Lord smelled a sweet savor; and the Lord said in his heart, I will not again curse the ground any more for man's sake; for the imagination of man's heart is evil from his youth; neither will I again smite any more everything living, as I have done. While the earth remains, seedtime and Harvest, cold and heat, winter and summer, and day and night shall not cease (Genesis 8:21-22).

In giving back, God provided them with tremendous bonuses, and not just any, but ones all mankind would be blessed with for generations. God elected to lift the curse from the ground, allowing agriculture to more easily thrive again. The thorns and toil would be now greatly reduced. God also put forth a universal promise of peace, including a declaration of reliable growing seasons for all time. More grace would be given, more prophets sent, more provision made, reversing a portion of the curse from the Fall. In an interesting declaration, God sums up man's primal condition, as a parent resigned to a difficult child, saying: *"For the imagination of man's heart is evil from his youth."* This edict suggests a new and general tolerance for the coming generations of mankind. But consider the context: *"While the earth remains."* The earth shall not remain forever. God has set a time and moment for earth's final and future end.

Moriah, Golgotha and the Temple Mount

What happened after man began to repopulate the earth? Let's take a quick look forward at one of the next important people we see in the Old Testament—Abraham (the grandson of Noah) and his son, Isaac. God showed Abraham that not only did man survive after the Flood, but that God would provide for them. According to the rabbis, a worship ceremony occurred at Mt. Moriah.[10] It was the same crest where the rabbis tell us Adam worshiped, and where later God asked Abraham to take Isaac, i.e. the "Land of Moriah." Consider that great act of faith, where Abraham was called to sacrifice his only son, Isaac, at this same mountain. On arrival, God then showed Abram the exact spot in the vicinity, "A place that I will show you" (Genesis 22:2). In Genesis 22:8, the narrative tells us that while on those ridges, Abraham paused and named the first "Elohim Yirah," *the Lord will provide,* in response to Isaac's question about the sacrifice, since he saw none with them. But this was not where they stopped! When they came to the precise place God showed Abraham, he then prepared to sacrifice Isaac, trusting in God completely. After the intervention by the *Angel of the Lord* (where a substitute ram was provided in Isaac's stead), we see the heart of God moved and exclaiming:

> *...for because thou has done this thing, and hast not withheld thy son, thine only son!* (Genesis 22:12)

We wonder how long it had been since God had seen such faith and devotion, contrasted with the dread of the Flood events not so many decades before. For our Lord, the landing day of Noah was *opposite* of the terrible time of rebellion and rejection. Here His redeemed knelt, sacrificed, and worshiped, and the heart of God was touched. We can please the Lord by a show of obedience and faith today and even amaze Him once in awhile!

Without a doubt, this principle had gotten deeply into the heart of Abraham, as it had Noah years before. At day's end we can be sure Abraham was equally thrilled and relieved from the burden of the last three, his son safe and sound, and as with Noah, it was again a big day on planet earth! Abraham then named this location: *"Jehovah Yirah"* or "the Lord who sees," suggesting Abram understood God saw him the entire time in this trial and knew he had never been alone. Could this site be Golgotha? Some scholars suggest so.* We may envision Christ hanging there thinking, "Oh my God, please see Me too!" As the crucifixion site is directly north of the Temple, it's said God would hover there observing the sacrifices, as He commanded in Leviticus that the Temple sacrifices be made in full view of Golgotha's ridge (Lev. 1:11). In essence, these two locations are likely the Temple and Crucifixion mounds of today, the latter higher by several hundred feet compared to Mount Moriah where the Temple was located. Moriah became the exact place where the Ark of the Covenant sat within the Holy of Holies, all within the Temple itself. This certainly was some very important ground to God! As apparent from these verses, God is ever searching and seeking those who will turn toward Him, as the scripture assures us:

For the eyes of the LORD run to and fro throughout the whole earth, to show Himself strong on behalf of those whose heart is loyal to Him (1 Chronicles 16:9).

Fig. 50 The Cross

God's single and central objective is simple: reaching out in love to every soul who will humble themselves and seek after Him!

Without a doubt, God had an armful of blessings and decrees awaiting our survivors; Noah's joy must have been overflowing, and his family so proud of him! *Note: From Warberton, Adam Clarke's Commentary p. 141

The Names of God

In the narrative we have the word "God" or "Elohim[11]" in the Hebrew. This name comes from *"El"* (Strong One) and *"him"* which means multiple or three in one, together creating *"Elohim."* But in these passages we now are given the word *Lord*, or in the Hebrew *"Yahovah,"* meaning God is pres-ent to act.[12] In English the word "Lord" is analogous to the lords of old Eng-land, who were known to provide a community dining table for all who entered in peace, day or night. The root in the Saxon is derived from *Loaved*, shortened to loaf or bread; these together meaning to supply or give out—*the Giver of bread.*[13] As such, we also have Christ, who is called the "Bread from Heaven."

More Blessing and Covenants

Seeing their good spirit, God now poured forth the next set of blessings, and in one of the most kind entreaties ever penned in mankind's behalf, He gives them more direction and promise:

So God blessed Noah and his sons, and said to them: "Be fruitful and multiply, and fill the earth. And the fear of you and the dread of you shall be on every beast of the earth, on every bird of the air, on all that move on the earth, and on all the fish of the sea. They are given into your hand. Every moving thing that lives shall be food for you. I have given you all things, even as the green herbs" (Genesis 9:1-3).

Then in another unexpected revelation, the Covenants and the bow are announced, the latter fixed in the heavens as a "sign."

*And God spoke unto Noah, and to his sons with him, saying, "And I, behold, I establish **my covenant** with you, and with your seed after you; And with every living creature that is with you, of the fowl, of the cattle, and of every beast of the earth with you; from all that go out of the ark, to every beast of the earth. And I will establish **my covenant** with you, neither shall all flesh be cut off any more by the waters of a flood; neither shall there anymore be a flood to destroy the earth. And God said, This is the token of **the covenant** which I make between me and you and every living creature that is with you, for perpetual generations: I do set my bow in the cloud, and it shall be for a token of a **covenant** between me and the earth. And it shall* *come to pass, when I bring a cloud over the earth, that the bow shall be seen in the cloud: And I will remember **my covenant**, which is between me and you and every living creature of all flesh; and the waters shall no more become a flood to destroy all flesh. And the bow shall be in the cloud; and I will look upon it, that I may remember **the everlasting covenant** between God and every living creature of all flesh that is upon the earth. And God said unto Noah, This is the token of **the covenant**, which I have established between me and all flesh that is upon the earth"* (Genesis 9:8-17 emphasis added).

Fig. 51 The remains of First Earth tower above this flood ripped plain, while the inverted *bow* reminds us of His love & covenants

Now we have the completion of the contract with Noah, the final installments and the bonuses. But more than bonuses to be used selfishly, these would reverse more of the curse and be a further blessing on all mankind! In the end, God wraps things up with a set of divine Covenants, assuring humankind of His care and watchfulness, mentioning them as *everlasting!*

Every generation since has seen God's sign, the "bow" formed in the sky for clear viewing. It's placed to remind man of these promises, inverted, at rest and not in hand. The rainbow stands as a permanent reminder of God's loving kindness, all the result of Noah's obedience and faith. The word we translate for "bow" is the Hebrew word, *qešet*, used in the Old Testament to mean a weapon used by a hunter or warrior. (See Genesis 27:3 and 1 Samuel 31:3 where the same word is used.) The "bow" of the ancients is not only a rainbow, but the moon's crescent also symbolized a bow *hanging* in the heavens for all to view at night. What a great thing God does! He hangs up His bow and remembers this image of peace both day and night!

The New World

A season would pass before the land could provide for them. God also decreed the use of meat for food, this for the first time in Genesis 9:3. So in their sacrifice of a seventh, mankind receives manyfold in return. This new food source would be vital to accelerate the expansion of humanity across the earth in the coming years. Note that America would have required far more time to achieve her expansion had not God placed the animals in plenty across the central prairies, thus providing a concentrated source of protein. The world would have a long way to go after the effects of the catastrophe before life could settle back into normalcy. The land would be prolific agriculturally. Livable space, however, would be at a premium, the climate cooler and storms more violent in the years immediately following the del-uge.

For instance, the book of Job mentions ice, sleet and snow in the Middle East, more so than any other book in the Bible. It's possible at this time glaciation began in the high latitudes. To offset the cooler temperatures, mankind could now find coal seams where the vegetation mats had been covered and compressed. (Coal now found to largely consist of tree bark, known capable of converting into this substance in hours.) As promised in the "Covenant," the Lord made every provision and more for our first family to thrive in the new world; despite the climate change, they would adapt.

With all these unexpected gifts and rewards, one can imagine their shock and surprise at the change in lifestyle these represented for them. We can be sure every soul felt a special appreciation in their heart to love and follow their God. Now seeing the faith of Noah come to life, they were certain God would keep His promises. He gave them a mission to fill the earth and enjoy their new life. His name would be invoked now as *Jehovah—the Lord Provider!* In our day we have these promises and more in Christ, who over and over spoke of faith and obedience as key for relationship, and further, as an expression of love to God (1 John 5:3 "This Love for God: to obey His com-mands"). Christ mentioned Noah and the Flood and its world-wide impact. Take notice that Christ Himself gave the *ultimate sacrifice*, more than build-ing a ship or offering his son as Abraham did.

We understand Jesus gave His *own* life, the final offering to complete the final Covenant, this in a single everlasting offering for the cleansing of all mankind. In this, Christ made provision for *all* to enjoy the same relationship and blessing Noah partook, our hero lacking the full atonement and receiving no promise of heaven. Now in Christ, we obtain *complete* atonement for sins, His sacrifice *completely* sufficient, as it says in the Bible, He gave *"once for all!"* (Hebrews 10:10) Further, God has promised eternal life in a place called heaven, and we can be assured that upon arrival far more blessings and gifts await the faithful there, just as Noah and family received when they landed in victory that great day long, long ago!

The Wedding

This day in the city of Ur, there's a celebration going on. It's a wedding, but not just any one—a prince and princess are joining in matrimony. Years after they have restarted their lives, Noah's son Shem is performing the wed-ding ceremony for his son Abram. Hundreds if not thousands are in presence as the music fades and the vows are given and taken. The Patriarch himself appears in full pomp and splendor, and gifts abound. He has them kneel be-fore him, placing his hands on the shoulders of the groom to bestow the blessing. The crowd goes quiet for the solemn moment, not knowing what the grand old sage may utter. He may have said something like the following: *Abram my son, as our great father Noah taught us, we must honor God's ways because He is Holy and His ways true and right. First and foremost our good father Noah obeyed our God without question as an example for us, and saved us to live in this present world, and serve God who gives us rain in season and protection from our enemies. He also bestows the bless-ings of marriage, sustenance and fellowship with Him. He shows us wisdom that we may prosper, and teaches us of His love. You must also pass these things to your children, that they have faith and obey the callings of the Almighty, so that we may fulfill our destiny and one day meet Him tri-umphantly in the next world, when the Promised One comes.* With this he raises his hands to heaven and continues:

I, Shem, son of Noah, entreat You Almighty One, Creator of Heaven and Earth and all that is within them, You who bless us with all we have and need, I ask that You may also bless, protect and multiply these children be-fore me, just as you promised my father, brothers and I that day on the moun-tain long ago. Give courage to my child Abram and multiply his seed, bless him and my child Sarah greatly, that they may prosper, live long and have good health. May my son never cower from his enemies, but always find courage in You, and be with him wherever he goes. Amen.

127

The ceremony turns to celebration. Shem calls Abram to his side and speaks privately with him, reminding him of the history of his ancestors: the Flood, the blessings and curses, obedience, and the faith and trials that may come calling him to faithfulness. The Elder carefully reconstructs the rich history of their family all the way back to Adam, reminding him of the promise of the Savior. (See Jude 1:14, speaking of Enoch's preaching.)

Decades go by, and Abraham awakes one morning finding the angel of the Lord before him. A message is given and the visitor departs. Without hesitation Abraham takes his one and only son, Isaac, says his goodbyes, and loads to leave. His destination is distant, the mountains of Moriah. Three days later they arrive, and Isaac notices no offering is with them. His father explains that the *Lord will provide* as they climb the longest climb any father could imagine. Isaac doesn't understand why, he only trusts—*completely.*

Why would anyone consider doing such a thing, taking the life of an innocent child, *his* only child? It made no sense; God had promised! He remembers the spoken words of Shem and decides he must have the blindest trust ever asked of a father. Abraham understood the outcome of Noah's long suffering and obedience. That payoff changed the course of mankind. Was it now his time? This kind of encounter was affirmed by the Patriarch and teachings from his childhood, so he must listen. Abraham understood that by acting in obedience now, no matter what the cost, he could possibly change the destiny of mankind, just as his ancestor Noah had. This was his ark. And he didn't fail us! As Isaac asked, God did provide; the substitute sacrifice represented in a ram that was caught nearby. Now through Isaac we have Christ, the *ultimate sacrifice* and example of faith and love, providing a rescue from the sins of humankind, just like the Ark did for Noah! With this we must proclaim: *Thank you for your faith, Abraham, thank you, Noah, and Thank You, God!*

Those who have gone before us have accomplished the more difficult work. Now in these days, God has made a way so simple *any* may enter into a relationship with Him, the same as Noah and better! The requirement? We must have faith in the reality of God's Son, Jesus Christ, who offers a most simple avenue, He said it Himself: *"The work of God is this, to believe in the Son He has sent"* and further, *"Without faith, it's impossible to please God"* (John 6:29; Hebrews 11:6).

This faith and relationship now comes through one portal, Jesus Christ. Same as the warning Noah received concerning the flood, we now have the testimony of Christ warning of a second pending judgment. This warning is just as grave and just as true as the one Noah received. If you wish to be saved, the requirements are simple. As Jesus said; *"If you keep My commandments, you will abide in My love, just as I have kept My Father's commandments and abide in His love"* (John 15:10).

The Contrast and Celebration

Now consider the story of Christ's holy conception and birth, this in *contrast* to the sinful actions of the fallen angels mentioned in Genesis 6. On the one hand, we have the actions of rebels and their illegitimate offspring, corrupting the earth through lust and power. On the other, we have the story of Mary and the conception of Christ by the Holy Spirit. Consider that from that *single* offspring, the world was saved and history changed forever through Christ. What a contrast between the two! What a difference a caring father like Joseph and a proper family can make in the world! The former marked by rebellion, fornication and disobedience; the latter marked by conformation, love and faithfulness!

How the blessing of God can bring true life to those within the watchcare of the Almighty! The Evil One has done everything possible to corrupt the true history of the earth and mankind's origin. The tactic has never changed, starting with his first words spoken in the Garden—that of lies, deception, and pridefulness. In the sum of it, God chose and blessed Noah based on his *obedience and faith; he believing in something not seen, no different in believing and trusting Christ in our time.* Such faith is within the grasp of every man, women and child; it attracts the eye of God toward us. By these, we have every gift Noah received and *far, far* more, because in Christ we have life, and life eternal. How is there more?

The Ark and Heaven

Now consider the wooden craft made by Noah and his sons, deigned to hold the animals and a few people for a year and then discarded. Now Christ promises a home far greater, not made by human hands to last a season, but one in construction for two thousand years and built to last forever! And think of this, all is made under the supervision of the Great Carpenter Himself, Jesus Christ! Be sure He will be there ready and excited to show the faithful their new abode, just as He proclaimed: "I go to prepare a place for you" (John 14:3). After all, He paid the price for our redemption, motivating Him to work tirelessly all these centuries on this fabulous place for *you*. Imagine His joy when he greets His people, redeemed by His terrible sacrifice! Be assured He's worked doubly hard on your behalf, having sacrificed so much in the earthly life, as such he also understands man's trials and what you have gone through. He also was treated unjustly, rejected, jailed, humiliated and murdered for no reason.

Entering Our Reward

Consider on the one hand the joyous occasion when Noah's family welcomed the animals aboard the Ark after so many years of mocking and hard labor, yet toiled on in faith, not yet seeing their reward. Now consider the grander celebration when the redeemed arrive at the entrance to heaven, the culmination of the Grand Scheme of God, truly the story of Noah played out!

The Bible is written in simple ways so any may understand its truths, from bushman to bureaucrat. It's designed to accomplish a primary goal that through a myriad of methods and means, it teaches God's will for us and the way to heaven. Such is accomplished in a picture of words that transects time itself. When it speaks directly to a point of fact, it's clear. When it's poetic or consists of verses of song, it resounds. When it records historical fact, it can be trusted. It's a book outside of time. It's practical. It has a beginning and an end. In one volume, it communicates libraries. It is the most important book in the world, and outsells any bestseller ever written and is read by more people than any other book written!

The Bible contains the story of mankind and his relationship with God since the beginning of creation. The Bible instructs man to be humble. It instructs man to be pure. It admonishes man to follow God's law of reciprocity, simply stated: *"Do unto others as you would have them do unto you"* (Matthew 7:12), the most simple summary of all God's law ever written! If we desire to be "like God," we must follow the example of Christ. He takes the "Golden Rule" even further, commanding us to love one another and forgive our enemies, snuffing out conflict from the start, then He says we will be; *"like our Father in heaven"* expecting that if He gives grace, His followers should also.

Conclusion

As we have learned within these pages, volumes of evidence exist in complete support of a young earth and the Flood catastrophe. The lines of disagreement lay philosophically between those that embrace a naturalistic view of origins and those who embrace the biblical one. The analysis from the science is up to you, but as Noah demonstrates for us, faith is sometimes beyond observation; we must trust in the loving character and existence of a good God, the Creator and Maker of the earth, who cares for mankind's good benefit at the end of it. As the Apostle Paul writes us:

For the invisible things of him from the creation of the world are clearly seen, being understood by the things that are made, even his eternal power and Godhead; so that they are without excuse: Because that, when they knew God, they glorified him not as God, neither were thankful; but became vain in their imaginations, and their foolish heart was darkened. Professing themselves to be wise, they became fools (Romans 1:20-22).

Paul then asserts this truth:

You, therefore, have no excuse, you who pass judgment on someone else, for at whatever point you judge another, you are condemning yourself, because you who pass judgment do the same thing! Now we know that God's judgment against those who do such things is based on truth. So when you, a mere human being, pass judgment on them and yet do the same things, do you think you will escape God's judgment? (Romans 2:1)

The State of Mankind:

There is no one righteous, not even one; there is no one who understands; there is no one who seeks God. All have turned away, they have together become worthless; there is no one who does good, not even one (Romans 3:23).

The Remedy:

You see, at just the right time, when we were still powerless, Christ died for the ungodly. Very rarely will anyone die for a righteous person, though for a good person someone might possibly dare to die. But God demonstrates his own love for us in this: While we were still sinners, Christ died for us (Romans 5:23).

The Gift:

For the wages of sin is death, but the gift of God is eternal life in Christ Jesus our Lord!" (Romans 6:23 NIV)

For God so loved the world, that he gave his only begotten Son, that whosoever believeth in him should not perish, but have everlasting life (John 3:16).

Your life is not an insignificant moment in time as the materialists want you to believe. You are important to God and live in a vital time frame, a time frame that includes predestined events like the *Flood* and coming *Fire* judgment. The mention of these repeated over and over in the Scriptures as a constant reminder for some six thousand years. My hope is that you learn to *trust God* with your life decisions based upon the Bible and seek to obtain all the gifts Noah received and more—the knowledge of Christ, the Savior, and then pass these truths onto your children.

The Noah Code

When we consider Noah's dilemma, this righteous man trapped in a society that would make ours seem holy; what were his options? Noah was humanly powerless to escape the unraveling world, so how could he protect his family from the inevitable? In his desperation and hopelessness, all Noah had left was a prayer and a life lived for God's glory, not knowing or seeing the bigger picture to come. We must marvel at such a mighty deliverance God provided in this hopeless situation. As with Noah, God sees every man, women and child on this planet. The Bible says the hairs on our heads are numbered; and every sparrow that falls is known to Him (Matthew 10:29-30). Noah trusted God, and see what great things happened in his behalf! The same caring and powerful Creator God awaits you through the work and sacrifice of His Son, found in the person of Jesus Christ!

Noah played a vital part in the physical redemption of mankind in the Flood event. But his part was only a step in the process, an image of much greater things to come in the work of Christ. The work and His victory as symbolized in this earlier event. This is the *Noah Code*—a code if put into practice will save your family and yourself from the coming end, and far more, pave the way for you to gain eternity!

The Bible teaches there will be a final worldwide Judgment, just as the Towers of Seth proclaimed to the people of the First Earth, don't miss the message for today and be left behind. Learn from the mistakes of those in history.

Noah's story is one that shows God is serious about man's actions. He will act to protect His people from moral corruption and Satan's wiles. The Flood stands as an example assuring all mankind that this same God, the

God described within the pages of the Bible, is ever ready to act and help us through life's difficulties, and act *Mightily!*

My hope is that as you consider the claims made within these pages, you will find them helpful in your search for truth, especially the truth that will lead you to the most important decision of your life—finding a saving faith in Jesus Christ, God's Son, sent for *you* and all mankind! The return of Christ like the Flood, *will happen*, as Christ stated:

"Just as in the days of Noah, so shall the coming of the Son of Man be!

May God bless you in your search for truth, and may every question of your heart be answered. God is faithful to answer as any father desires to answer his child because He loves you. He's your Father!

---

[1] P.J. Wiseman, *"Ancient Records and the Structure of Genesis"* (Thomas Nelson, Inc., 1985). This outstanding work is the general basis of the recently determined decoding of the ancient tablets.

[2] http://www.icr.org/article/ebla-its-impact-bible-records/

[3] P.J. Wiseman, *"Ancient Records and the Structure of Genesis"* (Thomas Nelson, Inc., 1985) p. 68,69

[4] John Woodward *The Natural History of the Earth* (1726) p. 42, 43

[5] Barnette and J. Baumgartner, Patterns of Ocean Circulation over the Continents During Noah's Flood," Third International Conference on Creationism

[6] From Nelson, *The Deluge in Stone* (1937) p. 90-91

[7] Chadwick, Arthur V 1993, *Megatrends in North American Paleocurrents*, Society of Economic Paleontologists and Mineralogists 8:58.

[8] Morris, John *The Global Flood*, Institute for Creation Research (2012) p.157

[9] Morris, John *The Global Flood*, Institute for Creation Research (2012) p.157

[10] Clark, Adam *Clarkes Commentary.* p. 77 ref. Genesis Chap 8:20

[11] http://www.hebrew4christians.com/Names_of_G-d/Elohim/elohim.html

[12] Bakers Evangelical Dictionary- Yahweh see also www.hebrew4christians.com

[13] Clark, Adam *Clark's Commentary* p. 27-29:42 Genesis 1:2, 2:5 (as in Genesis 2:5 where food provision is first mentioned)

Appendix

The following is a compilation of proofs obtained from a variety of sources and disciplines, so assembled for the edification and encouragement of the reader. Herein are assembled selections and observations from Archaeology, Geology, Paleontology and other disciplines, none of which will ever supersede the truth of God's Word. The author has liberally quoted from important works penned by the wiser and more experienced; their words on the various topics relating to the Flood impossible to improve upon, such art of writing being lost to us. May God bless any who are willing to search out this matter in good faith to their full and complete satisfaction, where the words of this author fail.

I

The True History of the World

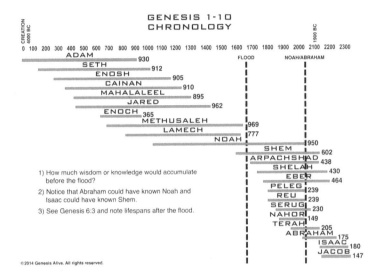

Fig. 52 Chronology of Patriarchal Life Spans (Genesis Alive image)

In this table we see the direct transmission of information from the pre-flood world to the present. Note that Noah and Shem were living during Terah's lifetime, (Abraham's father) Shem even surviving through much of Abraham's life. Potentially, Abraham was born before Noah's passing, though historians tell us Noah himself had moved to Northeast Turkey. (As far away from water as possible!)

Josephus on Early History

Josephus was a first-century Jewish historian, priest and soldier who fought against the Romans. Once the war was lost, he was captured and conscripted to serve in the Roman government. Later Josephus was directed to write a history of the Jewish nation, which we have today for a period reference and commentary relating to Jewish thought and history. One of his writings included a Table of Generations similar to the one included here.

Josephus noted many of the nations that formed after the Tower of Babel. He often listed the common Greek name for these places, providing a reference point of ancient history up to his era. From these works, we can connect those nations to those known today. For example, Josephus mentions that Gomer, one of Noah's grandsons, had descendants that the Greeks called *Galatians*. Josephus provides us with extra-biblical support to Genesis 10 and the division of family groups when God judged them by confusing their languages at the Tower of Babel. The following is a chart showing a corrected table of nations graphically. Josephus also mentions the Two Pillars of Seth.*

*The Antiquities of the Jews, AD 94 Flavius Josephus, Chapter 2

Relating to the great ages of the Patriarchs, Josephus writes: "Now when Noah had lived three hundred and fifty years after the Flood, and that all that time happily, he died, having lived the number of nine hundred and fifty years. But let no one, upon comparing the lives of the ancients with our lives, and with the few years which we now live, think that what we have said of them is false; or make the shortness of our lives at present an argument, that neither did they attain to so long a duration of life, for those ancients were beloved of God, and [lately] made by God himself; and because their food was then fitter for the prolongation of life, might well live so great a number of years: and besides, God afforded them a longer time of life on account of their virtue, and the good use they made of it in astronomical and geometrical discoveries, which would not have afforded the time of foretelling [the periods of the stars] unless they had lived six hundred years; for the great year is completed in that interval." (Note the Antikythera Device mentioned in Chapter two, requiring an extended life-age for the designers to test its accuracy).

Josephus Comments on the Long Lifespans of the Pre-Flood People

Josephus commentary: "Now I have for witnesses to what I have said, all those that have written Antiquities, both among the Greeks and barbarians; for even Manetho, who wrote the Egyptian History, and Berosus, who collected the Chaldean Monuments, and Mochus, and Hestieus and, besides these, Hieronymus the Egyptian, and those who composed the Phoenician History, agree to what I here say: Hesiod also, and Hecatseus, Hellanicus, and Acusilaus; and, besides these, Ephorus and Nicolaus relate that the ancients lived a thousand years."*

*The Antiquities of the Jews Flavius Josephus Chapter 3

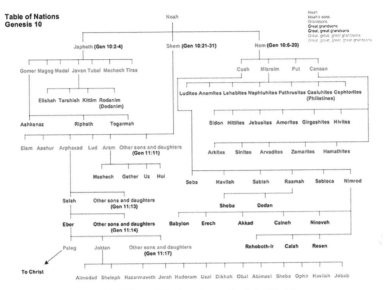

Fig. 53 Table of Nations from Noah to Christ.
Note: See Appendix XIX for information on recent finds in genetics echoing this Genesis 10 expansion period. (Courtesy Answers in Genesis www.answersingenesis.org)

The Nations of Genesis 10 and the Link to Modern History

Genesis Chapter 10 contains the most important chronological record in the Bible relating to the establishment of the nations after the Flood. From this chapter, we learn that Peleg, Abraham's great grandfather, was only three generations away from Shem, who we find still living well into Abraham's adult life. No doubt, at large family gatherings (such as the marriage of Sarah and Abraham), Shem was likely present to take part in the festivities.

There were ten generations from Adam to the Flood, fourteen from Abraham to David, fourteen from David to the captivity, and fourteen more from the captivity to Christ.* Considering that Creation took place about 4000 years before Christ's birth, we have the Flood beginning 1656 years after Creation week and 2349 years before Christ.** In Genesis 10, we have Noah's grandson, Mizraim, said to be the founder of the Egyptian race.

*Matthew 1:17
**Annals of the World, Ussher, 1658 edited by Pierce 2003 p.18

In a revised chronology, Egypt comes into existence soon after the dispersion from Babel, around 2100 BC. Eusebius, the famous 4ᵗʰ century historian writes us:

> *Egypt is called Mestraim by the Hebrews; and Mestraim lived not long after the flood. For after the flood, Cham (or Ham), son of Noah, begat Aeguptos or Mestraim, who was the first to set out to establish himself in Egypt, at the time when the tribes began to disperse this way and that...Mestraim was indeed the founder of the Egyptian race; and from him the first Egyptian Dynasty must be held to spring.* [1]

The Peleg Connection: A Time Cornerstone

Four generations after Noah, Genesis 10:25 and 1 Chronicles 1:19 record the birth of Peleg, his name associated with *division* "for in *his* days was the earth divided." The straightforward interpretation being the division of people and resultant nations derived from the Tower of Babel. (See Genesis 11.) According to the biblical chronology as deduced in Ussher's *Annals of the World*, (Second Age of the World, 1654) the Flood occurred in the 2349–2348 BC year, and Peleg was born soon after in 2247BC.

Babylon—First After the Flood

In 331 BC Alexander the Great journeyed to Babylon. It is recorded that here he received over 1900 years of astronomical observations from the Chaldeans, which they claimed dated back to the founding of Babylon. Based on this information, the founding of Babylon would have occurred in 2234 BC, or about thirteen years after the birth of Peleg. This was recorded in the sixth book of *De Caelo,* of Simplicius, a Latin writer of the 6ᵗʰ century AD and Porphyry, a Greek philosopher (circa 234–305 AD) who also deduced the same number, this according to historian and researcher Larry Pierce.[2]

The Founding of Egypt

Pierce also tells us: "Constantinus Manasses, a Byzantine chronicler (d. 1187) recorded the Egyptian state lasted 1663 years. Counting backward from the time that the Persian King Cambyses conquered Egypt in 526 BC, this gives us the year 2188 BC for the founding of Egypt, or about 60 years after the birth of Peleg. About this time Mizraim, the son of Ham, led his colony into Egypt. Hence the Hebrew word for Egypt is Mizraim or mit-srayim (מצרים) in Hebrew, 'the land of Ham.'" (See Psalms 105.)

The Founding of Greece

Pierce continues, "According to the 4th Century bishop and historian Eu-sebius of Caesarea, Egialeus, king of the Greek city of Sicyon began his reign in 2089 BC, 1313 years before the first Olympiad in 776 BC. If Euse-bius is correct, this king started his reign about 160 years after the birth of Peleg." Note that Babylon, Egypt, and Greece each spoke a different lan-guage. The early historians thus confirming the accuracy of the biblical ge-nealogies, showing us the Tower of Babel occurred before the founding of these important kingdoms. The most distant groups from Babel would have founded the latest, the people forced to split into groups according to their new language. In summary, first Babylon, then Egypt, and then Greece and Europe (after Father Japheth or "Jupiter"), all traceable to the present day.[3]

We may surmise they would have first moved only as far from Babel as needed (being agriculturalists and shepherds) determined by space and food supply. We can assume those with a pioneering spirit pressed outward, scout-ing out the lands. Remember God's command at the end of the flood: "Be fruitful, multiply and fill the earth" (Genesis 9:1). Whether they intended to obey the command or not, civilization spread out by migrations from Babel,(the "Futile Crescent" from a typical high school text), which is supported by archaeological evidence provided herein, demonstrating that a kinder gentler race first inhabited the old grounds.

Although secular historians ignore the events of Babel and the Flood, they do assume civilization started in the Middle East, likely near Babylon. The well-known historian Manetho, (as mentioned by Josephus) recorded the history of Egypt in the third century BC, wrote that the Tower of Babel occurred after the birth of Peleg and spoke of the flood as a known and obvious event, corroborating the Genesis account. In his history of Egypt he wrote: "After the Flood, Ham the son of Noah begat 'Aegyptus or Mestraim,' who was the first to establish himself in the area now known as Egypt at the time when the tribes began to disperse."[4]

The principal lesson for us being this: the Bible is an accurate and authoritative guide to history concerning these matters and we can use the biblical chronologies to determine history where the secularists have gone wrong that are often openly antagonistic to the Bible. The destructive work of humanists relating to these chronologies have overthrown the faith of not a few in recent times.

Mr. Larry Peirce[2] comments: "It is about time that this biblical (histori-cal) ground was reclaimed. If you could not trust the numbers in the chronologies of the Bible, why should you trust the words between the num-bers? What limits would you place on your unbelief?" Now let us consider the words of Christ regarding the authenticity of Moses' narrative:

For if you believed Moses, you would believe Me; for he wrote about Me. But if you don't believe what Moses wrote, how will you believe my words? (John 5:46-7)

The ancient writers provide independent support for the accuracy of the Bible narrative based on fact, not stories. Pierce mentions that the earliest revisionists were rabbis in Egypt who translated the Hebrew Bible into Greek, producing the Septuagint (LXX) in the third century BC, *arbitrarily* adding about 700 years to the biblical chronology for the period between Noah and Abraham, this to make it align with the works of Manetho. Un-fortunately for them, his chronology of the kings of Egypt, which differs from the Bible by several centuries, has even led some evangelical archae-ologists astray. Now, several secular historians are starting to realize Manetho's chronology is in need of drastic downwards revision for reasons he would not have known—some of the kings he thought reigned succes-sively *turn out to have ruled simultaneously!*

"Patterns of Evidence—Exodus" and the True History of Egypt*

Filmed and directed by Timothy Mahoney, this documentary reveals a number of late breaking finds relating to Egypt's Exodus period. The film challenges modernist thought and represents a revolution of factual support of the Bible in this arena. The revelations include:

- A complete city occupied by a people from Canaan (non-Egyptian) was un-earthed near Ramses, found to contain a palace with twelve pillars and twelve tombs, one of which in pyramid form (indicative of a leader) contained an image of an enlarged non-Egyptian man with a ruler's staff across one shoulder and a colored coat over the other.

- A papyrus written by a court scribe was unearthed in Egypt, matching the de-scription of the plagues of Exodus (blood in the Nile, frogs etc.).

- Names in stone and other papyrus documents match those recorded in the Ex-odus and Genesis account, including "Israel" as Jacobs's name. Mass graves near Ramses containing *Egyptian* remains were found, absent were those of the foreigners from this period, including evidence of an expedited departure. *Film http://www.patternsofevidence.com/en/

It seems apparent that just as the LXX's translators recopied what some Egyptian priests' information, and many modern biblical scholars have followed these "stories" told by secular historians and archaeologists who wrongly attempt to push the founding of Babylon and Egypt back to the wrong date. According to Dr. Carl Wieland, Egyptologist Patrick Clarke says that from the earliest times the ancient Egyptians quote: "called themselves and their land *km.t* (both pronounced as a throaty *Kham* (i.e. Cham or Ham)."[5] Clearly, not just Manetho, but what the ancient Egyptians knew of their history was passed to Moses, who was, as the martyr Stephen relates in Acts 7:22, "learned in all the wisdom of the Egyptians."

The Founding of Europe—The Descendants of Japheth

Amazingly, we find the best preserved Table of Nations located at the far extent of post-flood expansion—in England. As contained in the 8th century work, *History of the Britons* by Nennius. Within these chapters Nennius relates accurate genealogies, including a Table of Nations of Europe, collaborating with Genesis 10 with remarkable accuracy. For instance, Bill Cooper says that this work by Nennius is of "immense significance" that "seems to have escaped the notice of modernist scholars" either by accident or on purpose. Cooper spent three decades of study connecting the genealogies from Genesis 10, saying they maintain a fantastic 99% accuracy globally, and that no other human derived system of family origins even comes close to such an alignment.

Nennius is found to have cited an earlier source called *The Tradition of the Elders*, independent of the Bible, in which are found the names Jobhath, Baath, Easru and Sru corresponding to *Iobaath, Baath, Izrau and Ezra* in Scripture. They appear directly after none other than *Japheth*, this in the genealogy of the earliest Irish/Celts dating back to the time of Brutus in 1104 BC! Citing a little known 1917 treatise penned by renowned archaeologist Flinders Petie, entitled *Neglected British History,* Cooper says Petie vindicated the works of the so called "lairs and monks" (e.g. the works of Geoffrey of Monmouth and Nennuis, circa 800 AD). Petie accurately cited the references of older lost works and translated them into Latin, yet historians ignored this information. (From *After the Flood*, 1995 by Mr. Bill Cooper. p. 54-55.)

The Molmutine Laws

Dunvallo Molmutine was a British king who established a complex system of triplicate laws in the 5th century BC. These were amazingly similar to our Bill of Rights and Christian self-rule as set out in America by the Puritans in the 1600s. Interestingly, Molmutine mentions the *return of his country* to its previous pure moral roots in *500 BC!* So much for the image of primitive culture prevailing British early history, as this king is calling for a *restoration of civility* like in those times of old![6]

The History of Britain by Nennius, Chapters 17-18

"I have learned another account of this Brutus from the ancient books of our ancestors. After the deluge, the three sons of Noah severally occupied three different parts of the earth: Shem extended his borders into Asia, Ham into Africa, and Japheth in Europe. The first man that dwelt in Europe was Alanus, with his three sons, Hisicion, Armenon, and Neugio. Hisicion had four sons, Francus, Romanus, Alamanus, and Brutus. Armenon had five sons, Gothus, Valagothus, Cibidus, Burgundus, and Longobardus. Neugio had three sons, Vandalus, Saxo, and Boganus. From Hisicion arose four nations—the Franks, the Latins, the Germans, and Britons: from Armenon, the Gothi, Balagothi, Cibidi, Burgundi, and Longobardi: from Neugio, the Bogari, Vandali, Saxones, and Tarinegi. The whole of Europe was subdivided into these tribes.

"Alanus is said to have been the son of Fethuir; Fethuir, the son of Ogomuin, who was the son of Thoi; Thoi was the son of Boibus, Boibus of Semion, Semion of Mair, Mair of Ecthactus, Ecthactus of Aurthack, Aurthack of Ethec, Ethec of Ooth, Ooth of Aber, Aber of Ra, Ra of Esraa, Esraa of Hisrau, Hisrau of Bath, Bath of Jobath, Jobath of Joham, Joham of Japheth, Japheth of Noah, Noah of Lamech, Lamech of Mathusalem, Mathusalem of Enoch, Enoch of Jared, Jared of Malalehel, Malalehel of Cainan, Cainan of Enos, Enos of Seth, Seth of Adam, and Adam was formed by the living God."[7]

In summary, Dr. Bill Cooper responds to such omissions and the work of British revisionists in general:

"I cannot think of any other literate nation on earth that has managed to obliterate from its own history two thousand years or more of recorded history. Not even the sensors of Stalinist Russia or Maoist China were this effective in doctoring their own official accounts."[8]

So completes our short treatment of *The True History of Man* based upon Genesis. We can be assured without apology that *real history* beacons of the claims of the Bible.

[1] Ashton, J. and Down, D., *Unwrapping the Pharaohs: How Egyptian Archaeology Confirms the Biblical Timeline*, p. 73, 74, Master Books, Green Forest, AR, 2006

[2] Mr. Larry Pierce article www.creation.com/in-the-days-of-peleg

[3] Citing 1 above - Manetho's History of Egypt' in *Manetho, with an English Translation* by W.G. Waddell, Harvard University Press, Cambridge, Massachusetts, 1964, pages 7,11 Manetho, *The Book of Sothis*, Harvard Press, Cambridge, MA, p. 239. (Loeb Classical Library 350). See also Ussher, J, *The Annals of the World*, 1658, sections 1657–1762 am

[4] Unger, Merrill F. *Archeology of the Old Testament* Zondervan 1954, others

[5] Dr. Carl Wieland *Ancient Egypt Confirms: Genesis is History* article 2012

[6] http://www.thenationalcv.org.uk/Molmutius.pdf

[7] http://www.gutenberg.org/files/1972/1972-h/1972-h.htm

[8] Cooper, Bill *After the Flood—The Early Post-Flood history of Europe*, (1995 New Wine Press, England) p. 43 and as noted

II

Historical Records of the Flood

Shem, Noah's son, lived on both sides of the Flood and also throughout much of Abraham's life, possibly overlapping with Abraham's son Isaac. In this manner, the biblical account remained in *stasis* and was passed onto us through Moses. The handovers of the Genesis account passed directly from Isaac to Joseph (and thus into the Egyptian history) and finally to Moses. Moses was charged with combining the original works and putting them in the Hebrew language. God would not allow the narrative corrupted; the passage of information to us is clear, as Biblical Hebrew is considered a "dead" language.

Jesus gave direct credence to Moses' assembled works, confirmed to us in His own words John as chapter 5:46 & 47 show:

For if you believed Moses, you would believe Me; for he wrote about Me. But if you do not believe his writings, how will you believe My words?

And further:

And beginning with Moses and all the Prophets, He expounded to them in all the Scriptures the things concerning Himself (Luke 24:27).

We understand that within the books of "Moses," is contained the Book of Genesis, Christ authenticating the account as truthful. Specific to the Flood, Christ directly states in Matthew 24:

For as in the days that were before the flood they were eating and drinking, marrying and giving in marriage, until the day that Noah entered into the ark, and knew not until the flood came, and took them all away; so shall also the coming of the Son of man be.

In this passage we have Christ speaking literally and specifically to the Flood as an actual account, mentioning the Ark and the state of human affairs when the cataclysm began. He then takes it a step further, relating the event to *His* return: *"So shall the coming of the Son of Man be"*—hardly an analogy to a local or mythological event! The return of Christ has been heralded

144

for 2,000 years as the culmination of the history of man. His arrival will not be a local but *global* event, and *"so shall"*—meaning just as *sudden*.

If the Flood occurred in the scope the Bible describes, we would expect traditions of the account filtering down through the generations as man spread across the earth. Looking through Funk and Wagnall's *1950 Dictionary of Folklore, Mythology and Legend* under the heading "Deluge or Flood," we find: "A world cataclysm during which the earth was inundated or submerged by water: A concept found in almost *every* mythology in the world." When the histories of the antediluvians from around the globe are opened, we find flood accounts by the hundreds, and the following are a few for the reader's consideration.

Greece

Lucian is the author of record of *de Dea Syria*, including a history of the Scythians, Syrians, and Arabians, as well as Grecian records, in the section devoted to the traditions of the Deluge. He relates as follows: "Many say that this temple [that at Hierapolis in Syria] was built by Deucalion, the Scythian. That Deucalion, I mean, in whose time the greatest inundation of waters was. I have heard in Greece what the Grecians say concerning this Deucalion. The story they relate is as follows: 'The present race of men was not the first, for they totally perished; but is of a second generation, which, being descended from Deucalion, increased to a great multitude. Now of these former men they relate this story: they were insolent and addicted to unjust actions; for they neither kept their oaths, nor were hospitable to strangers, nor gave ear to suppliants; for which reason this great calamity befell them: on a sudden the earth poured forth a vast quantity of water, great showers fell, the rivers overflowed, and the sea arose to a prodigious height; so that all things became water, and all men were destroyed. only Deucalion was left unto a second generation, on account of his prudence and piety. He was saved in this manner: he went into a large ark or chest which he had, together with his sons and their wives; and when he was in, there entered swine, and horses, and lions, and serpents, and all other creatures which live on earth, by pairs. He received them all, and they did him no hurt; for the gods created a great friendship among them; so that they sailed all in one chest while the water prevailed.'"

Concerning the man Deucalion, the Greeks also continued to remember and celebrate the deliverance from the flood, related again by Lucian: "There is an ancient tradition among those of Hierapolis, (also is reported to be celebrated for a time at Athens, there called Hydrophoria [the root word for *hy-*

drophobia, a condition related to the drop of body temperature caused by exposure] which derives admiration. In their country a great chasm opened and received all the water, whereupon Deucalion erected altars, and built the temple of Juno over the chasm. In commemoration of this history, twice every year water is brought from the sea to the temple, and not by the priests only, but all Syria and Arabia. many come from beyond Euphrates to the sea, and all carry water, which they first pour out in the temple and afterwards it sinks into the chasm which, though it be small, receives an abundance of water. And when they do this, they say Deucalion instituted the ceremony, called in that temple, as a memorial of the calamity, and of his deliverance from it."

From Lucian—*de Dea Syria,* Tom. 11. p. 8 *Universal History,* Vol. 1. p. 882

Fig. 54 Commemorative coin image from Iconium, minted in memory of the Flood

Asia

At Apamaea in Phrygia, a pillar in recognition of deliverance from the great Flood was reported in a memorial, saying that the final resting place of the Ark was to be found nearby at Iconium (modern Konya, Turkey). In the second and third centuries before Christ, this city had coins struck relating to the matter on which were engraved the images of the ark: a dove, olive branch, and Noah and his wife exiting to dry ground, the name *Noe* stuck on the Ark. Called the *Place of Descent,* this is the proper rendering of the Armenian name of this very city. It is called by Ptolemy, Naxuana; and by Moses, Chorenensis; and by the Armenian historian, Idsheuan; but the place itself, Nachidsheuan (modern Nakhchivan, Turkey) signified the first place of descent and is a lasting monument of the preservation of Noah in the Ark, upon the top of that mountain at whose foot it was built, as the first city or town after the Flood.

From French archeologist Lenormant, *Les Origines de 1'Histoire* p. 440- 442, Josephus & William Whiston, 1737)

Chaldeans

Beorsus was a Chaldean priest who lived about 270 years before the birth of Christ. He relates as follows, "Before that famous devastation of waters, in which the whole world perished, many ages had passed, which were faithfully remarked by our Chaldeans. They write that in those times there was a great city of Giants, called AEno, (or Titans by the Italians— Ovis the poet) situated near Libanus. They governed the whole world, from the rising to the setting of the sun. These trusting to the greatness of their bodies and strength, and having invented arms, oppressed all, and being slaves to their lust, found out musical instruments and all kind of delights. They devoured men, and procured abortions on purpose to dress them for food. They promiscuously lay with mothers, daughters, sisters, men and brutes; and there was no kind of wickedness which they did not commit; they were despoilers of religion and of the gods. Then many foretold and prophesied and carved out upon stones the things relating to that destruction which was soon to come upon the world. But they [the Titans], following their old course, derided all such admonitions, though the anger and revenging of the gods were ready to fall upon them for their impiety and wickedness. There was one among the Giants who reverenced the gods and was more wise and prudent than all the rest; his name was Noa; he dwelt in Syria, with his three sons Sem, Japet, Cham, and their wives, the great Tidea, Pandora, Noela, and Noegla. This man, fearing the destruction which he foresaw from the stars would come to pass, began, in the seventy-eighth year before the inundation, to build a ship covered like an ark.

"Seventy-eight years from the time he began to build this ship, the ocean of a sudden broke out, and all the inland seas, and the rivers and the fountains bursting from beneath (attended with most violent rains from heaven for many days), overflowed all the mountains so that the whole human race was buried in the waters, except Noa and his family who were saved by means of the ship which, being lifted up by the waters, rested at last upon the top of the Gordyœan mountain. It is reported that there now remaineth some part, and that men take away the bitumen from it and make use of it, by way of charm or expiation, to avert evil. We must therefore allow from these premises that which both the Chaldeans and Scythians write of, that, after the earth was dried from the waters, there were no more than the above-mentioned eight persons in Armenia Saga, and that from these all men upon earth sprung and for this reason it is, that the Scythians justly say and call Noa the father of all the greater and lower gods, the author of the human race, the Chaos, and seed of the world."

In support of the account of Berosus and that of the Egyptians, we have Josephus commenting on these authors: "Now all the writers of barbarian histories make mention of this flood, and of this ark; among whom is Berosus the Chaldean. For when he is describing the circumstances of the flood, he goes on thus: 'It is said there is still some part of this ship in Armenia, at the mountain of the Cordyaeans; and that some people carry off pieces of the bitumen, which they take away and use chiefly as amulets for the averting of mischief's antics.' Hieronymus the Egyptian also, who wrote the *Phoenician Antiquities*, and Mnaseas, and a great many more, make mention of the same. Nay, Nicolaus of Damascus, in his ninety-sixth book, hath a particular relation about them; where he speaks thus: "There is a great mountain in Armenia, over Minyas, called Baris, upon which it is reported that many who fled at the time of the Deluge were saved; and that one who was carried in an ark came on shore upon the top of it; and that the remains of the timber were great while preserved. This might be the man about whom Moses the legislator of the Jews wrote.'" Josephus, Vol. I p. 10

Sumar

From Sumar, Gilgamesh a king in ancient Sumer related a written story as passed to him by his father, who knew of one Utnapishtim, a king from the pre-flood civilization and flood survivor (Noah or one of the sons?). The story goes that Ea, overlord of man and water, gave warning to Utnapishtim of God's plan to destroy all mankind. Ea told Utnapishtim to "build a boat" and to "Take up into the boat the seed of all living creatures…The god of the storm turned daylight to darkness, when he smashed the land like a cup. Utnapishtim looked at the face of the world and there was silence, all mankind was returned to clay, the sea stretched flat as a rooftop on every side was the waste of water. A dove returned finding no resting place, and later [a] raven did not return. When the Ark rested on a mountaintop, Utnapishtim offered a sacrifice to God." So in this account we have the major elements of the Genesis record, allowing for translation variations.[1]

Persia

Dr. Hyde, in his *Historia religionis veterum Perarum*, writes this account from Persia: "The orthodox among the ancient Persians believe a Deluge, and that it was universal, and overwhelmed the whole earth. But as they have various opinions and sentiments concerning all those things which are so remote in antiquity, they differ somewhat among themselves and run into fable." In the Book Pharh: Sur, the famous mountain, where Noah dwelt when the waters of the deluge broke out from it, is mentioned.

East Indies

Lord in his *Discourse of the Banian Religion* informs us, "That the Bramim say, that the four tribes, or casts, of which the first race of men consisted, degenerating from their primitive innocence; the Priest neglecting his piety, the Soldier becoming insolent and tyrannical, the Merchant practicing deceit in trade, and using false balances, and the Artisan spending the profits of his inventions in riot and excess; their impiety and wickedness grew at length to so insufferable a height, that God's indignation was justly provoked, and he sent a Flood, which destroyed all nations without exception. After which God, to repair mankind, created three persons of greater Excellency man those of the former generation to one of whom, named Bremaw, he gave the power of creating men and animals, which he executed accordingly: the first human pair proceedings one from his right side, the other from his left. The man was called Manow, and the woman Ceteroupa, and by them was the earth replenished."

India

"The God Routrcn, who is the grand destroyer of all created beings, resolved one day to drown all mankind, pretending he had just reasons to be dissatisfied with their behavior. He one day appeared to Sattiavarti, his great confident, and privately assured him, that a universal Flood would soon happen; that the earth would be covered with water, and that Routreris design was no less than that of thereby destroying all mankind, and every kind of animal. He nevertheless assured him, that he himself need not be under the least apprehensions; for that in spite of Roulren, he would find opportunity to preserve him, and to take such measures, that the world should afterwards be re-peopled. His design was to make a wonderful ark rife up on a sudden, at a time when Routren should least suspect any such thing, and to store it with a large provision of souls and feeds of beings, eight hundred and forty millions at least. As for Sattiavarti, he, at the time of the Flood, was to be upon a very high mountain, which he pointed out to him very exactly. Some time after, Sattiavarti, as had been foretold him, perceived a numberless multitude of clouds drawing together, but beheld with unconcern the storm which was gathering over the heads of the guilty, when the most dreadful rain that had ever been seen poured down from the skies; the rivers swelled, and spread themselves with rapidity over the surface of the whole earth, the sea broke its appointed bounds, and mixing with the rivers, which now had left their channels, soon covered the highest mountains.

"Trees, animals, men, cities, kingdoms, were all drowned in a word, all animated beings were instantly destroyed. In the mean time, Sattiavarti, with some of his penitents, had withdrawn to the appointed mountain, where he waited for the succor which God had promised him. However, this did not prevent his being seized with some short intervals of terror. As the water gathered strength continually as it rolled, and each moment drew nearer to his Asylum, he was every now and then in a panic. But that very instant which he thought would be his last, he beheld the ark that was to save him: no sooner did he set his eyes upon it, than he immediately got into it, with all the devotees in his company, and also the eight hundred and forty millions of fouls and feeds of beings, Sattiavarti waited very quietly in his Asylum, 'till such time as the waters were run off from the surface of the earth.'"

Miiller -Sanskrit Literature, 425, Lenormant, *Les Origins,* 421-423

Hawaii

From these islands come the account that after the death of the first man, the world became very wicked. Only one good man, Nu-u, remained. He built a great canoe with a house and took in the animals. As in the biblical version, the waters overcame the earth, leaving just Nu-u and his family alive.

Egypt

Fig. 55 The Ark in Egypt (Image courtesy Allen Austin, from his volume *Genesis in Egypt*)

In this image Noah is holding up the Ark with seven passengers and the Scarab or self powered one. Supposedly the bones of Adam were removed from the great Pyramid before the Flood and saved within the Ark. One theory relates that Adam's bones were later resurrected with those at the first Easter by Christ. Why would Adam not be the first whom Christ spoke life into after the Resurrection?

In Egypt, a story relates of one Nun, who "Was responsible for the primeval flood, which covered the entire earth and destroyed all of mankind except those in Nun's Ark."[2] In both the Egyptian and biblical Genesis, God repented of creation and conspired to destroy all living things by water, with the exception of Noah (Nun) and his family. In the Egyptian story, Noah is referred to as Nun and the waters as Nu. The earliest hieroglyphs are very extensive with the Noahic story, the dimensions of the Great Pyramid closely relating to that of the Ark.[3] Typho,* which name the Egyptians explain by interpreting as the Sea, and they call the salt of the sea, Typho's foam. Agreeable to this interpretation is what we are further told, "Typho was once in possession of the portion or province which belonged to Ofiris; by which they mean, that Egypt was once covered with the Sea. Which opinion, say these philosophers, is probable enough, from that great number of seashells, which are not only dug out of their mines and found upon the tops of their mountains; and that their fountains and wells, though many in number, have all of them a brackish or salt taste with them, as containing sea-water, which once covered their whole country."

*The name Typho signifies a deluge or inundation; and Typhoon, or as the Latin Poets (from which we get our word typhoon) call him, Typhteus, is represented as a monstrous giant warring against heaven. He was at last overcome by Jupiter, and as one says, lies now submersed in water. The Arabs of this day express the general Deluge by the word Al *Tufan.* (Universal Hist. Vol. I. p. 209.)

China

The Chinese maintained their history and science in a set of 4,000 plus volumes referred to as the *Book of All Knowledge*, dating back to 2250 BC. The Yihking account records the consequences of mankind's rebellion against the gods: "The Earth was shaken to its foundations. The sky sank lower towards the north." The account also records that the solar system motions were changed. Could this have been referring to the alteration of the axis? The earth was shaken and broken-up; the waters from its center were violently forced skywards and overcame earth.[4]

Another record tells that a man, Fuhhi, his wife, three sons and daughters were the only survivors of a great flood. After the catastrophe, they repopulated the world.

Accounts further make mention: "Now he called his name Noah, saying, 'This one will give us rest from our work and from the toil of our hands arising from the ground which the Lord has cursed'" (Genesis 5:29). The Chinese antiquities reach no further than Noah's time, for Fohhi was their first king. Their writers generally agree that Fohhi lived about 2952 years before Christ. According to Archbishop Usher, Noah was born in 2948 BC and died 2016 years before Christ, falling pretty near within his life span of 600 years. There is no history to challenge the assertion that Noah and the Chinese Fohhi are the same. They record Fohhi was conceived in a rainbow, acknowledging the rainbow's first appearing. They say Fohhi had no father, meaning Noah was the first man in the new world. Fohhi is said to have carefully bred seven forts of creatures, which he used to sacrifice to the supreme spirit of heaven and earth. The Bible informs us that Noah took seven of every clean beast fowl of the air aboard. Chinese history supposes Fohhi to have settled in the province of Xeuji, which is the northwest province of China, near to the mountains of Ararat where the Ark rested. Such collaborate with other accounts (e.g. modern Nakhchivan, Turkey).

We may assume then that his offspring traveled east and populated China. This assertion is supported by the fact that Uppusuin, the Babylonian king, mentions his travels to visit Noah as long and tedious including the crossing of a mountain range.

© www.Bible.ca

船 ＝ 八 ＋ 口 ＋ 舟
Large Ship   Eight   Person   Boat

Fig. 56 The Chinese identified with Noah in their earliest records. His final home is said to have been in Western China. (Image used by permission © www.Bible.Ca)

In Chinese, the name Noah means, "Man through whom the weed curse is removed" (as above). One Chinese character has a cross added within a box to describe the Garden of Eden, the source of the four rivers. The Chinese have always been perplexed why their word for boat has long contained the characters for eight people.

A story is told by Gutzlaff, viz., that he saw in a Buddhist temple in China, "in beautiful stucco, the scene where Kwanyin, the goddess of mercy, looks down from heaven upon the lonely Noah in his ark amidst the raging waves of the deluge, with the dolphins swimming around as his last means of safety, and the dove, with an olive branch in its beak, flying towards the vessel. Details of the flood event found nowhere else are mentioned in these records, including the sky turning black on the northern horizon, possibly indicating the collapse of the atmosphere as reflected in the super-cooling of the high latitudes; this is evidenced by the mass freezing of tens of millions of quadrupeds such as the wooly mammoths.

(See Appendix XV. Howorth, *Mammoth*, Hardwick, *Christ and other Masters*, iii. 16 & others)

Russia

It is said the Vogels in the Urals of Russia have this tradition: "After several years of drought the great women said to the man, it will rain presently, how shall we save ourselves? The other giants are assembled together in a town to take counsel. What must we do?" The great man said, "Cut in two a hollow poplar and make two boats. A man, with his children must enter into the boat and must cover himself with ox hides and prepare provisions for seven days." Others preferred to find someplace of vantage whereby they would save themselves, but this was in vain, for the great man, who was their elder, assured them no place existed anywhere. "We shall be overtaken by the holy waters. For two days has the noise of the surgings been heard. Let us enter into the boats without delay." The earth was presently submerged. On the seventh day the waters began to abate, but alas! there was no longer on the earth trees or plants. Animals and fish had disappeared. On the verge of starvation the survivors prayed Numitarum to recreate the animals and fish, trees and plants, and their prayer was answered.

Revue de Philologie et d'Ethnographe i 12,13) translated from French

Alaska

Fig. 57 The Alaska interiors first magistrate, Judge James Wickersham (left), first climb attempt leader; and missionary Rev. Hudson Stuck (right) who summited McKinley with his team 10 years later

Chief Koonah's Denali, renamed Mt. McKinley in honor of the assassi-
nated civil war hero president, an ardent supporter of that great territory.
Rev. Hudson Stuck, along with Harry Karstens and native guides Walter
Harper, Robert Tatum and John Fredsonof summited the peak in 1913. A
cross, carried by the guides, was placed on the peak.

From Alaska, we have a witnessed testimony as recorded by Judge James Wickersham[5] while camping with the Tena natives en route to climb McKinley in 1903. Here Wickersham met Chief Koonah, blind sage of the Athabasca tribe, who related the following Flood account abbreviated here: "Long ago, before Denali, the High One, was raised to the sky, one Yako dwelt in the land where the Tena live. He was gentle as a young caribou, strong as a bull moose and as wise as a beaver. [On] the bank of a great river [he] measured thereon the length and width of his magic canoe…wrought from day to day…caulked it with the gum of the Forest." Koonah relates that Yako traveled East to seek a good wife from the evil tribes who had daughters that were very beautiful. He was given the daughter of the second chief of the Raven tribe, one Tsukala, her mother wishing to save her away from the evil influences of the king, one 'Totson.' Hereon the local women, led by King Totson's daughter, attacked the mother but perished by a magic act of Yako, creating a giant wave that swept them away. King Totson, now enraged and (who lived underground, noted as "killer of men and animals" who enjoyed the "spilling of the blood of men and animals"*) perused Yako, and the ocean raged against him.

"He attacked Yako and the magic canoe to no effect, expending all his arms. Then with Yako's back turned, Totson thrust his last 'glistening' spear to finish his adversary. But alas, Yako used his magic and turned a huge wave to rock that deflected the spear, which sailed upward far into the heavens. With this last thrust, two waves came from either side and overcame Totsen, turning him into the raven, the waves now turning into mountains."

Koonah relates that one of the two mountains was Denali. Interesting here is that Noah's wife is mentioned. The account claims she was a princess and the detail suggests some truth to the story. Her Tena name was given as Tsukala, and according to lore, she waited on Yako faithfully and became a powerful grandmother. (Tsukala translated is *grandmother* in the Tena language.) The sage claimed the mountains were made as a result of the flood, including Denali, the High One. It should be noted that Denali is considered to be raised in the catastrophic subduction as related to the Flood.[6] Scientists maintain that Mt. McKinley was raised so abruptly that her sediments were stripped off her steep flanks, suggesting catastrophic origin.

*Author note: The book of First Enoch mentions this behavior in pre-flood times. This resulted in God acting to end the outrages, giving Michael and Gabriel authority to cast the rebels into gloomy dungeons and to give notice to Noah of the pending flood. See 2 Peter 2:4, *"For God did not spare the angels who sinned; on the contrary, he put them in gloomy dungeons lower than Sh'ol to be held for judgment."* (CJB)

Further west we have the summit of Mt. Everest consisting of sea floor, its buttresses full of ground sea creatures such as trilobites and other shells.[7] Maybe this peak is Yako's second wave turned to stone as the Chief relates to us. Along this line of discussion, we must mention that the Matterhorn and Mythen group of the Swiss Alps consist of material completely out of order compared to the Geologic Column, which date their summits far older than the rocks they sit upon. The suggested explanation for this enigma: their origin is from the African continent![8]

From the Inuit Eskimos who lived west of the Mackenzie toward the Colville River, Arctic Alaska, we find accounts more closely resembling the biblical one than many of the East: "The water having poured over the terrestrial disc, human dwellings disappeared. They fastened several boats to one another. The wind carried them away. The waves traversed the Rocky Mountains. Presently the moon and earth disappeared. Men died in the terrible heat, they also perished in the waves. Men bewailed what had happened. Uprooted trees floated about in the waves. Men having fastened boats together trembled with cold. A man threw his bow into the water and said, 'Wind, this is enough, be still!' It is enough and the end had come."

155

Dialects des Tchiglit... by Mile & Emile Petitot, 1876, French Missionaries to the NW Territories, Canada

Fig. 58 The Summit of Mt Everest is *Sea Floor*

North American Native Accounts

The Native Americans make often mention of a Deluge which happened in their country. Most record that all men were drowned in this event, mentioning a few saved in a great canoe landing on a high mountain to the west.

George Catlin reported that the Mandan's had an extensive ceremony closely resembling the Flood event. Catlin reports they painted a man all white and he proceeded to every lodge, proclaiming to each in a loud voice that a Flood had overcome the world, he having the full attention of every man and child from slave to chief of the village complex. He said that he was the "only survivor of a universal calamity," and narrated the full story about the watery disaster in detail, explaining that he "landed his big canoe on a high mountain to the West," and was seeking tools to make a new craft in order to be ready if the event reoccurs. He said that every lodge must donate some item just in case. The ceremony concluded with our featured character entering a lodge in the village center, made with a roof resembling a boat. Within said lodge were four tortoise shells filled with water, each representing the four quarters of the earth and 10 days time. The story goes, "Then after dedicating the gifts, took the whole and through them into the river." His given name means "the only man."

The O Kee Pa ceremony, Catlin, George *A Religious Ceremony and other customs of the Mandan's* 1967 Ewers editing

Note: Catlin states this tradition was not unique to the Mandan's, stating: *"of the 120 tribes I have visited in the North, South and central America, there does not exist a single tribe that has not related to me the distinct traditions of such a calamity, in which except one, two or three or eight persons were saved above the waters on top a high mountain."* He further mentions that many pilgrimaged to the mountains to imitate the event.

Among the Lenni Lenape tribe, it was recorded as follows: "Long ago came a powerful serpent, when men became evil. The strong serpent was the foe of these beings, and they became embroiled, hating each other. Then they fought and despoiled each other and were not peaceful. Then the snake monster brought the snake-water rushing. The wide waters rushed wide into the hills, everywhere spreading and destroying. Men and beings all go forth on the flood of waters moving afloat in every way, even on the backs of turtles [this not an impossibility, as giant tortoise existed in those times, 15x20 feet size]. The monsters of the sea were moving and destroying some of them. Then the daughter of a spirit helped them in a boat... the waters ran off again."
Bancroft, *The Native Races of the Pacific States* p. 86

Lake Tahoe natives tell of a time when their tribe inhabited the whole earth and were strong, numerous and rich. But a day came when a people rose up stronger than they and defeated and enslaved them. Afterwards the Great Spirit sent an immense wave across the continent from the sea, and this wave engulfed them all but a small remnant. After the deluge was over, taskmasters made the remaining people raise up a great temple so that the ruling caste should have refuge if another flood came upon the earth.
Bancroft, *The Native Races of the Pacific States* p. 547

Mexico

From the Aztecs of Mexico: "When mankind was overwhelmed with the deluge, none were preserved but a man named Coxcox and a woman called Xochiquetzal, who saved themselves in a boat and having afterwards reaching land upon a mountain called by them Colhuacan, had there a great many children…these children were all born dumb, until a dove from a lofty tree imparted to them languages, but differing so much that they could not understand one another."[9]

Well known Mexican historian and descendent of the last king Ixtlilxochitl (1570-1649) states as follows: "It is found in the histories of the Toltecs that this age and the first world lasted 1716 years; that men were destroyed by tremendous rains and lightning from the sky, even all the land without exception of anything, and the highest mountains were covered up and submerged in water to fifteen cubits; and add how men came to multiply from the few who escaped from this destruction in a *toptlipetlocali* which nearly signifies a closed chest: and how, after men had multiplied, they erected a very high *zacaulti*, which is today a tower of great height...presently their languages were confused, and not being able to understand each other, they went to different parts of the earth. The Toltecs, consisting of seven friends with their wives, who understood the same language, came to these parts, having first passed great land and seas, having lived in caves, after enduring great hardships in order to reach these lands. They wandered 104 years through different parts of the world before they reached Hue Hue Tlapalan, which was in Ce Teepatl, 520 years after the Flood."

'Histoire des Chichimecas et des ancients rois de Tezcoco' (2 vols., Paris 1840) by Alfredo Chavero

An ancient Aztec legend came from a document called the *Codex Chimalpopoca* relates as follows: "All mankind was drowned and turned into fishes, the water and sky drew near to each other. In a single day all was lost. The very mountains were swallowed up in the flood." It mentions the man Nota and his wife Nena who were told, "Make no more pulque, but hollow a great cypress into which you shall enter in the month of Tozoztli. The waters shall near the sky." And God "will shut them in." The Aztecs made a plate resembling a man, woman and horse in a craft of some kind called "The Stone of the Sun," depicting their origin.

The Pimas of Northern Mexico also relate that a certain prophet was warned three times by an Eagle that a deluge was coming, but each time the warning went unheeded. He told the man that the entire Gila Valley was to be flooded but still no heed. The tradition records: "Then there was a peel of thunder and an awful crash, and a green mound of water raised itself over the plain. It seemed to stand upright for a second and cut by lightning, fell on the prophet's hut. When morning broke there was no one left alive but one man, Szenkha, who saved himself by floating on a ball of resin. Then the waters fell."*

*Accounts of Alfred Murray as cited from Nelson, *Deluge Story in Stone* 1968 p. 183-7 likely originated from Bancroft, *The Native Races of the Pacific States* iii p. 64-79

South America

When the universal deluge occurred, one man with his wife and children escaped in a canoe and from them the world has been peopled. Also they taught that there was one Lord in heaven, who sent the rain and caused all the celestial motions. There was likewise a very beautiful woman in heaven, with a child, but they went no farther, nor did they know anything of their own origins. Bordering upon Terra-Firma is Peru. The ancient Indians (speaking of the Peruvians) it is reported, "had received by tradition from their ancestors, that many years before there were any Ingas [Kings], at the time when the country was very populous, there happened a great Flood, the sea breaking out beyond its bounds, so that the Land was covered with water, and all the people perished."

Brazil

The Brazilians inhabiting the inland countries scarcely knew anything of religion or an Almighty Being, this according to the Spaniard missions. They have some knowledge remaining of a general Deluge, it being their opinion "that the whole race of mankind were extirpated by a general Deluge, except one man and his own sister, who being with child before, they by degrees re-peopled the world."

Cuba

Antonio de Herrera in his *History of America* (as translated from Spanish by Capt. John Stevens), relates this interesting account as follows: "That the people of Cuba knew that heaven, the earth, and other things had been created and said they had much information concerning the Flood, and that the world had been destroyed by water, by three persons that came three several ways. Men of above seventy years of age said that an old man, knowing the Deluge was to come, built a great ship, and went into it, with his family and abundance of animals; that he sent out a crow, which did not return, staying to feed on the dead bodies; and afterwards returned with a green branch with other particulars, as far as Noah's sons covering him when drunk, and the other scoffing at it; adding, that the Indians descended from the latter, and therefore had no coats nor clothes: but that the Spaniards, descending from the other that covered him, were therefore clothed and had horses. What has been here said was told by an Indian of above seventy years of age to Gabriel de Cabrera, who one day quarrelling with him, called him dog; whereupon he [the native] asked, Why he abused and called him dog, since they were brethren, as descending from the two sons of him that made a great ship, with all the rest that has been said above. The same he repeated in the presence of several Spaniards, after his master had reported it." A good word for all, no matter what background or faith.

Summary of the Historical Record

These accounts show that our ancestors carried the Flood account across the world with amazing accuracy and unity, even celebrating the event. Further, the fact that these festivities often align with a particular calendar day and involve vivid symbolic detail of the Flood, all in remembrance of Noah and family disembarking the Ark. The event of Christs accent a logical and more perfect succession of the former, which accomplished to save only eight and cargo; but with the new, potentially rescuing *the entire world*. In other words, God passed the global salvation baton from Noah to His own Son, this in the person we know as *Jesus Christ*. There will be no other chance for mankind.

[1] Sanders, N.K., *The Epic of Gilgamesh* (Penguin Classics, London 1972), pp. 108-113

[2] Mercatante, A.S., *Encyclopedia of World Mythology and Legend* (Child & Associates Publishing, NSW, Australia 1988) p. 613

[3] Austin, Allen *The Middle of the Earth: Genesis in Egypt* Xulon Press

[4] Berlitz, C., *The Lost Ship of Noah*, (W.H. Allen, London 1987), p. 126

[5] Winkersham, James, *Old Yukon, Tales, Trail Trials* (Washington Law Press 1938), p. 243-253

[6] http://geology.about.com/library/bl/peaks/bldenali.htm

[7] Wikipedia.com *Mt. Everest Geology*

[8] Morris and Whitcomb, *The Genesis Flood* (P&R Press 1961), p. 199

[9] Frazer, J.G., *Folklore in the Old Testaments: Studies in Comparative Religion, Legend and Law* Abridged Edition (Avenel Books, New York, NY 1988), p. 107

III

The Great Divide of History—Man in Europe

A noted member of the British Geological Society, Henry Howorth and many of his peers maintained that in Europe and across the globe, a clear and unique *event horizon* appeared in the fossil and geologic records, best explained by a Flood. Their case was well documented and contained hundreds of human artifacts and remains found in caves, not to mention the extinct mega-fauna with them: the great hyena, cave bear, sloth, cave lion, broad fronted bison, wooly rhinoceros, mastodon, and finally the mammoth. All were swept from the face of the earth concurrently and simultaneously by rushing waters. Apart from this evidence was even more: the stupendous quantity of animal fossils at specific levels and in "fissure" deposits. These skyward facing crevasses that were found full of a mixture of all types of mammals, birds and even men, were exactly what one would expect in evidence of a global Flood.

As a contemporary of many other greats of the day such as Cuvier, Buckland, de Sires, DuPont, M. de Cartailhac, M. de Mortillet, Prestwich, Falconer, Adams, and others including Darwin, Howorth quoted them prolifically, creating a powerful testimony in light of this controversy that blazed at the time. And so we have the words of these Masters for the reader to consider, and they not without due respect and consideration in this matter, as many of their findings are timeless relating to the topic at hand, and now for the first time in many decades brought back to light.

Europe—The Great Divide

First, they uncovered a *divide* between the two periods, one that most all observed and openly documented. One, an older time identified by the findings in the caves and in the layers and Loess deposits of the world. This mostly is evidenced by what these able investigators found in the caves—a clear event-line of human history. The primary and direct evidence was the presence of man and the extinct beast together in the caves, both entombed in the same blocks of stone. Some attempted to explain this away, saying the bones were brought together by man himself in the process of hunting and consumption, or they were carried there by predators over eons of time, or further, brought into position by burrowing animals. But as the reader will soon notice, these flimsy explanations soon failed in evidence and were demolished one by one. Secondly, they found evidence of a new and more sophisticated man, one that came on the scene abruptly and unrelated to the first, this in the layers above the former, a fact cementing the Flood account in the minds of many.

Howorth tells us: "At all points, therefore, the evidence is complete that man and his companions in the Mammoth-age differed completely from man in the succeeding period: differed in habits, in tastes, in art, and in the animals which were his companions. This difference is *everywhere* acknowledged... What is much more important is the startling fact that the two sets of men, their remains, and their animal companions, are sharply and definitely separated by a complete *gap*. There is nowhere on record a well-certified instance in either the Europasian or the Mediterranean region in which the remains have been found mixed. Upon this subject there is a concurrence of opinion among the best judges."

"The summary of the combined archaeological and fossil evidence of both man and beast is clear, a watery catastrophe wiped both off the face of the earth later replaced by a gentler group of inhabitants bringing domestication, agriculture and art with them, absent the mega-fauna such as the mammoths and super sized predators, cave bear, hyena and others."

Howorth goes on concerning the Human-Mammoth epoch, now quoting these "judges." "Dr. Garrigou says emphatically that in the 252 caverns which he explored, he always found these two periods [referring to pre and post flood], were always strata-graphically separated; the Palaeolithic objects [early stone age] were always found with the old fauna and the Neolithic ones [modern stone age] with the more recent one."[1]

Quoting M. de Cartailhac (a well-known French archaeologist and geol-ogist): "In the south and south-west of France, the abyss which separates the age of chipped from that of polished stone is well marked. The caverns, and possibly the country itself, were temporarily deprived of inhabitants. The new people were a pastoral race. There is no analogy, no point of contact between them and their predecessors... It was they (i.e. the Neolithic people) who for the first time introduced pottery."[2]

Another recognized French naturalist, M. de Mortillet (Louis Laurent Gabriel de Mortillet, August 29, 1821 – September 25, 1898), a museum director in France, wrote extensively on the interpretation of the fossil record, promoting a chronology of earth's natural history based on four divisions. His primary work *Le Prehistorique* (1883) comments on this gap, he states:

"Between the Magdalenian (Pleistocene) and the Robenhausen (Neolithic) there is a wide and profound lacuna, a great hiatus, a *complete transformation*. With the former age disappear the quaternary animals, the great bear, Mammoth, the megaceros; with it migrated northwards the reindeer, glutton, and musk-sheep; and towards the mountains, the chamois, ibex, and marmot. With the latter there appeared not only polished stone implements, but also pottery, monuments, dolmens and menhirs, domestic animals and agriculture; a very complete change."[3] Continuing on the subject of transformation he says: "Up to now we have seen the different periods pass gradually into one another by a process of gradual development. This is no longer the case when we pass from the Magdalenian (Miocene), the last of the geological stages, to the (Pleistocene), the first stage of the present state of things. Between these two there is a complete difference, an *undoubted revolution*"[4] [emphasis mine].

Mortillet maintained that "in the earlier period we have a uniform type of man; in the later, one showing great diversity. In the former, a population that was in migration. In the latter, one much in stasis. In the former, a race of hunters and fishermen, without agriculture; in the latter, agriculture well developed. In the former, no monuments and no traces of sepulture; in the latter, abundance of both."

Speaking of the geologic conditions found, Mortillet states: "In many caves we have a layer of barren loam, marking the gap between the two periods.[5] We can trace a gradual passage from Neolithic times into the succeeding Bronze Age, but no such transition has yet been detected between the relics of the new and the old stone periods. The implements of the one period are never found commingled with those of the other, nor do the characteristic faunas of the two ages ever occur together in one and the same undisturbed deposit.

"The cave deposits testify to the remarkable fact that the Old Stone Age did not graduate, as it were, into the New Stone Age. The records of the latter epoch are separated very markedly from those of the former. No sooner do we pass from the uppermost deposits of Pleistocene age to the more modern accumulations, than all at once we find ourselves in quite another world. The hyenas and lions, the rhinoceroses and mammoths, have disappeared, and we are now face to face with a group of animals that we recognize as being the common indigenous European forms of our own day. Palaeolithic man has likewise vanished, and his place is supplied by races considerably farther advanced on the road to civilization. Neolithic man was not only a hunter and fisher like his predecessors, but he possessed some knowledge of agriculture, and of the arts of weaving and making pottery. His implements show more variety of design, and are upon the whole much better finished, being frequently ground at the edges, and often smoothed and polished. He was also accompanied by domesticated animals, and in some cases occupied well- constructed houses..."

The famous Scottish geologist and naturalist James Geikie in his volume *Prehistoric Europe* (1881), comments on the event horizon seen in these caves: "The implements of the former, i.e. Neolithic period, occupy invariably a superficial position, they occur either lying loosely at the surface or embedded at no great depth, in accumulations which can be shown to be of very recent date, geologically speaking. In undisturbed cave deposits they are *never* commingled with the relics of the older period, but are not infrequently separated from these by *sheets of stalagmite* [emphasis mine], accumulations of earth and debris, or beds of clay, silt sand, gravel, and other materials. Thus in Kent's Cave [England], we have seen that the archaic and more modern remains rested upon a bed of granular stalagmite, in and underneath which only, did Palaeolithic implements and the bones of the extinct mammalia occur. All these had been sealed up and the cave had been long abandoned before it was again tenanted by man. In the interim, many large and small blocks had fallen from the roof and accumulated upon the floor."[6]

Commenting regarding the contents of these *hundreds* of caverns and sub-surface finds, Geikie continues: "Between Palaeolithic and Neolithic man there is thus a wide gulf of separation. From a state of utter savagery we pass into one of comparative civilization. When Neolithic man entered Europe, he came as an agriculturist and a herdsman, and his relics and remains occur again and again immediately above Pleistocene deposits, in which we meet with no trace of any higher or better state of human existence than that which is represented by the savages who contended with the extinct mammalian."[7]

To those who embrace uniformity and reject the Flood model, such a break is very disharmonious to their theory. In the study of man, those who reject the Flood account hope for a *continuum*, having little or no explanation for this gap. They often resort to disease, pestilence, meteor bursts, earthquakes or war, anything but a flood to explain this widely observed phenomena. Yet according to these early observers, they will find little to support such ideas in the digs, none but that of a flood of transcontinental proportions. As these authorities ranged further across Europe, they found only more of the same, and when they peered globally they returned home astonished; the story was the same!

Apart from man himself, we must remember that a *whole fauna* disappears suddenly, and is replaced as suddenly by another. Howorth tells us there is not a single instance of mammoth or rhinoceros found with the remains of Neolithic man, [modern man] and not a *single instance* of domesticated animals found associated with the remains of Palaeolithic or pre-flood man. James Geikie also supports this understanding: "This is a simple assumption; so much so, indeed, that I fear [Mr. Dawkins] must have made it without due consideration; for even granting that Palaeolithic man was scared out of Europe by the terrible apparition of Neolithic invaders, (as has been claimed since) are we to suppose that this had the same effect upon the fauna and flora? Did the reindeer, musk-sheep, mammoth, hyena, and cave-bear at once vanish from the scene?"[8] *

*Note: Also these included the woolly rhinoceros, with a skin so thick only large caliber weapons are able to penetrate its smaller cousin in Africa today, forcing a new class of rifles to be developed once Europeans came there to hunt. To deal with these animals, the 4" long .375 caliber Holland & Holland round was developed, now the legal *minimum* caliber allowed to hunt today's monsters, monsters that were dwarfed by the extinct versions, these supposedly "slaughtered" by man with spears according to the modernists.

Axes and Implements Found Deeply Buried in European Sediments

Tools and implements of the early populous of Europe were found deeply buried and scattered in the gravels of that place, suggestive that their owners perished with them by flood waters. The early researchers comment extensively on these important artifacts, often in the face of stubborn criticism from those who insisted on a local flood; such was explained as water sourced from receding *glaciers,* a mistaken theme that caught on in America later on. It became apparent that no amount of evidence would sway them, enjoying their new cosmology of earth separated from the biblical account, always and ever ready to reject the Flood. Truthfully, their new pyridine was not new at all, but that of the Greek philosophers of past times, recently resurrected. We now know the real goal of the uniformists was to detach themselves from the Church and Bible in specific, clearing the way for a new philosophy to drive science.

Howorth rejoins the debate in his energetic and straightforward style, exasperated by the blind faith of the uniformist group, they now explaining this deposition of "axes" done accidentally by dropping their tools over the sides of boats while fishing! Howorth continues: "Many of the axes, it has been remarked, do not lie on their sides, but are found as it were hanging in the beds [suspended] and resting on their edges in a way only compatible with their having been dropped out of water. The same conclusion seems deducible from the regular distribution of the flint implements in the gravels of the Somme, &c. These implements are there scattered…through the lower beds of the gravel, and the view which this fact has suggested to the champions of uniformity is that they were dropped out of their boats when fishing by the palaeolithic folk. This notion is surely most original.

"That palaeolithic [pre-flood] man, should deliberately sow flint tools out of his boats in such profusion, and with such a catholic regard to universal distribution, is certainly either a fresh proof of the unsophisticated character of early life, or of the naive and unsophisticated ingenuousness of the champions of uniformity…that the beds in which the stone implements occur are found in situations where no river flows, and where no river that we can postulate as possible ever could have flowed. The white patina which covers the axes when it attains a certain thickness invariably proves that they have been exposed for a long time to the air. [Author note: a condition showing they had been in use for a time before burial.] Thus, those which we find in the gravels covered with this [ageing evidence] were already old when buried. That is to say, were not dropped about at haphazard by fishermen, but were swept away very often from the surface of the land by the torrent, which deposited them where they are found."*

*Author note: Often documented at eight, nine, or even twelve meters of gravels, (25-40 feet) these are axe heads, unlikely to have migrated there by their own weight.

Howorth continues: "How can anyone seriously point to a complete, absolute, and sudden gap as a proof of a vast, unbroken, and continuous period of time having elapsed between one state of things and the other. There is literally no relevance of any kind between the facts and the inference. The logical hiatus is as complete as is the physical one. A change progressing over a long period might be expected to show continued proofs of change, but not a complete gap. A gap means a break in the continuity—a break in the uniformity of the evidence; and those like ourselves who believe in empirical methods, believe further—that a gap in the evidence, unless accounted for very clearly, means a substantial gap in the facts themselves. To me, nothing can be plainer than that the complete and sharply defined disappearance of a type of man with a distinct fauna and flora, and its being replaced by an equally sharply defined new type of man, with a new and distinct fauna and flora, means the sudden, the widespread, and complete destruction of the one, and an entirely separate and distinct new beginning caused by the old desolated district being reoccupied by a fresh migration."

Howorth then expands the options: "That it means, in fact, some cataclysm such as I have argued for on so long, and which is supported by an ever-increasing and ever-converging array of facts. I do not know anything else in nature competent in the first place to destroy human life over a wide area without obliterating or injuring the remains, and at the same time competent to entomb them in continuous masses of loam or gravel. The mode in which the implements occur is equally suggestive with the mode of occurrence of the human bones. I believe that the same potent cause which swept away the mammoth and the rhinoceros, the cave-bear and the hyena from Europe, also swept away Palaeolithic man, and that this cause was as sudden as it was widespread. It seems to me that the human skeletons and bones which occur un-weathered in precisely the same condition as those of the wild animals which accompany them, must point precisely the same moral."

Human Finds Emerge

Howorth continues: "Like those of the extinct animals, the human bones are buried deeply in undisturbed loess, &c. There is no pretense for saying that the human skeletons which have been hitherto found and which were for the most part disintegrated and scattered, were buried artificially. The ground where they have occurred is undisturbed ground, and it does not seem arguable therefore that the remains of man, anymore than the remains of the accompanying extinct animals, were artificially buried. If not artificially buried by his companions, I cannot understand how his remains, un-weathered and fresh, should have been overlain by great depths of loam and loess in situations far above the level of the rivers and their overflow, and in districts where such overflow, even when it occurs, only deposits layers of loam the thickness of brown paper at the most, except as I argued in the case of the extinct animals, *by the operation of a great flood of waters.*"

Agreement on a New "Gentle Race"

The most important geologists, archaeologists and zoologists of the day largely concur that an event of global proportions wiped out one form of man and animal; then quite as rapidly, was subsequently replaced by another, more gentle race that focused on agriculture, domestication, art and permanent places to dwell. Further, it is one accompanied by the wildlife and domestic animals of the present day!

These observations seem a perfect image of none other than the descendants of our favorite family! Now consider three things basic to their lifestyle: a) that of building the Ark, b) the cultivation of crops, and c) engaging in the science of animal domestication! Now considering the reports that these "new" inhabitants made a "sudden" appearance, a fact so obvious that the majority of these naturalists found *consensus* in their observations of this amazing change of heart and lifestyle! Their unified summary was nothing less than amazing proof that the biblical account *is* fully aligned with true archaeology and devastating to secular explanations. And quote: "by operation of a great flood of waters."

---

[1] Cited from Howorth, *Mammoth*, Compte Rendu, Int. Cong, of Arch. Bologna, 96.
[2] Cited from Howorth, *Mammoth*, Id. Brussels, p. 452, 453.
[3] Cited from Howorth, *Mammoth*, Id. Brussels, p. 441
[4] Gabriel de Mortillet, *Le Prehistorique*, 1882 p. 479, 480
[5] Gabriel de Mortillet, *Le Prehistorique*, 1882 p. 481- 482.
[6] Geikie, *Prehistoric Europe*, 23, 24, 118—120
[7] ibid. 6. P. 379.
[8] ibid. 6 p. 647, 548, 252

IV

North American Early Man

Now we shall cross the Atlantic and visit the evidences found in our native land, North America, searching the layers for an event horizon such as found in Europe in that hemisphere. The question being posted, did man meet the same demise in America as that found in Europe? The answer may only be found in the rocks.

Common to the European and American sites, we find the presence of man and the extinct quadrupeds: those of the sloth, mammoth, mastodon, camel, large predators and the horse, now vanished and encased in solid rock. The same Flood deposited sediment types as across the globe. Looking again to the words of those closer to the evidence, we have the following accounts for the reader's consideration. Fortunately for us, these documents came at a time when such thought could be published openly without worry of snubbing, transfer or loss of employment, as is the case today.

Lyell and the Bias

Charles Lyell first visited this country in 1850 and witnessed with his own eyes (to his consternation) the recovery of human remains 30 feet below the surface in association with extinct animals, just as in hundreds of locations across Europe! Speaking of the discovery, Lyell records: "It appeared to be the bone of a man, in the same state of preservation, and was of the same dark color as the other fossils, and was believed to have come like them from a depth of about thirty feet from the surface."[1]

Lyell goes on to urge that until other like specimens could be found, this case must be *overlooked*. He rationalizes the site as possibly that of a native graveyard. At this juncture it's worthwhile to quote the presiding witness who made the discovery in the first place, Dr. Dickeson. Documenting this find in contradiction to Lyell's comments, Dickeson stated the human remains were taken from a uniform and undisturbed bed of blue clay, two feet *below* the skeletons of the megalonyx (mastodon) and other extinct quadrupeds. The discoverer tells us: "The bone is that of a young man of about sixteen years of age, as determined by its size and form. That this bone is strictly in the fossil state, is manifest from its physical characters, in which it accords in every respect of color, density, with those of the megalonyx and other associated bones. That it could not have drifted into the position in which it was found is manifest from several facts: 1) the plateau of blue clay is not appreciably acted upon by those causes that produce ravines in the superincum bent diluvium, 2) That the human bone was found at least two feet below three associated skeletons of the megalonyx, all of which, judging from the apposition or proximity of their several parts, had been deposited in this locality. And lastly, because there was no admixture of diluvial drift with the blue clay, which latter retains its homogeneous character equally in the higher part that furnished extinct quadrupeds, and in its lower part that contained the remains of man."

Now, if this find supported Lyell's opinion of origins and the reverse was indicated, we can be sure this discovery would have been shouted from the rooftops, his visit to America a success for "science," no less than of the Beagle of Darwin a few decades before! The last thing Lyell wanted to find was more of the same as in the Old Country, that is, more evidence of a Flood! Lyell's bias was exposed years later in his personal letters, his primary object found out: to eject the Bible from the classrooms of science at any cost, all the while appearing objective and wholly scientific. In that he did well, even compared to the floating of axe heads in the European finds mentioned.

Niagara Falls and "Principles of Geology"

Lyell, a lawyer first by trade, was a master of convincing language, which is evident in his many works. Darwin took his *Principles of Geology* on the Beagle voyage, which argued the concept of slow and gradual geological processes occurring over millions of years. Even modern evolutionists acknowledge that Lyell was biased and driven by anti-biblical presuppositions. The late Stephen J. Gould commented about this issue, that of Lyell in his perfect act in the portrayal of the objective scientist: "Lyell relied upon true bits of cunning to establish his uniformitarian views as the only true geology. First, he set up a straw man to demolish. In fact, the catastrophists were much more empirically minded than Lyell. The geologic record does seem to require catastrophes: rocks are fractured and contorted, and whole faunas are wiped out. To circumvent this literal appearance, Lyell imposed his imagination upon the evidence. The geologic record, he argued, is extremely imperfect and we must interpolate into it what we can reasonably infer but cannot see. The catastrophists were the hard-nosed empiricists of their day, not the blinded theological apologists."[2] One infamous example of Lyell's bias was his account of the rate of erosion of Niagara Falls, publishing a mathematical figure to suit his purpose. The commonly known erosion rate of the Niagara at the time of his visit was known to be between 3 and 5 feet/year. (One period averaged 18 feet/year.)[3] Lyell somehow arrived at the far reduced rate of one foot or 0.3 meters/year, and published such in his popular books. Since the gorge was 35,000 feet long, he intentionally helped people extrapolate (using his cooked data) that the gorge must certainly be 35,000 years old!

Later analysis of the Falls from 1842 to 1927 confirmed a higher rate of erosion, that of four to five feet per year. This rate placing an *upper limit* of 7,000 to 9,000 years for the gorge; we now know the average erosion factor is even *higher*, the calculated age agreeing with the ice cover of about 3,800 years ago, which is in agreement with the post-flood Ice Age. That Lyell's writings influenced Darwin is a well known fact; Darwin eventually linked uniformities' slow and gradual geological processes with his supposed gradual biological processes (e.g., finch's beaks), in the end giving us the delusion of Darwinian Evolution.

The North American Great Divide and Early Man

When archaeologists ventured across the American expanses in search of early man in the early 1900s and forward, the concept of a global Flood had been largely dissected out of most science texts thanks to the efforts of the new professors (as in Europe), who were disinterested in making bedmates with theologians, often rejecting the Bible outright as any sort of reliable guide.

There were exceptions, one being Sir J. William Dawson (October 13, 1820 – November 19, 1899) and past President of the Royal Society of Canada and noted geologist, who writes us:

"Further, we know now that the Deluge of Noah is not a mere myth or fancy of primitive man or solely a doctrine of the Hebrew Scriptures. The record of the catastrophe is preserved in some of the oldest historical documents of several distinct races of men and is indirectly corroborated by the whole tenor of the early history of most of the civilized races. As to the actual occurrence of the Deluge as a widespread catastrophe affecting, with a few stated exceptions, the whole human race, we have thus a concurrence of the testimony of ancient history and tradition, and of geological and archaeological evidence, as well as of the inspired records of the Hebrew and Christian revelation. Thus no historical event, ancient or modern, can be more firmly established as matter of fact than this."[4]

As an option to the Flood, a new explanation was needed to explain the deeply flood covered bones and artifacts. They elected the work of *glaciers* to accomplish this and many other amazing watery feats. These were responsible, they claimed, for the gravel burials of every man, animal and vegetable in North America, even capable of drowning stampeding herds of mammoths! (And as we will document later, the same such actions explaining deep human burials in Texas, Louisiana and elsewhere!)

Thus, a new system of geologic explanation was developed in order to classify and index such finds; glaciers and their melting becoming the central theme of much geologic work, too much. This is an interesting model but in contradiction with the general and obvious isolation of two epochs found in the layers in North America exactly as that found in Europe. The deeper were acknowledged as the eon associated with the extinct species: e.g. the broad front bison, the sloth, the mastodon and of course, the ever present mammoth, all found buried catastrophically under thousands of tons of water deposited gravels, these as far as Texas, quite a distance from any glacier! To deal with these problems, new definitions were assigned to cover over the obvious.

The Thermal Changes: First, it was acknowledged that there was an earlier moist and warmer period: this was designated the *Altithermal Period.* Here was, archaeologists agreed, a period called the *Thermal Maximum* said to begin some 7,000-7,500 hundred years ago, suggesting the exact conditions the Bible suggests present in the First Earth! Next, they admitted to a cooler period that followed the former, defined the *Medithermal Age,* which is suggested to have began some 4,000 years past, again, right on target with the biblical Flood![5]

---

[1] Lyell, Antiquity of Man, p. 238.
[2] S.J. Gould, *Natural History,* p. 16, February 1975. (cited from www.creation.mobi/article/276)
[3] Philbrick, S. S., *What Future for Niagara Falls?* (Geological Society of America Bulletin, 85:91–98, 1974).
[4] Sir John William Dawson, *The Historical Deluge in Relation to Scientific Discovery*, p. 4.
[5] Wormington, Hannah M. *Ancient Man in North America* (Denver Museum. of Nat'l History Press 1957), p. 20

V
Human Artifacts in North America Potentially Related to the Flood

Ancient American Man, Soda Bar, Trenton, and the Nampa Image

In further study of evidence relating to the race of people who occupied America before the Flood, we now come to a series of artifacts that are unexplained by the concept of great ages, glaciers and the notion of uniformity.

The Soda Bar Find

Soon after Lyell's visit to America, miners discovered human remains twenty-two feet below the surface in the Soda Bar Colorado gold mines in 1860.* The skeletal remains were found lying facedown beneath gravel and boulders in the rocky deposits at Soda Bar, high in the Colorado Rocky Mountains. Still intact were the larger bones and skull, found to be fully modern. Witnessing the find, Mr. L. Berthond,* reported to the Academy of Science at Philadelphia in 1866: "[it] was a point conclusively shown, namely, that prior to the cause which covered Soda Hill, Soda Bar, and Dry Diggings Hill with its enormous beds of gravel, sand and boulders, and its native gold, man roved and dwelt in this region."[1] Along with the bones a pine tree was found two feet beneath in strata called "red rock." The tree observed had its bark charred and disintegrated upon contact with the air. It would not be a stretch to surmise the tree was exposed to tremendous heat, then covered by sediments carried by moving water, nor to guess that the body was deposited then covered by the water transported gravel and boulders. Hence this find represents yet another important discovery conveniently omitted from the modern literature.

---

*Berthond concluded: "We confess that our preconceived notions of the antiquity of this Globe have received a severe shock by this discovery, and have modified our views as to the antiquity of the strata in this part of the Globe in this part of the continent..."

The Trenton Event Horizon

A decade after the Soda Bar finds, we move to the Trenton Gravels of New Jersey, the site of a number of significant discoveries including artifacts, tools and deeply buried skeletal remains. For the first time in America, a clear distinction was made in reference to older palaeolithic tools of early man and those of Neolithic man of modern habitation.

First brought to light by Dr. Charles C. Abbott of New Jersey (author of *Primitive Industry, a study of artifacts from the America Northeast Coast,* 1881), also a member Boston Society of Natural History, Fellow Royal Society of Antiquaries of the North Copenhagen and other professional associations. Abbott's work seems definitive. According to Lewis of the American Survey Office, a witness to these finds and of Abbott's work in general, goes on to tell us about the artifacts themselves: "in their shape and character they are quite unlike those of the [current Native Americans] of the Atlantic coast. He has found them embedded at various depths in the apparently undisturbed gravel of the cliff at Riverview Cemetery, and in other places near Trenton. They are of palaeolithic type, and differ from Indian stone implements by being larger, ruder, and made from a different material. They are composed of grey argillite, a rock which is found in places farther up the river...They occur in positions which render it extremely probable that they belong to the same age as that of the deposition of the gravel, or at least to an age when it was overflowed by a flooded river."

Abbott himself wrote: "There are two points which offer strong evidence in that direction. The first is the fact that modern Indian implements, Neoliths, are never found associated with these Palaeoliths in the gravel. Although abundant at the surface, it is stated that they never occur at a depth of more than a few inches in the undisturbed soil, while the Palaeoliths are found often ten or more feet from the surface. This fact alone argues a different age for the two classes of implements. The second fact is that when found below the surface of the ground these Palaeoliths always occur in the Trenton gravel and never in the older gravels. All the evidence that has been gathered points to the conclusion that at the time of the Trenton gravel flood, man in a rude state lived upon the banks of the ancient Delaware. Many of the Palaeoliths found in the river gravels of Europe are of similar type. As a rule, probably the implements of the Trenton gravel are somewhat more rude."[2]

The narrative in Dr. Abbot's volume (Abbot's Primitive Industry) continues, adding that geologically, the Trenton Gravels cover a large uniform area extending all the way to the coast and basically involve the southern half of New Jersey. He also differs that these gravels had a glacial origin, an explanation often evoked to deter students from considering such a result of the Great Flood. This mistaken theme has continued to this day.

Again we have Dr. Abbott in his volume *Abbott's Primitive Industry* describing the discovery of a human jawbone in the Trenton Gravels. He provides several important remarks in overview for the reader: "These gravels are, so far as we can make out, exactly on the same horizon as the implement-bearing gravels of Europe, and bear just the same relation to the so-called glacial beds. In them were found similar remains of extinct animals. Remains of the bison have also occurred there."

Abbott summarizes: "The conclusion that the Indians were preceded by another people is based upon the fact that it is not practicable to trace any connection between the characteristic chipped palaeolithic implements and the polished, pecked and finely wrought objects of Indian origin: the one form certainly not having any necessary connection with the other. The wide gap that exists between a full series of each of the two forms is readily recognized when the two are brought together, and no one will hesitate to acknowledge it... The fact that the implements were deposited with the gravel is shown, not only by the undisturbed character of the latter, but also in that they have been found under the *great boulders* which pervade the gravel" [emphasis mine].

Abbott refers to one weighing 100 lbs. and a second boulder, of much larger size, located five feet above the first, twenty-one feet below the surface and both in contact. He adds, "The character of the mass, which was that of the bluff on the bank of the river near Trenton, was such as to render it impossible that this specimen could have reached this position subsequently to the deposition of the containing bed." The relics are isolated, in that the cause, which buried both boulders and implements, was earlier than the appearance of Neolithic man, is shown by the fact that no relics of the latter are found with the old implements.

Abbott then speaks directly to the issue: "It is here strenuously maintained that the forces that caught up these later gravels also gathered in fact the rude implements that now give such interest to the deposit. It is evident, from the condition of some and the depth at which many are found, that they were made prior to the foundation of the containing bed, and were lost or discarded when the floods swept down the valley... These implements are indicative of man's presence and have been placed in their present positions, varying from three to forty feet in depth, by the same agency that laid down the gravels... Every geologist who has written about these gravels has, so far as I know, invoked the agency of immense floods of water to account for them, most of them adding a corollary to which I completely demur, (is in disagreement) that the flood of water proceeded from a melting glacier."[3]

By rejecting the glacial flood explanation and embracing the European connection, Abbot is leaving the reader with but one alternative, that of a worldwide flood explaining the deep burial of these artifacts.

Divide Found in New Mexico

At the Sandra Cave in the Las Huertas Canyon, New Mexico, were found a variety of man-made implements together with the fossil remains of such animals as the horse, camel, bison, mammoth, ground sloth, and wolf. The cave was initially discovered by treasure hunters on the lower slope of Bishops Cap, the principal a Mr. Roscoe Conkling of El Paso, TX. Intrigued by its soft floor, a party was formed and returned to the site along with an expert witness.

Excavations commenced in the presence of a recognized authority, Mr. William Bryan, invited to be on hand to witness any potential fossils of importance and to verify the geological sequence of the excavation. Digging down through the layers, bones of animals now extinct began to be exposed and removed. To the shock of all present, suddenly a human skull cap appeared at the 12 foot level. Further down in the water deposited sediment layers, a hard sandstone lens was encountered. When this layer was broken through, another skull was found, along with remains of other animals including a camel at nearly 21 feet in depth. Several archaeologists commented that this finding was of national significance, but for one reason or another, Bryan's impressive report* never made it into the textbooks or literature and was sidelined into obscurity.

*Bryan, William Alanson; *Science*, 70:39-41 1929 New Mexico

The Nampa Image

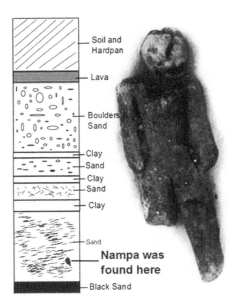

Fig. 59 The Nampa Image, pumped over 300 feet to the surface
in a well drilling operation, confounding evolutionary explanations

The "Nampa Image" pumped 300 feet to the surface through a 6" well casing before many witnesses. Without question this object was made by humans who lived before the Flood. The strata dated approximated 2 million years old, using evolutionary models.

This idol image from the Nampa, Idaho, area was brought to the surface in a well drilling operation in 1889. The stone doll came from the 300 plus foot level of the well boring. Quoting Frederick Wright: "The record of the well shows that in reaching the stratum from which the image was brought up, they had penetrated first about fifty feet of soil, then about fifteen feet of basalt, and afterwards passed through alternate beds of clay and quicksand down to a depth of about three hundred feet, when the sand pump began to bring up numerous clay balls, some of them more than two inches in diameter, densely coated with iron oxide."

According to the United States Geological Survey, the age of this stratum was considered "Plio-Pleistocene," supposedly deposited some 2 million years ago. Note the well log shows the image was found below multiple water deposited beds of *sand,* and far below a 15 foot layer of solid *lava.*

This volcanic layer could be part of the aforementioned Columbia Basalts, spanning over 90,000 square miles of the Northwestern United States.

In this find, we have evidence that a civilization existed before the catastrophe that covered the idol, confounding current geological and archeological models and fully supporting the biblical one. Note that the Demenski, Georgia, find of human remains, (complete skeletons and skulls) were assigned the same age range as the Nampa Image. Demenski has forced paleoanthropologists to rework the coveted evolutionary tree of man, this in favor of an entirely new model.[5]

Axe Head from an Illinois Well

In the process of digging a well down through soil, four farmers hit bedrock at 70 feet. In getting ready to set a blast charge at the well bottom, an axe head was found lying on the bedrock in the lowermost clay layer, which indicates a water deposit. The four witnesses led by the landowner, a Mr. A.B. Young of Green County, Ill., who elected to proceed to the local judge and took out a sworn affidavit by their own insistence, and then turned over the relic to a Mr. McAdams, a scientist from a local institution.[6]

Fig. 60 The Calaveras Skull, the most controversial
human remains find of the 19th century

Table Mountain California, Gold Mine Skeleton Finds

The Calaveras Skull was discovered in 1866 in deep gold-bearing gravel beneath a mesa with a volcanic tuff cap. In February 1866, the skull in question was removed by Mr. Mattison in Calaveras County, CA and was claimed to have been extracted from a layer of gravel 130 feet below the surface under the lava cap of Table Mountain Butte. The image of the Calaveras Skull (Figure 58) was taken in the original gravel matrix. The skull was found in 1866 at Bald Hill near Angels Camp in Calaveras County, California.

Later, a human jaw was also removed and inspected by Professor J. D. Whitney, the California State Geologist at the time. The jaw was given to a Dr. Snell by miners, who also stated it came from the gravels beneath the lava cap at Table Mountain. As this site gained publicity for the sheer quantity of human artifacts and remains found; noted geologists of the day George H. Baker, Professor O.C. Marsh, a Professor Putnam and W. H. Dall, were noted as attesting to the fact that the Calaveras skull was found *in place* beneath a stream of gravel deep underground. The relative position of the strata indicated these were over 30 million years old according to the evolutionary time scale, invalidating all the models then and now.

Speaking about these finds in August 1879, then AAAS President and respected paleontologist Dr. O. C. Marsh stated: "The proof offered on this point by Professor J. D. Whitney in his recent work (Gravels of Sierra Nevada) is so strong, and his careful, conscientious method of investigation so well known, that his conclusions seem irresistible. At present, the known facts indicate that the American beds, containing human remains and works of man, are as old as the Pliocene of Europe. *The existence of man in the Tertiary period seems now fairly established.*"[7] Of course, this find never found itself into the most basic textbooks on the subject, establishment science unable to embrace finds that were unacceptable to the preconceived models of today.

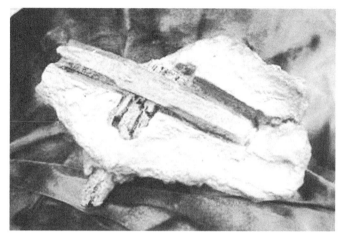

Fig. 61 The hammer in this specimen is said to be impossible to forge
in today's atmosphere (image courtesy Creation Evidence Museum Glen Rose, TX).

The London, Texas Hammer

A hammer encased in a rock dating approximately 100 million years old
was discovered in June 1934, by a Mr. Max Hahn near London, Texas.
Noticing a rock with a wooden handle protruding out of it, Hahn returned
home where he opened the stone with hammer and chisel, exposing a hammerhead. The hammerhead was analyzed and found to be composed of
96.6% iron, 0.74% sulfur, and 2.6% chlorine. Metallurgy tests suggest the
forging process may not be replicated in today's conditions.

Sheguiandah Island, Canada Artifacts

Turning to the late 1960s and 70s, an amazing group of artifacts were
discovered on Sheguiandah Island, this place on the Canadian side of the
border. The discoveries included a great number of tools and artifacts deeply
buried under multiple layers in water deposits. Most were arrow/spear points
and bowls (pestles). Discovered below four layers of supposed "glacial till"
[which are often miss-identified and are exactly the same as 'flood deposits,'
simply renamed], the last layer above them was a uniform deposit of granite
boulders 30 inches in diameter! Many tools and arrowheads were unearthed
in these "stratified clays." Thomas E. Lee, champion of the find was also a
casualty thereof. Lee, after being dismissed from his position over documenting this discovery, states: "These finds would have forced embarrassing
admissions that the archaeologist's of the day did not know everything, and

that North American man occupied these parts 100,000 years too early." Lee further stated, "Tons of artifacts vanished into the storage bins...it would have forced the re-writing of almost every book in the business. It had to be killed. It was killed." (Lee 1966)

Establishment scientists decided the Sheguiandah finds[8] were too radical for definition, and the dig assigned the "non-site" category: a special place for findings that don't conform to the ideals of the establishment. Lee and his former director at the Canadian National Museum were forced from their jobs over these finds, all for simply trying to do the right thing, let the evidence lead where it may for the betterment of science. The archaeological establishment wouldn't have them. They were made an example of, it seemed—conform or you're *out*.

Fig. 62 Dinosaur and human footprints found near Paluxy, TX
also found in Arizona, Kentucky, New Mexico and at Mt. Whitney[9]

Fossil Humanlike Footprints.

Professor W. G. Burroughs, head of the department of geology at Berea College in Berea, Kentucky, reported in 1938 that he had identified a number of prints in the vicinity of that place. These consisted of human foot impressions mixed with those of animals. Similar finds have been reported in Australia, El Salvador, Nicaragua, Massachusetts, Nevada, St Louis, MO. Texas, California, New Mexico, Arizona and Turkey.

Corliss, William, *Handbook of Geological Enigma's* Sourcebook Project 1980 p. 668-9 & Morris *The Genesis Flood* 1961 p. 174-5

[1] Cited from Mammoth, Howorth. Proceedings, Acad. Nat. Sc. Philadelphia, 1866, 344, 345.

[2] Cited from Mammoth, Howorth 1887, the Proc. Acad. Nat. Sc. Phil. 1880, 306, 307.

[3] Abbot, Charles C. *Abbott's Primitive Industry*, George A. Bates Pub.1881 p. 512. Id. 506 Id. 477 Id. 477, 479, 480.

[4] Bryan, William Alanson; *Science*, 70:39-41 1929

[5] Wright, Frederick, G. *American Antiquarian* 11:379-381 1889, and *Scientific American*, Nov. 9, 1889.

[6] Cited from Corliss, *Handbook of Enigma's*, McAdams, William AAAS 29:720-721 1880

[7] Holmes, W. H *Smithsonian Institution Annual Report*, 1899 p. 419-472

[8] Corliss, William, *Handbook of Geological Enigma's* Sourcebook Project 1980

[9] C. L. Burdick *The Naturalist*, Vol. 16 1957 cited in *The Genesis Flood* Morris, 1961 p. 174-5

VI

General Finds of Man
Around the Globe

Unique Finds Suggesting a Global Flood:
Ships and other Artifacts

Complete ships have been discovered by early explorers in several parts of the globe. One was reported from Greenland. The author Mercurins Centralis describing: "such was the mast, dug out of the top of a high Hill in Greenland, with a pulley hanging to it." In 1460, near Bern, Switzerland, Baplista Sulgosus, Ludovicus Moscardus, and Theodoras Moretus, reported that in a mine 50 fathoms deep, an entire ship was dug out complete with broken masts, anchors, remains of 40 mariners and their merchandise. Fulgosus mentions this find occurred in his own time and was seen by many grave and sober men, from whom (in reassurance) he received a personal account of it.

Confirmed by Whiston in 1737, citing Dr Robert Plot, (first Professor of Chemistry at Oxford) and also John Davy. *Philosophical Transactions,* No. 77 Chap. z. § 71

Group of Artifacts from a Quarry in France

Jacques-Louis, Comte de Bournon (1751–1825), was a French scientist once elected Fellow of the Royal Geological Society. He made record of an interesting discovery in a stone quarry that was providing material for the rebuilding of the Palace of Justice in Paris. He states: "The stone was a limestone of deep grey, and of that kind which are tender when they come out of the quarry, but harden by exposure to the air. The first which were wrought presented no appearance of any foreign bodies, but, after the workmen had removed the ten first beds, they were astonished, when taking away the eleventh, to find its inferior surface, at the depth of forty or fifty feet, covered with shells. The stone of this bed having been removed, they found stumps of columns and fragments of stone half wrought, and the stone was exactly similar to that of the quarry: they found moreover coins, handles of hammers, and other tools or fragments of tools in wood. But that which principally commanded their attention, was a board about one inch thick and seven or eight feet long; it was broken into many pieces, which was that of the

183

boards of the same kind used by the masons and quarry men: it was worn in the same manner, rounded and waving upon the edges. Here then, we have the traces of a work executed by the hand of man, placed at a depth of fifty feet, and covered with eleven beds of compact limestone: everything tended to prove that this work had been executed upon the spot where the traces existed. The presence of man had then preceded the formation of this stone, and that very considerably since he was already arrived at such a degree of civilization that the arts were known to him, and that he wrought the stone and formed columns out of it."

Ref: Cremo, Michael A.; Thompson, Richard L. *Forbidden Archeology* Torchlight Publishing 2011, American Journal of Science, 1820 Vol. 2 p. 145- 146.Used by permission.

Human Skull in Brown Coal

A human skull encased in coal was unearthed near Saxony and later placed in the Mining Academy Museum in Freiberg as noted: "In the coal collection in the Mining Academy in Freiberg (Stutzer was Professor of Geology and Mineralogy in the School of Mines at Freiberg, in Saxony), there is a puzzling human skull composed of brown coal and manganiferous and phosphate limonite, but its source is not known. This skull was described by Karsten and Dechen in 1842." Otto Stutzer's set to oath: "I (the present author) have personally verified the existence of this object via correspondence with Prof. Dr R. Vulpius, Professor of Coal Geology at the Freiberg Mining Academy."[1]

Stutzer, Otto *Geology of Coal*, University of Chicago Press 1940, p. 271

Human Marks in Stone Quarry

In November 1830, two individual letter shapes were found extruded into a slab of marble in a quarry 12 miles northwest of Philadelphia. The marble block of 30 cubic feet was removed in the normal course of business and taken to a sawing facility. When the workers there noticed the letters inset into this slab, they set the block aside and called in witnesses. The rough cut was taken from a depth of sixty to eighty feet deep.

Browne, J.B. *American Journal of Science* 1:19:361 1831.

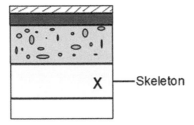

Fig. 63 Reck's Skeleton was chiseled out of solid rock in Olduvai Gorge, Tanzania

Reck's Skeleton

In 1913, Professor Hans Reck of Berlin University was undertaking field investigations in the now famous site at Olduvai Gorge, Tanzania. One of his team noticed a protrusion and exposed a portion of a skeleton embedded in the strata. The workers labored to extract the remains out of hard rock with hammers and chisels, unearthing a fully modern human. The find was located in a layer classified as far too "old" by evolution standards, below finds of creatures the evolutionists claim are transitional to modern humans. In spite of this hard evidence, scientists claimed a recent burial for this find, now rarely mentioned in the literature. The Reck discovery would be quite destructive to modern interpretations of human origins, undermining Darwinian evolution at its basic level. The thinking of the day couldn't tolerate a fully human skeleton located in strata dated at a time thought only to contain apes. Such rejections outline the bias of the science establishment, challenging its credibility as a whole regarding honest fossil interpretation and origins science in particular.
http://en.wikipedia.org/wiki/Hans_Reck Cremo & Thompson *Forbidden Archeology*

Castenedolo, Italy Finds

In 1860 geologist Giuseppe Ragazzoni from the Brescia Institute visited the area of Castenedolo, Italy, and made his remarkable discovery of four modern humans below 10 layers of water-deposited sediments. Quoting Ragazzoni: "Searching along a bank of coral for shells, there came into my hand the top portion of a cranium, completely filled with pieces of coral ce-mented with the blue-green clay characteristic of that formation. Astonished, I continued the search, and in addition to the top portion of the cranium I found other bones of the thorax and limbs, which quite apparently belonged to an individual of the human species." Later excavations revealed more "modern" human remains, the total to include a man, woman and two children. This discovery was highly controversial at the time and was later suppressed. Later Giuseppe Sergi, a well-known anatomist from Rome, visited Ragazzoni in 1883 and verified the remains of the individuals, an adult male, female, and two children. A noted authority of his day, Sergi believed the Castenedolo skeletons were authentic. As the skeptical reactions flowed in from others around the world, he later summarized "By means of a despotic scientific prejudice, call it what you will, every discovery of human remains in the Pliocene has been discredited."

Robert A.S. Macalister in his *Textbook of European Archaeology* 1921, records his honest frustrations with the Castenedolo finds: "Whatever we may think of them, they have to be treated seriously...unearthed by a competent geologist, Ragazzoni, and examined by a competent anatomist, Sergi, *there must be something wrong somewhere* if they really belonged to the stratum in which they were found, this would imply an extraordinarily long standstill for evolution. It is much more likely that there is something *amiss* with the observations." Finally and honestly Macalister asserts: "The acceptance of a Pliocene date for the Castenedolo skeletons would create so many insoluble problems that we can hardly hesitate in choosing between the alternatives of adopting or rejecting their authenticity."

Ref: Cremo, Michael A.; Thompson, Richard L. *Forbidden Archeology*)Torchlight Publishing 2011) p. 422-32 Used by permission

Savona, Italy Skeleton

In 1850, while excavating for a church in Savona, Italy, a fully modern human skeleton was unearthed 10 feet below grade in a layer thought to be "millions" of years in geologic age. Geologists of the day put the age of the layer over 3 million years old, assuming uniformity. The presenter of the find, Arthur Issel observed: "The body was discovered in an outstretched position, with the arms extending forward, the head slightly bent forward and down, the body very much elevated relative to the legs, *like a man in the water.*" Animal bones were also found scattered with the human remains at the same layer. As this skeleton appeared to be washed in by water and was found face down trapped against a rock, it gives strong evidence that this person perished in the Flood. Savona is 75 miles inland from shore.

Ref: Cremo, Michael A.; Thompson, Richard L. *Forbidden Archeology* (Torchlight Publishing 2011) p. 422-435 Used by permission

Heidelberg Mandible

Dr. Otto Schoetensack, lecturer on Geology in the University of Heidelberg, often visited a fossil rich deposit in a gravel pit near Mauer for study. In 1907 "the desired evidence was obtained, for 20 meters below the surface soil, and above the floor of my sand-pit, there was found the lower jaw of primitive man, in good preservation, and with all its teeth." Concerning the authenticity of the find there cannot be any doubt; the bed in which the mandible was covered by a series of deposits, amounting in all to 78 feet. Twenty-four different strata classified as Pleistocene were numbered above the find. In the lower strata, remains of the following extinct animals were found: lion, an extinct form of cat, a dog, two forms of bear, a species of bison, an early Pleistocene form of horse, and a rhinoceros. Arthur Keith in his *Antiquity of Man* states: "No revelation of prehistoric man could be more convincing than the discovery of the Heidelberg mandible. We have no shadow of doubt as to its authenticity or significance."

George McCready Price, *Evolutionary Geology and the New Catastrophism,* 1926

Cave Finds in France

Prof. Hugo Obermaier of the University of Madrid, and author of the volume, *Fossil Man in Spain* (Yale University Press, 1925), accumulated a great deal of material on man's early existence. Obermaier reports the discovery of a cave in France where human remains were found with cave bear, cave hyena, cave lion, leopard, great deer, mammoth, wolf, woolly rhinoceros, and reindeer. Prof. Obermaier also documented a 1865 find with human remains near Colmar along with woolly mammoth, bison and other animals in Alsace, these within a deposit of loess over two meters (six feet) below the surface. Obermaier also noted that a complete human skeleton was found near Strassburg, located within a sediment deposit intermixed with rounded rock and associated with the remains of a mammoth in 1914.

Weimar, Germany

In 1914, human fossils were found in a quarry near Weimar, Germany, at a depth of over eleven meters or 34 feet. Associated with these remains were found wood ashes, flint implements, the remains of a rhinoceros and a cave bear. Two years later in the same vicinity, the skeletal remains of a child were uncovered together with the fossils of a rhinoceros, a cave bear, and other prehistoric animals.

Finds of Humans and Extinct Animals: Europe

According to Howorth, in 1774, Esper published the discovery of a human jaw and shoulder blade, along with remains of bears, hyenas and others near Nuremberg.

Rosenmiiller relates in his 1804 memoir on the cave bear, documenting that human bones were found with both a cave bear and cave tiger.[2]

A Professor Crahay located a human lower jaw in the loess exposed in a cut opened for a canal dugout between the years 1815 and 1823. Along with the human remains were found a number of elephants, deer and oxen. The jawbone was later placed on display at the Leyden Museum and the find published in the Bulletin of the Belgian Academy in 1836.[3]

M. Risso reported he unearthed a large number of human bones from fissures near Nice, as disclosed to the French Academy on the geology of that place. Many of these remains were sent to Cuvier for examination.

Again according to Howorth, M. Ami Bou'e reported to the Bulletin of Geol. Soc. of France that in 1829, he had made further discoveries of human remains in the clay at Krems, published in the "Annales des Sciences Naturelles," vol. xviii. Other discoveries were reported by Razoumofski at Baden near Vienna, that of human skulls in connection with extinct animals.

In 1828, Howorth reports the naturalist Tournal of the Museum at Narbonne published a report documenting the remains of extinct animals in the cave of Bize, along with pottery and human remains. M. Marcel de Serres examined the artifacts and declared them of the same mineral condition as those of the extinct animals.[4]

In 1829, speaking of the caverns near Gard, France, M. Christol provided a general treatise regarding human remains from these caverns and published his discovery of human bones and pottery mixed with those of the hyena and rhinoceros in the Poudres cavern. Other discoveries of human remains were reported by M. Emilien Dumas at the cave Souvignargues, near Sommie'res (Gard), and also Dr. Pitore reported the same at Fanzan, near Gesseras (He'rault).

In 1833, M. Schmerling published the volume entitled "Recherches sur les ossements fossiles decouvertes dans les cavernes de la province de Liege," concerning his exhaustive excavations in Belgium. He also documented that the bones of man existed in precisely the same mineral condition as the hyena, cave bear, mammoth and rhinoceros antiquitatis. He states: "the human remains of most frequent occurrence being teeth detached from the jaws, and carpal, metacarpal, tarsal, metatarsal and phalangial bones separated from the rest of the skeleton."

In the cave at Engis, Schmerling also unearthed the remains of three individuals; one of the skulls was found by the side of a mammoth's tooth, complete and buried in a breccia five feet deep. With them were several bones of a horse, reindeer and the remains of a rhinoceros. These skulls were kept in the University of Liege. Human remains were found in other caves as well, this according to Sir Charles Lyell's reports on these discoveries, quoting him: "Speaking generally, it may be said, the human bones, where any were met with, occurred at all depths in the cave mud and gravel, sometimes above and sometimes below those of the bear, elephant, rhinoceros, hyena, &c. Breaking through the stalagmitic floor, bones and teeth of the cave bear and other animals which Schmerling had described were speedily discovered." Lyell further mentions that after several weeks' digging in the same locale, that Lyell's companion, Professor Malaise of Liege, found three fragments of a human skull and two perfect lower jaws with teeth, all associated the bones of bears, large pachyderms and ruminants, and so precisely resembling these in color and state of preservation, as to leave no doubt in his mind that man was contemporary with the extinct animals."[5]

Tournal's 1833 Call for Reason

Quoting M. Tournal's works of 1833, Professor Fairholme tells us: "[The] French geologists were so powerfully struck with the mixture of human and other bones, in some of the caves in the south of France, that a more strict scrutiny was instituted; and the results were published in a paper by M. Tournal, jun., of Narbonne, in No. 52 of Annates de Chimte et de Physique, from which the following is a short extract: In speaking of human remains, M. Tournal says, "The heads of the geological world would have it that they were, in all cases, recent, and accidental; and their opinions had the effect of deciding the point as a subject unworthy of further discussion. However, the discovery of the caves of Aude, of Herault, and of Gard, in the south of France, offers to the observer a crowd of human bones, and of ancient pottery, mixed up in the very same mud with those of hyenas, tigers, lions, stags, and a number of other animals of lost kinds. Attention was, therefore, again called to the subject, and MM. Marcel de Serres, Jules de Christol, and myself, after an attentive and conscientious examination, have come to the conclusion, that all these objects are of the same date, and, consequently, that man was contemporaneous with the animals now lost from the surface of the globe. Our conclusion was principally based on the equal alteration of the bones, and on the manner of their deposit in the caves. We have not hesitated, therefore, notwithstanding the repugnance which our observations may occasion, to proclaim our belief, that man exists in a fossil state." [6]

*Annates de Chitnle, February 1833

At Kostritz, of the Elster, in Upper Saxony, in 1820, Baron von Schlotheim published at Gotha in the *Annals of Philosophy* for 1823 stating: "Man was unquestionably found in a fossil state in this deposit. Of those of quadrupeds, von Schlotheim relates those of the rhinoceros, lion or tiger, hyena, horse, ox, deer, hare, and the rabbit; as also the bones of the owl, and other birds…[and] those of a small elephant, subsequently placed in the Museum at Berlin. Mentioned are fragments of the arm and thigh bone of man, recovered in a gypsum crevice at the depth of eighteen feet from the surface of the country, and "eight feet deeper than two phalanges of the rhinoceros." Fairholme reports, "A portion of a human cranium, and of a leg bone, have also been procured for the British Museum, and may be seen in the same case, as the more entire specimen found at Guadaloupe, which has now, at length, been placed in a situation suited to its high interest and value. These were marked with the name of Dr. Schottin." He states further, "In the possession of Prince Reuss, I saw a fine specimen of the rib of a young person, about fourteen or fifteen years of age, from which I made a drawing the size of nature; as also of two bones…which now belong to Dr. Schottin. They consist of the tibia and the radius of an infant, or infants of not more than three or four months old, and only from three to four inches in length. It is in the collection of Prince Reuss, the proprietor of the district; and it was described by Dr. Schottin, in No. 4 of the history of Leipsig, page 415 (1829)."[7]

In 1835 M. Marcel de Serres published his account of the bone filled caverns in France and elsewhere in Europe: "Essai sur les cavernes a ossemens."[8] Documenting eighteen individual locations where remains of extinct animals and that of man were found together, (according to Howorth) Serres tells us: "Il parait done bien etabli, soit d'apres ces faits, soit d'apres ceux que nous avons enumeres dans nos differents travaux, que 'homme a ete contemporain des especes perdues, dissemin£es avec ses debris, dans certaines."

M. Dupont mentions a great quantity of human remains found in state with land animals in one or more locations. From Trou du Frontal, he remarked that the bones of the thirteen human skeletons were found in inexpressible disorder. And speaking of the Trou de la Rosette, he says the occupants of this cave were "overwhelmed by a deluge. It was," he says, "unanimously admitted that they had been mingled with the stones and earth by a great *inundation*"[9] [emphasis added].

Fig. 64 M. Tournal's works of 1833. Saxony Human remains (See ref 7, p. 49, 50)
No. 1: The radius of an infant of not more than three or four months old
No. 2: The tibia of an infant of about the same age as that of No. 1
No. 3: A rib of a young person of the age of about fourteen or fifteen years

Africa

In 1921 while men were working in a mine known as the "Bone Cave" in Rhodesia, Africa, a great number of fossilized and partly fossilized remains were unearthed, including the elephant, lion, rhinoceros, antelope, and human remains. An excerpt of the article reads: "Until lately no remains of the cave man himself have been noticed at Broken Hill, but at the end of last summer Mr. W. E. Barren was so fortunate as to discover and dig out of the earth in a remote part of the cave a nearly complete human skull, a fragment of the upper jaw of another, a sacrum, a tibia, and the two ends of a femur. These specimens have just been brought to England by Mr. Ross Macartney.[10]

China

In Honan, China, human remains were found in a deep loess deposit with the remains of the wild boar, the bison, and the mammoth.

West Indies—Human Fossil Block

Just offshore of Guadeloupe, West Indies, lays a formation of limestone dated as Miocene, or about 25 million years old. Records show that in the late 1700s many human skeletons (indistinguishable from modern humans) were excavated from this deposit recorded as being a "British mile" in length. One of the quarried specimens, ensconced in a 2-ton slab, was shipped to the British Museum and placed on public display in 1812. Later on, with the popularity of evolution, the slab was quietly removed to the basement. The discovery of these remains has been well documented in the scientific literature and witnessed by a number of authorities. Bill Cooper *'Human fossils from Noah's Flood'* Creation Ex Nihilo, 5 Jan. 1983 p. 119-153, and same ref. Vol. B 1990, p. 108-137.

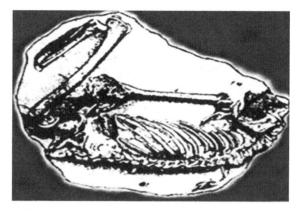

Fig. 65 The Guadeloupe Skeleton, displayed at the British Museum until evolution became "scientific," then quietly removed to the basement. The display also included a skull from the Saxony finds, removed at the same time (See ref. #7).

[1] Whitcomb, J.C. and Morris, H.M., *The Genesis Flood* (The Presbyterian and Reformed Publishing Company, Philadelphia, 1961), pp. 175-176

[2] Mortillet, Gabriel *La Pre Historic* vol ii. 8, 3

[3] Lyell, *Antiquity of Man*, 240.

[4] From Mammoth vol ii. 8, 3

[5] Lyell, Antiquity of Man, 65-72.

[6] George Fairholme, *New and Conclusive Demonstrations of the Mosiac Deluge* (London, 1840), p. 37

[7] Cited from Fairholme, *New and Conclusive Demonstrations of the Mosiac Deluge* (1840), p. 41

[8] Noted citation p. 179, 180

[9] From *Mammoth* p. 221, citing Dupont, *Etude sur les Caverns de la Lesse* (October, 1865), p. 7

[10] *Nature*, (Nov. 1920 1 issue 108), p. 371-372

Ancient Man in North America

Iron Cup in Coal

Frank Kennard found this artifact in the course of work while prepping coal in 1912; he states: "While I was working in the Municipal Electric Plant in Thomas, Oklahoma in 1912, I came upon a solid chunk of coal which was too large to use. I broke it with a sledge hammer. This iron pot fell from the center, leaving the impression, or mold of the pot in a piece of the coal. Jim Stull (an employee of the company) witnessed the breaking of the coal and saw the pot fall out. I traced the source of the coal and found that it came from the Wilburton, Oklahoma Mines."

Signed: Frank J. Kennard, sworn to before me in Sulfur Springs, Arkansas, this 27th day of November, 1948. Julia L. Eldred N.P. My commission expires May 21, 1951 - Benton Co."

Footprints in Stone

Sites reaching from Virginia to Pennsylvania, through Kentucky, Illinois, Missouri and westward toward the Rocky Mountains to California, impressions and prints have been found on the surface of exposed rocks. It is a well-known fact that once limestone is heated to a specified temperature, it assumes a pliable mortar like state for a short time. In such a state, this mortar has been known to freeze the impressions of water ripple marks or even 20 foot waves, not to mention the imprints of animals. In Utah and Australia, thousands of dinosaur prints preserved in this manner have been found, suggesting the animals were fleeing, the phenomena a byproduct of the Flood, according to reports by M. Oard of CMI.

Adapted from Ingalls, Albert C. *The Carboniferous Mystery*, Vol. 162, *Scientific American*, January 1940, p. 14

Shoes in Stone

A report entitled: "Mystery of the Petrified 'Shoe Sole' in 5,000,000 Year Old Stone," by Dr. W. H. Ballou states as follows: "Some time ago, while he was prospecting for fossils in Nevada, John T. Reid, a distinguished mining engineer and geologist, stopped suddenly and looked down in utter bewilderment and amazement at a rock near his feet. For there, as part of the rock itself was what seemed to be a human footprint! Closer inspection showed that it was not a mark of a naked foot, but was, apparently, a shoe sole which had been turned into stone." The Triassic rock bearing the fossil shoe sole is now recognized as being far more than 200 million years old. Mr. Reid took the specimen to the American Museum of Natural History where the expert staff seemed amazed but skeptical. Supposedly a report was written about the find by the American Museum, but when Mr. Reid inquired about it, no document could be found. The sole imprint was so clear a wear spot was visible at the heal pressure point. The artifact has been left a mystery to secular scientists, but not to those who hold the Bible as authoritative.

Ref: Cremo, Michael A.; Thompson, Richard L. *Forbidden Archeology* (Torchlight Publishing, 2011) pg. 807-8

Sole Print Including Trilobites, the Meister Story

William Meister was collecting trilobites near Antelope Springs, Utah. Upon breaking open a clast rock, the two parts fell open and there before his eyes were the impression of shoe soles impregnated with trilobites, an animal dated back 500 million years! Geologist after geologist studied the imprints and rejected them, simply due to their idea that trilobites mingled with humans just can't be and contradict the entire basis of the Geologic Chart! One geologist familiar with the area visited the site and reported that the surface rocks are of the same nature as the artifact, so Meister was exonerated from any kind of fraud. One geologist admitted that he "could not accept it," and added no geologist would.* Corliss, William R. *Handbook of Geological Enigma's* Sourcebook Project 1980 p. 642

*Author note: For more information on this and other finds see; *In the Beginning, compelling evidence for Creation and the Flood*, Dr. Walt Brown, 2008, p. 36. On-line www.creation-science.com/onlinebook The Center for Scientific Creation: Home of the Hydroplate Theory This encyclopedic volume is available for viewing free of charge.

Florida Man and the Osprey Man Finds

In 1916, human skeletal remains along with artifacts in association with extinct fauna including a mammoth and mastodon, were found in deposits near Vero, Florida. James W. Gidley and Frederick B. Loomis (1926) reported that after working in comparable deposits, they decided that the animals had not become extinct until after the end of the Pleistocene. A crushed human skull, found near Melbourne, Florida, lay in the upper portion of the Melbourne bed. All were apparently found below an undisturbed stratified (water layered) deposit.

Early in 1886 this locality was visited by Prof. Angelo Heilprin and Mr. Joseph Wilcox where several parts of a fossilized human skeleton were actually found in situ. Professor Heilprin described the find as follows: "I was conducted to a spot where it had been reported a human skeleton lay embedded in the rock. The rock I found to be a partially indurate ferruginous sandstone, removed but a short distance from the sea and but barely elevated above...I was much surprised to find actually embedded in this rock and more or less firmly united with it the skeletal remains of a mammalian which I had little difficulty in determining to be the genus homo. Most of the parts, including the entire head, had at various times been removed by the curiosity seekers of the neighborhood, but enough remained to indicate the position occupied by the body in the matrix. The depression which received the head was still very plainly marked, but unfortunately the outline had been too much disturbed to permit of any satisfactory impression being taken from it. I was able to disengage from a confused mass of stone and skeleton two of the vertebrae, which Doctor Leidy has kindly determined for me to be in all probability the last dorsal and first lumbar. The distinctive canellated structure of bone is still plainly visible, but the bone itself has been completely replaced by limonite. The same locality was visited again the following spring by Mr. Wilcox, who obtained several specimens of fossilized human bones, among which was a fairly well-preserved calcaneum. Finally, on still another occasion, Mr. Wilcox secured at Hanson's landing 'a piece of the rock containing the end of a human thigh bone, also altered into limonite,' which specimen he gave to the University of Pennsylvania."[1]

Nevada Man
In 1930, Dr. Mark Harrington found human remains together with the fossils of a now extinct ground sloth and extinct camel in a gypsum cave sixteen miles east of Las Vegas, Nevada.[2]

Grand Rapids, Minnesota
Three miles north of Pelican Rapids, Minnesota, on July 16, 1931 (Jenks, 1936) the first skeleton in North America was found that could be geologically dated and the deposits attributed to the Pleistocene. The almost complete skeleton associated with two artifacts was found at a depth of ten feet in glacial silts* unearthed by highway workers while digging a roadbed. The skeleton was later determined to be a girl, estimated at fifteen years of age lying on her side, covered in uniform water deposited sediments. The artifacts that were found with the girl, a dagger or knife and a conch shell, gave no indication of age. The knife was eight to nine inches long made of elk antler and perforated at one end. The artifacts were found lying along the ribs and vertebrae in the abdominal area of the skeleton. The carbon content in the elk antler dagger was largely inorganic carbonate so, according to the researchers, it was not possible to determine its age. The degree of

mineralization suggested antiquity. (Wilford, 1955)[3] The clays were dated approximately eighteen to twenty thousand years old. Due to the dates given to the clay and on the basis of radiocarbon dating, most geologists regard the deposit as being less than eleven thousand years old.

*Author note: Finds such as these were typically identified as glacial. It seems obvious that this person perished in flooding, but no one witnessed how. It's unlikely that the child expired by drowning and was slowly covered in till yet remained intact.

Human Skull Found at Stanford, Menlo Park, CA

While excavating for a building project, scientists from Stanford discovered mastodon remains 22 feet below ground level near the campus. The observing scientists recalled an earlier find of a modern human skull found by Bruce Seymour, a Stanford University student, who found this skull twenty feet below the surface in the bank of San Francisquito Creek, at the same depth and strata of the Mastodon. The skull was cemented in a gravel stratum on which an alluvial cone had been formed. Bailey Willis (a competent geologist that had worked closely with Hrdlicka*) visited the locality, and determined that a considerable period of time must have been required for the formation of the alluvial cone which overlay the gravel, and for the cutting of the present creek bed. He suggested that the skull might have been deposited more than 4,000 years ago. According to Wormington, Willis is a capable geologist, likely to be "extremely cautious in supporting claims for the antiquity of human remains." (Wormington 1957) The skull, which was studied by T. D. McCown (see *Early Man in the New World,* 1950) determined it was a "male between thirty-five and forty-five years old." The physical and chemical condition of the specimen made it appear unlikely that it could be very recent. Researchers discussing the implications quoted Dr. J.W. Gidley as stating: "If this mastodon is of the late Miocene or early Pliocene as D. Blackwelder says it is, that sets it (the skull) back some two or three million years. *And we have no evidence man has been here that long.*"

Science, 69: supl. ii, Feb, 1 1929, Revisited by Robert F. Heizer (1950) and Corliss, William R. *Handbook of Geological Enigma's* Sourcebook Project 1980 p. 673 including observations and comments from Wormington as noted

*Ales Hrdlicka was first to pioneer the idea of "Neanderthal Man" and the Asian migration to the Americas. He became a department head at the Smithsonian. See www.britannica.com/EBchecked/topic/273648/Ales-Hrdlicka

Illinois Man

In December 1862, The *Geologist* reported: "In Macoupin County, Illinois, the bones of a man were recently found on a coal-bed capped with two feet of slate rock, ninety feet below the surface of the earth. The bones were covered with a crust or coating of hard glossy matter, as black as coal itself, but when scraped away left the bones white and natural." The coal layer in which the skeleton was discovered was said to be over 250 million years old (according to evolutionary dating).

Cremo, Michael A.; Thompson, Richard L. *Forbidden Archaeology* Torchlight Press 2011 p. 454

New Orleans Man

The original report on this find, usually credited to D. B. Dowler, is by Prof. D. Drake, reads as follows: "In 1844, I visited two gas tanks, each 60 feet in diameter and 16 feet deep, recently sunk in the back part of the city [i. e., New Orleans] and received from the intelligent superintendent, Doctor Rogers, an account of what was met with in excavating them. At first they encountered soil and soft river mud, then harder laminated blue alluvion, then deep black mold resting on wet bluish quicksand. The roots and the basis or stumps of no fewer than four successive growths (or stacks) of trees, apparently cypress, were found standing at different elevations. The first had a diameter of 2 feet 6 inches, the second of 6 feet, the third of 4 feet, and the fourth of 12 feet, at a short distance up, with a base of 28 feet for the roots. It is embedded in a soft deep-black mold. When cut with the spade much of this wood resembled cheese in texture, but hardened on drying. At the depth of 7 and 16 feet burnt wood was met with. No shells or bones of land animals or fish were observed, but in a tank previously excavated, at the depth of 16 feet the skeleton of a man was found. The cranium lay between the roots of a tree and was in a tolerable state of preservation, but most of the other bones crumbled on pressure. A small ossilium, which I saw, indicated the female sex.*[4]

*Note: A similar "buried forest" is found near the shores of New Jersey, where for years loggers extracted the timbers of huge trees flattened to a horizontal from some earlier watery catastrophe. Such buried forests also exist along the central Oregon coast near Pacific City.

Charleston, North Carolina Man

Emil Schmidt, in his Zur Urgeschichte Nordamerikas gives nearly all that is known concerning these specimens. It appears that Prof. F. S. Holmes, geologist and paleontologist, of Charleston, while exploring the banks of the Ashley River about 10 miles above the city, discovered human bones, fragments of pottery, etc., together with the bones of the mastodon. Professor Leidy, who was sent by the Philadelphia Academy of Sciences to examine the locality, actually found human bones associated with those of the mastodon, but there appeared in the same connection also a fragment of porcelain. Later, in following his investigations in the same region, Professor Holmes discovered further evidences of the coexistence of man with extinct animals: these were particularly a human lower jaw, a tibia, a femur, some stone implements and potsherds, which were dug out personally from an undisturbed old deposit. The lower jaw was that of an adolescent and showed a prominent chin and strong muscular impressions; the teeth were normal. The femur also showed strong development. It seems that Professor Holmes has never published his account of the finds just mentioned, and there is consequently but little to aid us in the effort to reach a conclusion. Schmidt was inclined to accede to the opinion that the bones were geologically ancient and suggested that they belonged to a man of the Champlain period. This view cannot be sustained in the absence of more definite information. Chemical and detailed physical characteristics of the skeletal parts are wanting, and the fate of the bones is unknown. They are not in the Charleston Museum.[5]

Quebec Man

According to Doctor Usher, a fossil human skeleton, "which was dug out of the solid schist-rock on which The Citadel stands," was preserved in the museum at Quebec. There are no particulars in print concerning the find; the skeleton is not preserved in the Laval University Museum, the only museum in the city containing objects of natural history, and nothing could be learned concerning it during the writer's recent visit to Quebec. The absurdity of the statement that a human skeleton was "dug out of the solid schist-rock" will be apparent when it is remembered that the rock is Silurian.*

*W. Usher, *Geology and Paleontology in Connection with Human Origins*, chap, xl, Nott and Gliddon's *Types of Mankind*. Note: Silurian Rock is considered to be over 300 million year of age.

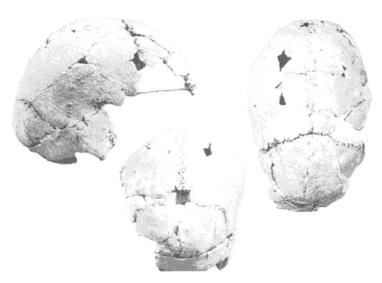

Fig. 66 Elongated skull from a young women unearthed 60 feet deep near Midland, TX. Five others were also found deeply buried in Texas (Image - Wormington, *Ancient Man in North America* chap. X)

Texas Finds and Midland Man

The "Midland Man" was actually a female. In 1953, Keith Glasscock recovered artifacts and human remains in a grey sand "blow out" near Midland, TX. The finds were located below five layers of water deposited sediments, totaling nearly sixty feet of overburden (see Wormington p. 243). The skeletal remains, parts of a skull and two fragmentary ribs, are thought to be the oldest in North America. The location was named the Scharbauer site after the property owner. Remains of extinct antelope, horse, mammoth and bison were found with the subject. A number of arrow points were also recovered. Chemical analysis of the bones showed the human and animal remains were contemporary of each other. Here again we have a sedimentary waterborne deposit, containing human remains, found to be buried at a time period closely associated with other such finds in North America. In addition, the team mentioned that the skull was of the elongated type, as found in other Texas excavations buried catastrophically in water borne tombs.

Also in Texas, skeletons with very long, narrow heads were unearthed in number. The subject was of considerable study and comment by Hooton, 1933**; Roberts, 1945***; and Woodbury, 1935. The remains were found in deeply buried silts (water deposits), but are little mentioned or publicized. (Wormington *Ancient Man in North America* 1957)*

*Note: Skulls of similar appearance have been found and are on display in Peru
** "Notes on Five Texas Crania" Vol. 5 p. 25-39
*** "Deep Burial in the Clear Fork of the Brazos River" Vol. 13 p. 9-30

Los Angeles Skeletons

In 1914, a complete human skeleton, animal bones and artifacts were found in a Los Angeles area tar pit. Later in 1924, at Angeles Mesa, six skeletons were found (Heizer, 1950) at depths of nineteen to twenty-three feet below the surface. Later, more finds surfaced as part of the excavation in 1936 when workmen were digging a storm drain beneath the Los Angeles River. This find revealed more human bones, including a partial human cranium and seven fragments of other bones at depths of twelve to thirteen feet below grade. The bones and cranium were mineralized and coated heavily with sandstone and conglomerate. Extinct animal bones were also discovered two months later in the same stratum. A. Lopatin, of the University of Southern California excavated two teeth later identified as those from an Imperial Mammoth. The geologic study of the associated stratum was conducted by Thomas Clements, a well known geologist who concluded they were of Pleistocene age (Wormington 1957).

Torrington, Wyoming

Four skeletons were discovered near Torrington, Wyoming, according to W. W. Howells (1938). The skeletons closely resemble those found at Lake Pelican. Unfortunately these bones were found during blasting activities but apparently were entombed in a sealed cave opened in the excavation process. Upon further investigation, the remains were determined to be that of an adult male, two females of differing ages, and an infant. It was stated that the remains and artifacts resembled many other such finds across the continent in their condition of covering and ethnicity.[6]

Tepexpan Man

In the Valley of Mexico near Tepexpan, an interesting find of human skeletal remains were unearthed (De Terra, Romero and Steward, 1949). The skeleton was found face down with the legs drawn up to the stomach. De Terra's conclusion was that the person had met an accidental death and the body had rested face downward in the mud. The silts where the skeleton was found were also associated with mammoth remains (encased in the same material) and worked obsidian. De Terra dated the formation around nine to ten thousand years old. Tests of the surrounding peat produced a radiocarbon date of 11,000 plus or minus 500 years of age.

Locations of deeply buried human remains in the US:

Fig. 67 Map of human skeletal remains associated with the Flood

Dmanisi Skeletal Finds of Georgia Republic—2013

Here we have the excavation of multiple and complete skeletal remains from a formation dated 2 million years past. The sensation for the anthropologists was that these include *complete skulls*, unlike the fragments used to construct the entire evolutionary human tree from Africa, now upturned with this new evidence, and evidence not unsupportive of the Bible narrative.

*CNN interview with Fred Spoor Shaking up evolutionary models - YouTube
https://www.youtube.com/watch?v=j9D_jBcZvTw

At this juncture, we will end our tour of the human graveyards, hopefully providing the reader ample evidence with this small treatise. These finds conclusively demonstrate that the destruction of life in the course of the flood was general, and in fact was inclusive of humans as reported so thoroughly by many past authorities.

At War with the Animals?

It's generally true that of the early North American human artifacts, many are associated with mega-fauna, weapons and arrow points. A perplexing thought is this: when we recall the decrees given by God in early Genesis, speaking only of a vegetarian based food sustenance; *"For to you this shall be your food"* (Genesis 1:28) and the acknowledged use of agriculture in those times, one must wonder what happened. Why is man found everywhere with a spear in hand? The intent of the First Earth was to be a *bloodless* co-habitation of man and animals. However, what is generally determined from these relics both in Europe and America seems to be nothing less than man was at *war* with the animals.

As earlier mentioned, the Bible teaches that as part of *judgment* man will be driven to live in caves. Perhaps an earlier rebellion forced man to live in nomadic existence and constant warfare. The Bible provides few details of life in the years leading up to the Flood, only that the people had digressed morally to a point where they thought *"only of evil continually"* (Genesis 6:5). Among the flood traditions in Appendix II, we learn more details concerning this period, when law and order in society apparently vanished from the earth. The point to be made is this: the remains we examine exist in the present and cannot tell their full tale. If we remember, the earth was first shaken by the opening of the great deep, and we may assume this means earthquakes struck the planet, possibly in magnitudes and frequencies never before experienced. Assuming this being the case, with rain falling in typhoon proportions and all available shelter destroyed, where else would the survivors go? It would be reasonable to assume most would flee to the caves as their last option to escape, both man and animal. The sad conclusion is that the people and these fearsome beasts would likely perish together in savage struggles, as so often indicated in the caves. The evidence for such constantly prevails in the excavations covered in this volume, suggesting the observed evidence actually represents a *short period frozen in time*, a mere *snap-shot of the life and death struggle for survival within the first weeks of the Flood year*. If this be the case, modern archeology and paleontology would be entirely in error relative to stories about early life, lacking this perspective. So it would *appear* early man lived in such a state constantly; but the in actual fact, this was not the case at all. Fires in caves would be an obvious response, all souls being soaked and cold due to the rain and resultant lower temperatures.

As demonstrated in earlier chapters, the evidence strongly supports that there were two distinct classes of man occupying earth in this period, each widely separated in technology, and subsistence (hunter/gatherer versus herdsman/farmer). Further mentioned was the warring between these sides, clearly mentioned in the book of 1Enoch, culminating in the decree given by God to imprison the responsible, destroy the guilty and notify Noah of the pending Flood. To this end, I will leave the reader to their own conclusions, the detailed evidence available to construct a full history of those days being in poverty, save the scant biblical record and a few sentences from other sources left for us to ponder. In view of this, it seems God wanted those times left forgotten, and we can hardly blame Him for that.

[1] Hrdlicka, Ales bulletin 33, *Skeletal Remains in North America* 1907 p. 54, 55

[2] Rehwinkel, Alfred M., M.A., B.D., LL.D. (1968-05-04). *The Flood: In the Light of the Bible, Geology, and Archaeology* (Gr 9-10 1951 1957) Concordia Publishing House.

[3] Cited from Wormington, *Ancient Man in North America* 1957 Wilford, Lloyd A. (1955 *American Antiquity*, vol XXI no. 2) p. 130-142

[4] Hrdlicka, Ales bulletin 33, *A Systematic Treatise on the Principal Diseases of the Interior Valley of North America*, etc., 76-77, Cincinnati, 1850

[5] Emil Schmidt, *Zur Urgeschichte Nordamerikas* A.rch. f. Anthrop., v, 250 et seq., 1871-72

[6] Howells, W. W. "Crania resembling Minnesota Man" *American Antiquity*, vol II no. 1 p. 318-326

VII

The Fossil Beds Related to the Flood

"The crust of our globe is a great cemetery, where the rocks are tombstones on which the buried dead have written their own epitaphs." —George McCready Price, *Evolutionary Geology and the New Catastrophism,* 1926

Though unable to speak, the rocks do tell us a story of a mighty calamity, one of untold magnitude that swept across the planet with unfathomable power.

"Fossils" 101

We know from the study of geology that over 70% of the rocks making up the continents are "sedimentary," that is, "water deposited." These start out as features in the surface of the earth, then water and/or flood erosion turns them to water borne silt, sand and clay. Pushed by current, these elements sort according to their specific gravity with the heaviest settling and dropping in layers first. After the water recedes, they dry out and are lithified, or hardened in time to *stone*; within these sediments turned rock we find the buried animals and plants we call fossils.

Dr. Henry Morris in the classic work *The Genesis Flood* tells us:

"Almost all sedimentary rocks of the earth, which are the ones containing fossils and from which the supposed geologic history of the earth has been largely deduced, have been laid down by moving waters. This statement is so obvious and so universally accepted that it needs no proof nor elaboration." —The Genesis Flood, p. 124

Fig. 68 Fossilized jellyfish, evidence of rapid burial
(Image courtesy Creation Ministries International www.creation.com)

How Fossils Form

Fossils are formed by a sudden covering of mineral-saturated water. Most fossil deposits indicate the animals were *alive* at the time of burial. As mentioned, we find multiple classes of animals mixed together, aquatic and terrestrial, avian and insect, exactly as one would expect in such a Flood. In simple terms, fossils are the remains of animals killed and rapidly buried in sediments. They contain minerals that provide for cementing like limestone. All these need is water working the minerals to create a rock hard substance. In summary, all it takes to make a fossil:

• Quick burial
• Water & minerals
• Short time period

Fossilization can take place very quickly, in a few years or even days. Science students fossilized a bone in a few days time in a classroom setting.[1]

The Great Fossil and Fissure Deposits

We now begin with the evidences from the great fossil deposits, investigated as long as men could write down their observations about them. We begin with the caverns, caves and fissures filled with the bones of men and animals found around the world in the early days. In the first years of fossil hunting, a phenomena known as "Rubble Drift and Ossifurous Fissures" caught the eye of the naturalists, especially Oxford Professor Joseph Prestwich. Prestwich's work was followed closely by Cuvier, de Serres, Falconer and many others, including the investigations on Malta by Dr. Lieth Adams. Prestwich published an important treatise on the subject entitled: *"On Certain Phenomena bearing on the Close of the Last Geological Period and their Bering on the Tradition of the Flood"* in 1895, dedicated to the categorization of this odd form of bone deposit.

Prestwich explains: "We may assume that all the animals, of whatsoever description, fled before the advancing flood and sought safety on the higher un-submerged grounds and hills, though many were overtaken and perished. At the same time there is reason to believe that the unequal strains produced by the great earth movement disturbed and rent the rocks, for gaping fissures were formed, especially where strong divisional planes in the strata favored vertical disruption. Thus, the hills of Devonian limestone near Plymouth; the Cretaceous and Jurassic limestones of the South of France and Italy and of the Rock of Gibraltar; the Tertiary and Cretaceous limestone of the northern coasts and Islands of the Mediterranean, together with the limestone ranges of the North African coast, were rent in many places and to variable depths."

Prestwich continues: "As the flood waters increased in depth, and the greater became the destruction of animal (and some human) life, decaying bodies and detached limbs would be scattered over the submerged surface, more particularly on those spots where the animals had ineffectually sought refuge. As the land emerged again, sometimes, as we shall show, slowly, and at others more rapidly, the effluent waters swept into the open fissures the debris of the old land surface, together with the remains of the drowned animals, had the fissures been of older date remains of an older fauna would have been preserved or less force and violence. Nor could this have been the work of long time, for the entombed bones, though much broken, are singularly fresh, and the time was not sufficient to allow of the formation of any marine sedimentary deposits. In the same way that the surface rubble was swept into fissures, so when any hollows or depressions were present on the surface it lodged there, as for example that in the old gully or ravine on the slope of the Chalk hills above Didcot. Where not caught, as it were in situ, the rubble was swept down to lower levels and formed banks of breccia on the slopes, and at the base of the hills, as in the instances quoted at Mont Genay, Mentone, and Gibraltar. At this latter place the force of the effluent current is well exemplified, it having carried down from the heights above a brecciated mass of rubble 100 feet thick with blocks 12 feet or more in diameter. It is in a breccia of this character, situated at the foot of the hills at the back of Palermo, that the extraordinary mass of Hippopotami bones occurs."

We find in this rubble not only the remains of the animals which were overtaken and destroyed by the waters, but even the delicate land shells which lived in the grass and amongst the fallen leaves of the old land surface.

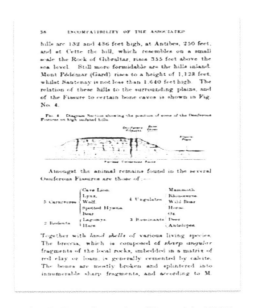

Fig. 69 From the works of Prestwich, (1895)
one of the many fossil filled vertical fissures found across Europe

This diagram makes note of four distinct groups of mammals found within this fissure: cave lion, lynx, wolf, hyena, bear; lagomyx, hare, mammoth, rhino, wild boar, horse; ox, deer and various antelopes, all cemented together with land shells.

The Mountain of Bones

Generally, these consisted of skeletal material found stacked up in basins, caves and vertical fissures, often brim full of shattered bones. In earlier times this phenomenon was well acknowledged, there being dozens of these bone-filled, skyward facing fissures in England, France, Germany, Malta, at Gibraltar, Spain, Germany, Greece, Portugal, Italy and Russia.

For example, on the Greek island of Cerigo, a local hill was referred to by the locals as the "mountain of bones," being over one mile in circumference and literally stacked with the remains of animals a thousand feet high. These deposits and fissures are known to contain a wide variety of animals, a close description of one of many in France, M. Marcel de Serres relates in his *Essay*: "By the side of a fragment of beaver, otter, or of rabbit, we find the bone of a wolf, of a deer, a horse, or even a rhinoceros. Again, by the side of a hyena, or of a lion, we find the bone of a tortoise, of a frog, of an ox, or an elephant. The remains of the most divergent species, in regard to habit and mode of life, are found mingled in the most confused manner. The mixture is so complete that we can only explain it by invoking currents of water, which have borne the bones along, or have disintegrated and dispersed the skeletons after the death of the animals."[2] In the same reference M. Rosenmuller tells us they were found "everywhere" from the cave entrances to the deepest and remote crevasses, sometimes many feet in thickness."[3]

The French observed that the mass of the deposits appeared to be held in suspension by water for a time but then subsided, leaving a deposit of assorted gravels and stones associated with the remains as a conglomerate, like a ring in a bathtub. In general, such deposits also show the action of "tremendous forces" smashing the individual bones to pieces and leaving them in state. In many cases, the deposits are covered in a thick case of stalagmite mineral, sealing it in time like a semi-clear epoxy, and creating a geo-chronometer isolating the past event from the post-flood age.

Describing the deposits at Kent's Hole [England], McEnrey (a contemporary naturalist with Buckland) says: "They had suffered considerably from pressure, after having first undergone violence from the force which impelled and congregated them in this narrow creek. They were found driven into the interstices of the opposite wall, or piled in the greatest confusion against its side." Such evidence is hardly explainable in terms of uniformity and geologic age subdivisions that have animals evolving, dying natural deaths, migrating and suffering accidental falls. Buckland further observed that a similar deposit is found all over Europe, common with the debris in the caves in Germany and of Plymouth.

In Burgundy, France, a steep isolated promontory over 1000 feet above the valley floor has a natural fissure on the summit. (See fig. 69) Early on, naturalists describe it as filled to the brim with the remains of bears, foxes, wolves, horses, oxen and other animals. This deposit (and many others like it in France) "was surely made by waters passing over the top of the edifice, the animals moving to high ground and drowning them," according to many observers.

Similar deposits exist in Sicily near Palermo, where in the San Ceri caves more than 20 tons of hippopotamus bones were mined out for commercial purposes. Commenting on the San Ceri find, Prestwich mentions:

"My supposition is, therefore, that when the island was submerged, the animals in the plain of Palermo naturally retreated, as the waters advanced, deeper into the amphitheater of hills until they found themselves embayed, as in a seine, with promontories running out to sea on either side and a mural precipice in front. As the area became more and more circumscribed the animals must have thronged together in vast multitudes, crushing into the more accessible caves, and swarming over the ground at their entrance, until overtaken by the waters and destroyed." Prestwich adds that the fresh condition of the bones proves that "the event was geologically, comparatively recent."[4]

One observer mentioned that the water level must have exceeded 1,000 feet across England and over 3,000 feet on the European continent in order to create these deposits, mostly thought to be a last sanctuary for the wildlife before perishing in the Flood. On Gibraltar, fissures in number reach over one thousand feet high, full of animal bones, and in one place, along with human artifacts.

Howorth goes on to mention the contents of the caves: "The fact that in some caves the smaller passages, where neither man nor carnivorous animals could creep, are found choked with confused debris, bones, pebbles, etc., that even the main passages are found sometimes filled up, and with portions of the bone debris attached to the roof, points clearly to water as the only possible agent by which they have been arranged."

Howorth continues: "Dr. Falconer explored the cave of Maccagnone, in Sicily, and in it found human traces consisting of ashes and flint implements in a breccia containing the bones of Elephas antiquus, hyena, a large ursus, and especially containing immense numbers of the bones of the hippopotamus. He concluded that 'the cavern had been filled right to the roof, the uppermost layer consisting of a concrete of shells, bone splinters, with burnt clay, flint-chips, bits of charcoal, and hyena coprolites, which was cemented to the roof by staligmitic infiltration. There was nothing to indicate that the different objects in thereof were other than of contemporaneous origin' and further observes: 'a great physical alteration in the contour occurred, altering the flow of superficial water and of the subterranean springs, changing all the conditions previously existing, emptying out the whole of the loose, incoherent contents, and leaving only the portions agglutinated to the roof. The wreck of these ejecta being visible… containing fossil bones, below the mouth of the cavern.'" Howorth again asserted that none other than a "flood of water" could be the explanation for these finds.

Near Odessa, Russia, a cavern as such was discovered full of animals such as cat, hyena, horses, boars, mammoth, rhinoceros, deer, wolves, plus smaller creatures such as rodents, hares, martens, otter, foxes and insects mixed together in no order. Further over 4500 bone remains of bears were found, suggested from approximately 100 individuals. Another cave was said to contain the remains of 2500 bears alone, confined by torrents of water and perished.

The event was (in Cuvier's opinion) "sudden, instantaneous, and without any gradation." At a village near Brunswick, Germany, a collection was discovered that included multiple tusks of elephants up to fourteen feet long and twelve and three-fourths inches in diameter, piled in no order. Within these were mixed the remains and teeth of the rhinoceros, horse, ox, and the stag, these all in a confused mass, but none rolled or broken.

Near Stuttgart, Germany, a fissure was located containing elephant, rhinoceros, horse, deer, ox, and small carnivores. A Professor Rehmann reported in the Bulletin of the Geological Society of France the unearthing at a *single site* included the remains of badger, wolf, fox, cave-hyena, mammoth, rhinoceros antiquitatis, lynx, marmot, leopard, and several kinds of birds, red-deer, reindeer, a kind of antelope, ibex, bison, horse, ass and cave bear, these found mixed and showing no traces of rolling or weathering nor were they assignable to differing time periods. This find was in the loess of the Danube Valley near Langenbrunn.[5]

Howorth reports remains of more than a hundred Rhinoceros Antiquitatis individuals were found buried together at Seveckenberg, near Quedlinburg. At Esper near Aichstedt in the Altmiihl valley where found (Howorth mentioning "as elsewhere") the remains of elephants mixed with hyenas.[67] Dr. Buckland speaks of "Mammoths' teeth of all sizes from the milk-teeth to those of the largest and most perfect growth, some of them showing all the intermediate and peculiar stages of change to which the teeth of modern elephants are subject, as being met with in the pits at Ilford. In the gravel-pits at Oxford and Abingdon, teeth and tusks and various bones of the elephant are found mixed with the bones of rhinoceros, horse, ox, hog, and several species of deer, often crowded together in the same pit, and seldom rolled or rubbed." He goes on to describe a find at Warwickshire in 1815, where fifteen feet below the surface, two magnificent mammoth heads were found with numerous bones of the ox, horse, the teeth of the Siberian rhinoceros, elephants and a number of stags' horns.[8] Such finds showing that a variety of age groups is quite common among the fossil sites, precluding explanations of die offs by any other factor than simultaneous flooding, the animals being of mixed and sometimes adversarial species, found cemented together in sea shells or limestone.

It seems there was no end to the caches of fossils in the Old World, for as often as a foundation was dug, a road bed cut, or a mine opened, the remains of the previous period were found. The volumes of discovery filled the libraries of the greatest naturalists of the day. Such finds were not limited to the land surface, as the sailors working the grounds between Lowestoft to Dunkirk named the seafloor the "burial ground" due to the fact they caught up so many bones of the fauna of the past Epoch. The same findings are recorded by those who sailed the Russian north and east coasts. The same may also be said of some parts of the east coast of the United States seaboard.

The Rock of Gibraltar

Speaking to the Gibraltar caves in his memoirs, Dr. Hugh Falconer investigated the fissures there for the Crown. Falconer describes the cave structures: "The 'Genista' Cave forms part of a great perpendicular fissure, which, by the vigorous measures adopted by Capt. Brome, has either been excavated or traced downwards to a depth of upwards of 200 feet below the level of the plateau. It was full of the fossil remains of quadrupeds and birds, the former of which are now wholly extinct. The fossil remains establish beyond question that the rock was formerly either peopled by, or the occasional resort of, large quadrupeds like the elephant, rhinoceros, aurochs, deer, ibex, wild horse, boar, & [also] hyenas, leopards, the African lynx…either peopled or resorted to the rock in considerable numbers…a certain proportion of them were strewed in hollows along the lines of natural drainage when heavy rains fell; the latter, for the time converted into torrents, swept the bones, with mud, shells, and other surface materials, into the fissure and subsequently solidified into a conglomerate mass…It is now a pinch to find sufficient food at the end of the hot seasons for the flocks of goats which are reared on the Rock. Some of the species must have peopled the rock in vast numbers. We infer, upon a rough estimate, that we have passed through our hands bones derived from at least two or three hundred."[9]

"Human remains were found in great abundance in the upper chambers. They appear to have belonged to between thirty and forty individuals. They were accompanied by stone implements of the polished-stone period, broken querns, a large quantity of pottery, marine shells of edible species, and some other objects enumerated in Capt. Brome's Report. No way of access from the surface by which these materials could have been introduced has been discovered…"

Speaking further about the Gibraltar remains, Captain Brome, who alerted the authorities of the rich finds and spent considerable time excavating the fissures, reports the contents of Genista cavern number 2: "The remains [animal and human] presented precisely the same appearance as those found in the first cave, as regards being semi-cracked, not rolled or water-washed, and very few with signs of having been gnawed. Everything almost was fragmentary, very few whole bones being met with. The scattered, broken state of everything found, together with the fact that the objects were almost invariably discovered near and under the sides of the cavern and passages, appears to me to indicate that these appearances would only have been caused by some convulsion accompanied by flood."[10]

Author note: The annual precipitation for Gibraltar is approximately 30"/annum.

Fig. 70 Gibraltar's skyward facing fissures produced mammoth, hippo, rhino
and a plethora of other remains including human

Lacking pasture or river bed, their method of transport leaves only one alternative, a long distance ride by water. The English officer in charge stated: "[it] appears to me to indicate that these appearances would only have been caused by some convulsion accompanied by flood."[11]

Dr. Falconer passed into the next life with dignity in England soon after studying the Malta fissure findings; he identified a giant extinct swan there, proposed to be given his namesake: *Cygnus Falconer*. After his passing, a 1,000L fund was instantly raised to commission a bust in his honor.

Dr. Falconer's Change to Catastrophism

Falconer's thoughts on faith and science in 1854: "It has never yet been pretended that there has been a divine revelation expounding the knowledge of the natural world. The Almighty has given us reason, and left us, by the adequate exercise of that power, to investigate the laws and order of Creation. True religion and true science can never be irreconcilable. For the Almighty has so ordained that reason can safely reproduce all that has been lost, and restore to the [fossil] tooth all that was correlative to it in life. But, remember that what I have said here bears solely upon our knowledge of the physical world, and not to doctrines of faith for our moral and religious guidance."

Palaeological Memoirs of the Late Hugh Falconer Vol. 1, 1868 edited by Charles Murchenson

Fig. 71 Dr. Hugh Falconer 1808-1865, tireless explorer, servant to all

For the Almighty Creator, infinitely beneficent in regard to the wants of his creatures, and thrifty in the use of means, has left imperishable monuments and inscriptions of the past operation of his laws, more durable than the pyramids, and more legible than the hieroglyphics of the Egyptian porphyries. He has engraved on our natures, as well as in the record of revelation, "Seek, and ye shall find; knock, and it shall be opened unto you." In the exercise of this high endowment of our nature, we glorify in the highest degree the attributes of our Creator. —Dr. Hugh Falconer 1840

The Change

Falconer wrote in his memoirs, "But in the interval between my first visit, in 1858, and Mr. Prestwichs' late reconnaissance of the Gower district, I had opportunities of examining the cave collections of the Mendips in the Museum at Taunton and in Mr. Beard's possession near Banwell, the remains of the Devonshire caverns Torquay and Plymouth, the Durdham Down collection at Bristol, the Cefn collection formed by the late Mr. Lloyd and now in the possession of Colonel H. W. Williams Wynne and the Kirkdale collection at York besides gleanings from all these and other localities in the British Museum and in the rich collection left by Buckland at Oxford. I had also seen the indubitable remains of 'E'. antiquus and e. primagenuis, associated in the beds of marine volcanic Tuifflc at Monte Sacro and other localities in the environs of Rome. *The result was to prepare me for a great change of opinion and for the conviction, that notwithstanding apparent anomalies in the restriction of certain species to certain caves, all the extinct mammalia of the Gower caverns might belong to one fauna, and to the same unbroken geological period.* I have had constantly, throughout the descriptive details of the caverns, to refer to its presence, sometimes in vast accumulations, in the immediate vicinity of the caves, and to its intrusion, so to speak, into their interior, as a flooring cemented by stalagmite…some, like Mr. Godwin-Austen, regard it as being sub-aerial deposit, while other able observers view it as an aqueous deposit, the result of *tumultuous transport*" [emphasis added].

Falconer—*Memoirs* Vol. II, 1862

Malta

Now a thousand miles east of Gibraltar, we have Dr. A. Leith Adams reporting extensively on the fissures and caves of Malta, publishing several works on the topic. His observations differ little from those fissures of like nature elsewhere in Europe and abroad, even compared to those observations on Gibraltar itself. "The excessive numbers [of the gigantic dormice and pachyderms] in the Maltese caves indicate a luxuriant undergrowth and preponderance of cereals, soft nuts, and arboreal vegetation inconsistent in the extreme with the present capabilities of the island." Later he added, "Including even the entire cultivated districts, I do not think that combined they could produce sufficient natural subsistence for a tithe of the river-horses, elephants, and dormice represented by the exuvia even of the Malek and Mandira deposits."

In other words, Adams is telling us the quantity of animal remains is so daunting that the entire island would be unable to support their thousands as represented in the bones found! Mentioning the incomplete skeletal remains in the fissures [like at Gibraltar, indicative of a catastrophic death], Adams comments: "Upon close examination of these deposits we find that very few complete skeletons remain, disproving these deaths being accidental."[12]

Discussing of the range of fauna ages found in Malta, Dr. Adams further points out "their wholesale destruction at all ages of their existence, from the newborn to the aged. In the Maluk cave were detached teeth of the river-horse, from the molar just cutting the gum to the old trefoil-crowned tooth of the adult." He also speaks of the tremendous quantity of avian bones found.[13] [14] Similarly, Falconer says he had remains of the pigmy elephant from at least twenty individuals in Malta, and the entire dentition of every stage, from the fetal age upwards, not a single link missing.

Quoting French naturalist M. Dolomieu regarding Malta, Adams tells us: "M. Dolomieu supposed that a great convulsion must have taken place in the neighborhood of Malta, causing a wave to pass over the island, and washing off all the soil, which he said would account for its bare aspect."[15] Adams also mentions the presence of shark's teeth, along with the remains of fish and frog, turtles and large numbers of shells, not to mention stones not local to the area. Boulders were noticed on top and crushing some of the elephants, suggesting more catastrophic actions, unmentioned in the literature of the area today yet very suggestive of tremendous water action.

Now thinking of these islands and peninsulas such as Malta, Certigo and Gibraltar, and M. Dolomieu's (and later Dana's) giant wave theory, its previous environment and habitations of tens or hundreds of thousands of quadrupeds as Dr. Adams points out, a picture starts to unfold that is here observed as elsewhere around the globe, relating to water, lots of it, in the form of a catastrophe.

In conclusion of the subject of the Ossifurous Fissures, we give the final word to Dr. Adams, who toiled long and hard to provide us with these objective truths to ponder. This passage provides us with a faithful picture from his informed perspective looking across the now barren plains of Malta:

"Here, the geologist, standing on the bare limestone cliff and looking across the deep blue waters of the Mediterranean, might speculate on a time when Malta was a portion of a continent extending far, far beyond the misty horizon; of a land abounding with mountains, rivers, lakes, woods, and forests, where strange pigmy elephants kept company with gigantic compeers, and where also river-horses in hundreds and thousands lived and died; of myriads of destructive rodents, huge fresh-water tortoises and aquatic birds swarmed on the land or on the water; how, per chance, for unreckoned ages had all sojourned in safety on this ancient post-Miocene land, until suddenly (it may be by degrees), it began to sink below them, and they were finally cut off from both continents; then, dying by starvation, they crowded together, and as pinnacle after pinnacle of rock was disappearing under the waves, boisterous billows washed their carcasses into the hollows and rock fissures where we now find them."[16]

In summarizing the evidence of these cave and fissure deposits, Howorth, a scientist personally familiar with the sum of these striking observations, calls for reason:

> The destruction of a fauna, great and small, old and young, the piling of a mixed medley of its remains upon one another in a state of freshness without signs of weathering or decay, is in the case of the caverns, as in that of the surface beds, only consistent with some widespread flood. Such a flood would scour the country and mix gravel and bones together; would force the bones, &c., into the inner recesses of the caverns and drive the forces, as Falconer found them driven, into the roofs of the caves; would rush through the valleys and enter any holes there were in their sides; would drown great beasts, and would as easily carry their carcasses along; would sweep up land-shells and fish as well as mammals, and pile all together in heterogeneous masses.[17]

Now we leave the deposits of our land fauna and look to the marine creatures, the ones who would likely escape any local catastrophe and live on… but no, they are found in the mountains and in the plains, like so many mammoths and mastodons. How did *they* perish?

1

The Fossil Beds Related to the Flood

[1] http://www.icr.org/article/hands-lesson-rapid-fossil-formation
[2] Cuvier cited from Mammoth, Howorth, *Essaiy sur les Cavernes*, etc. 54, 101
[3] ibid 2 p. 101
[4] Prestwich, *On Certain Phenomena Belonging to the Close of the Last Geological Period* (Macmillan and Company 1895), pp 50-52
[5] Falconer, Hugh Bull. Geol. Soc. France, xxix. 332
[6] Howorth, *Mammoth* p. 166
[7] ibid 9. p. 127
[8] Cited from Howorth, *Mammoth* Compte. Bendn, Int. Con. Arch. Pesth, 42. 177
[9] Dr. Hugh Falconer Memoirs Vol II p. 558, 559
[10] Cited from *Mammoth*, Howorth 1887 International Congress of Prehistoric Archaeology, 1861, 130, 131.
[11] ibid 13
[12] Dr. Leith Adams, *The History of the Deposition of the Contents of the Fissure-Cavern of Mnaidra, in Malta*, p 235, 236
[13] ibid 15 p. 204
[14] ibid 15 p. 182
[15] ibid 15 p. 154
[16] ibid 15 p. 146, 147
[17] Howorth, H.H *Mammoth* 1887 p. 212

VIII
Marine Reptiles and Whales in the Mountains

Further evidence of high water comes in the form of the upper altitude deposition of marine reptiles and whales, including that of the plesiosaur, found in the last decade at altitudes exceeding 6,000 feet. The largest known (50 feet long) was found at such heights in Mexico, a concern for one need-ing (as the evolutionist) to sink a mountain range, catch him, then raise it back up, this to lift these giants to such heights..

In the aftermath of the Flood, we can expect there were huge floating biomasses. Additionally, we know from experience that reptiles sink imme-diately when drowned, where mammals bloat and then resurface before dis-membering. In these stages, the corpses are exposed to be consumed by carrion eaters such as sharks etc.. This phenomenon explains why reptiles are often found deeper and more complete in many cases, they typically, but not always, found in the deeper layers than mammals. (Such as those found at the National Dinosaur Monument, Vernal, Utah, where Park service signs explain their common association with sea bottom creatures, such as coiling shells.) Their death, (according to Park signage), a result of drowning at a *river* crossing, this involving the 600,000 square miles of Morrison Formation, a fast moving undersea mud flow!

Yale head of Geology Benjamin Silliman gave the series of talks named *Geological Lectures* on the topic in 1829. In these, he mentioned the occur-rence of whale remains found at high altitudes:

"There can be but one opinion: geology fully confirms the Scriptural history of the event...Whales, sharks and other fishes, crocodiles and am-phibians, the mammoths and the extinct elephant, the rhinoceros, the hip-popotamus, hyenas, tigers, deer, horses, the various species of bovine family and a multitude more, are found buried in diluvium at a greater or less depth; and in most instances under circumstances indicating that they were buried by the same catastrophe that destroyed them: namely a sudden and timely *deluge*."

Silliman mentions as proof the fact that a skeleton of a whale was found on top of Sanhorn Mountain in the North Sea, "three thousand feet high." Silliman further observes there was no possible cause other than a deluge that could have conveyed a whale to that elevation. In one locale he says a

218

whale fossil was also collocated with mammoth remains.[1]

Professor James Dwight Dana, Harvard Professor of Geology and writer of the famous "Manual" series, speaking of the remains of the Zeuglodon, says: "Remains of these gigantic whales are very common in the 'Jackson beds' of the southern United States. The large vertebrae, some of them a foot and a half long and a foot in diameter, were formerly so abundant over the country in Alabama that they were used for making walls or were burned to rid the fields of them." He further relates concerning the Jackson beds: "The most common, called the Zeuglodon, was probably about seventy feet in length. Their remains occur in Mississippi, Alabama, Georgia, and South Carolina; and a species of the genus is found in the Tertiary of Europe."[2] And are also found in the foothills of Vermont.

Dana's last revision reads: "Incalculable violence and great surgings of the ocean should have occurred and been often repeated... The survivors within a long distance of the coast line would have been few."[3]

At 5,000 feet high in the Andes, marine animals and whale fossils were unearthed together with rodents, porcupines, rhinoceroses, camels, marsupials and giant sloths; all in sediments on a high plain in these mountains. Scientists suggest that the chain "rose very rapidly" from the sea.[4]

Fig. 72 Whales in the mountains? (Image Gabriel Barathieu CC lic. 2.0[5])

In 2010, a group of animals including more than 80 fossilized whales were discovered piled together in a narrow 60 by 800 foot strip in the Atacama Desert in Chili, the driest desert in the world. Other fossils at the site included sharks, a porpoise, a 17 foot wingspan bird and an extinct dolphin. What event could quickly bury these creatures in sediments providing their excellent state of fossilization? If this happened over time, the animals would decompose and/or be scavenged, so how may this heap of mixed creatures have perished? In another site at the western base of the Andes, 800 miles north of Atacama, at Cerro Blanco, Peru, were unearthed 346 fossilized whales, a ground sloth, porpoises, sharks, turtles, seals and penguins at 3,800 feet above sea level.[6] From erosion patterns, researchers detected that a diatom/ash mix catastrophically covered the animals, but how did it move uphill to nearly 4,000 ft and cover whales with over 250 feet of sediments? What concentrated such large and diverse creatures, (many still in soft tissue)[7] and how were they fossilized in these Mountains?*

*See http://expertscolumn.com/content/cemetery-whales-chile-mystery-science

Dr. Walt Brown, author of *In the Beginning, Compelling Evidence for Creation and the Flood* (2008) suggests a qualified answer. As an engineer researching rock mechanic's working at MIT, his comments on the subject deserve some consideration. He states: "The rapid continental drift phase ended with the compression event, the sudden crushing, buckling, and thickening of crashing hydroplates. Mountains, such as the Andes, were pushed up in less than an hour. Evidence of that compression event can be seen in thousands of similar places on earth. Not only did part of the seafloor rapidly rise to become the Andes Mountains, the overlying water was also lifted. It then drained down the rising slopes and back into the sea, sweeping with it stranded sea creatures and drowned land animals. Larger animals (whales, etc.) tended to become lodged in these streams, while smaller animals (fish, etc.) were swept into and out of ponds created by large animals damming up the flow. Sediments (especially diatomaceous earth easily swept off the rising seafloor) filled these ponds, fossilizing the larger animals."[8]*

*Dr. Brown's on-line edition: *In the Beginning, Compelling Evidence for Creation and the Flood*, Institute for Creation Science, Phoenix, AZ www.creationscience.com

Vertical Whale Fossil Found in California

A report published in the 1976 issue of *Chemical and Engineering News* documents a whale find in a mining pit near Lompoc, California. Workers uncovered an 80 foot Baleen whale entombed almost vertically in the diatomic filled structure. The remains of four other whales were also found in the presence of many other marine animals. Whale deposits in groups have been found in Oregon, Peru, France, Chili and recently in Norway. Whales are often found mixed with various other marine mammals and turtles, signifying a catastrophic, and not a gradual, end.[9]

Plesiosaurs

Plesiosaur is the most common large marine fossil in the world, commonly found buried in waterborne deposits at high altitudes.[10]

Fig. 73 The most prolific marine reptile fossil in the world, the lively Plesiosaur (left), found entombed in rock at high altitudes. On the right, the Mosasaur, found in soft tissue both in North and South America

Remains of these magnificent creatures have been found across the earth, including at high altitudes, seeming to have been buried alive in flood deposits. Like that of the whales, these finds constitute a testament to the Flood. In addition, a pregnant Plesiosaur was found complete on the plains of Kansas (a seemingly unlikely place, but actually known as a fossil hunter's paradise), now on display in the Los Angeles Museum. In describing these animals, researchers tell us Plesiosaurs are unique aquatic reptiles, giving birth to single, large offspring like whales. In the discussion of fossils from all over the world, from Egg Mountain in the USA to Malta, Brazil, Siberia, China, Europe and almost everywhere across the globe, a common denominator is to be noted, that is, the season of the catastrophe.

"Plesiosaurs have no known living relatives but were common in the world's oceans." [11]

Two plesiosaurs were recently discovered in the Montana highlands; already noted was the Kansas find[12] carrying a young pup, (perplexing to evolutionists, who previously assumed marine reptiles were egg layers) and more very recent findings far north near Prairie City, Alberta, and another near Mitchell, Oregon.[13] Three and possibly four of these were located at altitudes over 5,000 feet. Think of a catastrophe so massive it has the power to capture a 25-50 foot Plesiosaur alive, then preserve it in mountain sediments! The largest plesiosaur specimen found to date was nearly *50 feet long*, unearthed in Mexico on a mountain far above 3,000 feet! Plesiosaurs appear, like the mammoth, to be another important index fossil of the Flood, considering this animal is found both near shore and on high ground around the globe, the most prolific large sea reptile known!

Soft body finds among dinosaurs, plesiosaurs, ichthyosaurs and mosasaurs are very challenging to millions of years based science, yet fit the global Flood model well.

A recent Mosasaur discovery found one of these creatures in a pre-served and amazingly fresh condition, the report stating in brief: "A newly discovered ten-foot-long mosasaurs fossil was discovered along the Mis-souri River in South Dakota. *Its 'remarkable' preservation not only kept the bones in articulated positions, but also retained some original soft tis-sues. This fossil also includes the contents of the animal's stomach—its last meal."*[14] Soft tissue marine mammals noted as "millions" of years old challenge the claims of evolution.[1516]

Fig. 74 Tyrannosaurus Rex, icon of Triassic Park, has been found in
soft tissue alongside sharks and fish, reported in the
papers but not in the textbooks.

T-Rex Bedmates with Sharks and Fish?

As reported from the Hell Creek (Fox Hills formation) area in eastern Montana, five species of shark and 14 species of fish were unearthed near the T-Rex finds, as reported in June 2015 by the Institute for Creation Re-search.[17] Citing a paper by Hartman and Johnson published in 2002,[18] and others, Dr. Tim Clarey* informs us:

It is now becoming obvious that the mixing of terrestrial and marine environments is not a rare occurrence. Discoveries in Morocco and Europe have now shown that most dinosaurs are found with marine fossils or buried in marine sediments in the rock record." He concluded: "Genesis (chapter) 7 and 8 describe this process better than any secular scientist could imagine. *http://www.icr.org/aaf June 2015 *Acts&Facts* Vol. 44 no.6 p.16

Interestingly enough, evolutionary paleontologists are quick to date the layers where these animals were found as tens of millions years attempting to correlate them with a segment on the *Chart*. This is because they maintain the life form *they say* lived in that time frame, according to evolution and the paper on which the Geologic Chart is printed, not on objective reasoning or observation.

Fig. 75 The Famous Agate Springs Nebraska Site
(Image Deluge Story in Stone 1968)

This bone bed was discovered in 1876 by a retired US Cavalry officer while riding the range on the family ranch. It contains the bones of rhinoceroses, camels, giant wild boars and others buried together in a confused mass. The find is represented in a uniform layer horizontally transecting a hill base, obviously created by a moving mass of animals, and subsequently covered by layers of water deposits. It is estimated the site contains the bones of about nine thousand animals in a small area. By all appearances the fossil bearing layer once extended over a very wide expanse, which was then exposed to a massive runoff, subsequently removing the adjacent topography and exposing this segment of what once was a far larger deposit. The mixed and jumbled mass, so common to these sites, suggests these creatures had died in great numbers and were subsequently buried catastrophically, then exposed by a subsequent event, likely the returning stage of the Flood waters.

Fig. 76 The Karoo Mega-deposit, calculated to contain hundreds of *billions* of fossils (Image www.creation.com)

The Karoo formation in South Africa is a water deposited sediment bed thought to be nearly 20,000 feet thick and covers 200,000 square miles.[19]

It doesn't stop there; massive fossil graveyards of dinosaurs and mammals exist all over the world. The Morrison beds in North America, covering thousands of square miles from central Colorado to Utah; the dinosaur beds in Montana, Wyoming, Alberta, the Dakotas, Africa, Europe and China contain literally millions of dinosaur fossils piled together in great heaps, intermixed with shells and many other life forms. Ten thousand Hadrosaurs of all ages were found on Egg Mountain alone, jumbled together in a mass watery grave. Would such occur under normal, uniform conditions? The answer is no. One may trek for years before coming upon the natural remains of a single animal, let alone thousands, or in the case of the Karoo South Africa deposit—*billions!* Again, these all perished in *water* deposited sediments.

Hollywood Death Pits

In America, a death pit exists near Hollywood, with eagles, doves and approximately two hundred and fifty saber tooth tigers and fifty elephants. In Oregon there are beds with elephants, camels, cats, bison, mammoths and mastodon; whales and turtles, mice, lemurs, opossum, beaver and dozens of types of clams, to name a few, all are found in water sediment deposits.[20] Along the Arctic Coast, naturalists have found thousands of mammoths buried in the tundra silts; in Siberia, entire *islands* are made of bones, trees and carcasses of animals washed in jumbles by the thousands. In Antarctica, fossil beds abound. In California, petrified fish, fossilized with mouths open, backs arched and fins spread, have been found. *Many of these fish are partly on end with the body passing through two planes of rock-strata.* In modern geologic terms, such would mean that the fishes' tails are separated from their heads by millions of years. That, of course, is impossible. There are approximately five fish per square foot in this find, covering approximately four square miles. *This equates to more than one billion fossilized fish.* Similar finds are reported from the British Isles in the Old Red Sandstone deposits, where many square miles of deposit show the fish entombed in a stressed state.

The Buffalo Question—Where Are All the Bones?

Millions of buffalo were slaughtered on the North American plains in the last century, so thousands of fossil buffalo bones should be common, but are any great buffalo fossil graveyards to be found today? The answer is simply no. Their remains were disposed of by normal exposure to weather, scavengers, and decomposition in just a few years. So the question must be asked, what act created the great fossil graveyards of dinosaurs, plesiosaurs, mammoths and thousands of other species, laying entombed in water deposited heaps around the world, testifying that they all perished together in a great mass death?

"Fossils are an embarrassment to evolutionists." —Dr. Gary Parker PhD

At current count, over *a million* fossil deposits exist worldwide, covering every continent and extending from pole to pole, the primary covering element of these creatures being *water borne sediments*. Such deposits preclude any possibility of local catastrophic action, their quantity, uniformity and world-wide distribution telling of one causative: that of a worldwide destructive calamity using the driving force of water.

[1] Nelson Byron C. *The Deluge Story in Stone* Bethany Fellowship 1968, p. 85

[2] Price, George McCready, *"Evolutionary Geology and the New Catastrophism"* (Pacific Press Publishing 1926)), p. 253 Quoting from Nicholson *"Ancient Life-History,"* p. 300. and Dana

[3] ibid 3 p. 736

[4] www.nytimes.com/1987/03/12/us/whale-fossils-high-in-andes-show-how-mountains-rose-from-sea.html

[5] Wiki CC 2.0 Link to Image http://www.flickr.com/photos/barathieu/7277953560/

[6] Leonard R. Brand et al., "Fossil Whale Preservation Implies High Diatom Accumulations Rate in the Miocene-Pliocene Pisco Formation of Peru" (Geological Society of America, Vol. 32, February 2004), pp. 165–168.

[7] ibid 26, quote: "The most viable explanation for whale preservation seems to be rapid burial, fast enough to cover whales 5–13 m long and ~50 cm thick within a few weeks or months, to account for whales with well-preserved bones and some soft tissues." Brand et al., p. 167.

[8] *In The Beginning, Compelling Evidence for Creation and the Flood* (2008) p.101 ref. no. 128 http://www.creationscience.com/onlinebook/EarthSciences16.html#wp2218824

[9] Opt. Cited & Snelling, Andrew, *Creation Ex Nihilo* Technical Journal 1995 Vol. 9, no. 2, pp. 244-258

[10] http://i.dailymail.co.uk/i/pix/2011/08/12/article-0-0D65D8D700000578-61_468x286.jpg

[11] http://www.sciencedaily.com/releases/2011/08/110811142806.htm

[12] ibid. 31

[13] http://www.oregongeology.org/sub/news%26events/OregonPlesiosaur.pdf

[14] www.rapidcityjournal.com/news/article_fe339138-dd7c-11df-87de-001cc4c002e0.html

[15] Adam, Smith S. Morphology of the caudal vertebrae in rhomaleosaurus zetlandicus tail fin in plesiosauria (relating to finds of soft body in ancient Marine aquatic life) 2013 http://plesiosauria.com/pdf/smith_2013_plesiosaur_tail_fin.pdf

[16] "Plesiosauria" Wikipedia; en.wikipedia.org/wiki/Plesiosauria#cite_note-51

[17] Acts and Facts June 2105 issue Vol, 44. p. 16 Timothy Clary

[18] Hartman, J. H & J, J Kirkland paper #361 Geological Society of Am. Special Paper, p. 271-296

[19] http://creation.com/noahs-flood-africa , http://www.science-frontiers.com/sf105/sf105p10.htm

[20] *Oregon Fossils*, Orr & Orr 2009, p.103, 196-201, 223-2, *Oregon Geology*, Orr&Orr 2012, p.199

IX

The Trilobite and Nautiloid, Evolutionary Problems

In the Grand Canyon, there is a limestone layer called the "Red Wall" that runs over 250 miles from Arizona to near Las Vegas and containing tens of millions of nautiloids. This number derived from estimates based on an average of *one nautiloid fossil per four square meters*, with nearly one in seven fossilized standing upright. Geologist Dr. Steve Austin, one of the world's leading experts on nautiloid fossils, points out like many of the world's mass fossil graveyards, this enormous nautiloid deposition that covers more than 5,000 square miles provides indisputable proof of the rapid formation of this limestone layer, thought to be of great age for over a hundred years. Also, contrast this to textbook explanations which claim that such layers form extremely slowly, grain by grain settling to the bottom of some shallow and placid sea over millions of years.[1] Most of these creatures are of *uniform age*, suggesting they all perished within the same timeframe.

Dr. Austin explains their significance: "I believe the bed was formed by an underwater mud flow. The water was full of mud, what we call 'slurry,' and so was much denser than the surrounding water. The slurry rushed down the steep slopes of the underwater mountains, gathering speed like an avalanche. And it careens across the ocean floor as fast as a semi on the freeway. There's something like 40 or 50 cubic kilometers of sediment in that bed and it was all deposited rapidly. As the avalanche swept past, it trapped the nautiloids and carried them along. It works like a water cushion and has very low friction, so the mud flow careens across the flat surface of the ocean floor for hundreds of miles.

"Turbulent flow can't carry the mud so it dumps its load suddenly across the ocean floor. And that is what happened to the nautiloid shells. They were deposited quickly, frozen in time. One in every seven is standing vertical in the bed. The others tend to point the same way indicating the direction of the slurry flow. It's a very interesting arrangement of fossils. For a long time geologists have thought that limestone rock, like the rock containing the nautiloid fossils, takes many thousands of years to form. But this bed formed rapidly, like in minutes.

"This bed alone illustrates the title of my book, *Grand Canyon, Monument to Catastrophe*."

Fig. 77 Trilobites exhibit a very complex eye system, yet are located alongside sightless worms on the "Geologic Chart," stories crafted by evolutionists to explain their eyesight read like science fiction, not science text

Trilobites have been found in soft body, allowing their eye anatomy to be thoroughly studied. Turns out they have a very complex eye and lens system, capable of adjusting for underwater aberration. Below the trilobites in the sea floor sediments we find worm fossils, so evolutionists claim the trilobites evolved from these worms, yet no transitional forms are to be found. Extrapolating this logic, if one finds worms and moles together in the backyard, we should also assume worms, over millions of years, became moles! Such logic sounds ridiculous but is exactly what the evolutionists teach concerning these creatures. Now if we observed partial forms of a worm gradually changing into a mole, or further, a lizard jumping off a rock and growing wings and so forth, then the argument would obviously be over, but this is not the case among any major animal grouping. The workings of the cell and genetics must be in agreement showing such a mechanism, and the experimental science to back it. But no, there is no support from either experience or experiment to support the evolution of anything, only the mental progression to believe such things as displayed in crafty drawings.

Evolutionists don't offer an explanation for the complex transitions required to form organs such as eyes like these. Their story is one day a worm had a light sensitive spot on their skin, and that over great eons of time that spot evolved into an eye, then two—all by accidents. Refuting this notion as well as the Geologic Chart, we find the Trilobite in the very throws of life's beginning having a sophisticated lens consisting of chitin/calcite layers, providing the correct refraction and exact thickness giving this creature the ability to correct for underwater aberration. These eyes are said to also employ the laws of Fermat, Snell, Abbes and others.[2]

Extrapolated further to the human eye, with its 120 million sensors mixed in a 20:1 ratio of rods and cones for color and black and white light sensing, eyes have an incredibly complex nerve interpolation network, so the same logic applies. Darwin himself scoffed at such accidental eye developments, but not the evolutionary "scientists" of today; for them, time is invoked to solve every complexity. In an indirect way, "belief" in such a pyridine is a religion in itself, the definition of religion simply being; "a belief system based on faith."

The Failure of Evolution

Interesting enough, in a nearly 30 year University of Michigan study subjecting 45,000 generations of the E. coli bacteria to every thinkable environment and variable, the researchers were unsuccessful in effecting *any* evolutionary change to their subjects. Their only alterations noted were that of size and a small and previously known change of diet to that of citrus.[3] If you lived in a grocery store would you grow? If you were only offered one type of food source would you consume it? Yes, you would or perish; does such constitute evolution and survival of the fittest? Hardly. The lead researcher, Dr. Richard Lenski then goes on to describe evolution as a "hypothesis." He states: "Because bacteria reproduce so quickly, we use them in experiments to test evolutionary hypothesis." He goes on to associate finches beaks and humanoid evolution with this laboratories findings. But how?

Evolution fails in the scheme of microbiology and cell operation to describe a mechanism (other than mistakes) for its operation; it fails to account for the DNA and language convention; it fails to describe how the proton motors operate or came into being (operating in the E. coli mentioned); and finally, evolution fails to explain the absence of transitional forms in the fossil record, a record that screams catastrophe and death, not the eons of time the promoters of evolution have falsely told us occurred, as represented in the Geologic Chart!

In the mind of the unbiased, the sum of this evidence tells one thing: the Geologic Chart is a completely disproved failure, and those so adhering, utterly deceived. The author has personally visited these sites and held and touched the above named fossils with his hands. No transitional forms exist either at the bottom, middle or top of the Chart. Evolutionists, not wanting the average school child to question these potentially embarrassing points, have resorted to any story required in order to keep their faith palatable. These are important matters, for in this dishonest approach to "cherry pick" data in support of their faith, these institutions have resorted to contrive whopping deceptions, resulting in the minds of many youth being swayed from the truth. The truth being this: the honest evidence fully supports the

biblical account as written and stands against evolutionary precepts.
The findings reported here represent a small sample of the evidence supporting a past world-wide cataclysm; they are without apology and in perfect
synchronization with the chapters of Genesis.

[1] http://youngearth.com/grand-canyon-nautiloids
[2] Safariti, Jonathan *Refuting Evolution* (Master Books, 1999). p. 129
[3] http://myxo.css.msu.edu/ecoli/

X
Investigations of the Dinosaur Fossil Beds— the "Unreported" Finds

Dr. Carl Werner in his book series, *Living Fossils* (New Leaf Press, 2009), provides a revealing documentary summarizing the results of his many years research visiting over 60 museums, many institutions and actual fossil dig sites worldwide. In a stunning series of revelations, Werner documents a number of upending finds relating to fossil dinosaurs, their unlikely companions and telling statements from the scientists themselves. One example concerns "index fossils," these given certain Latin names and found associated with the dinosaur sites, such as at National Dinosaur Park near Moab, Utah. Comparing the anatomy of snail shells that occur with these dinosaur fossils which, according to the Park officials, perished while crossing a river, Warner identified *living* snails with the exact same anatomy as those associated with dinosaurs, simply re-identified with different Latin names!

Dr. Warner's books provide proof after proof of similar instances, culminating in the whale series, where Werner shows how the newly publicized whale evolutionary progression (recently upheld immutable in the literature and primary education textbooks) is literally full of holes, constructions and lacking in evidence. After documenting statements from key authorities testifying to this supposed "closed-door" case for evolution, Warner ends the chapter with an admission that the anatomy of the most celebrated whale "missing link" (and others identified as whale ancestors) are actually missing the key anatomy that makes them what is claimed! In truth, the specimen noted was no candidate for an intermediate type at all and has no close association with whales or marine mammals whatsoever! It seems the whole affair is a construction to gain publicity for evolution and a smattering of fame to boot! Since this exposé, a number of major museums were informed of the fraud, some acting to correct the error as demonstrated in their displays and signage.* And the scandal doesn't stop there. Warner personally viewed the actual remains that are out in public view yet noted a completed model exists out in the museum public display; the extra parts that prove evolution are a fabrication. In other words, the faked version is left intact for daily viewing by teams of schoolchildren, with signs declaring immutable evolutionary victory.   *Note: see www.thegrandexperiment. com

Dr. Werner challenged the very scientist who unearthed this "key" fossil with the facts; he openly admits the error, yet stands quietly by. To the evolutionist as the politician, it seems their "science" is becoming patently dishonest, winning in the short term but losing in the long. To the author, the sum of such activity exemplifies the desperate situation of that faith at this time in history. They are manufacturing what's needed to prop-up their theory, then resorting to lies in the foyer to sway school children!

Werner documents with stark reality the fact that researchers have found bird remains and other mammals co-located with dinosaurs, yet museums refuse to display them together, keeping this information from the public and out of the literature. Werner states: "If provided the complete evidence from the field, one should see displayed a *T. Rex* or a *Triceratops*, along with ducks, loons, flamingos or pipers as have been found in the same rock layers as these dinosaurs!" But such a display would be contrary to the Geologic Column and evolution; in reviewing the Geologic Chart; we find birds *above* and evolving *from* dinosaurs, such finds creating much difficulty for evolutionists. Birds sport a completely unique lung, are warm blooded, have feathers and hollow bones, difficult issues for evolution to solve, not to mention the co-habitual living arrangements now indicated with their purported ancestor, the dinosaur!

Fig. 78 Parrot and dinosaur remains have been found mingled together
at the same dig site, yet are rarely displayed so in museums.

Werner states:

"If provided the complete evidence from the field, one should see displayed a T. Rex or a Triceratops, along with ducks, loons, flamingos or pipers as have been found in the same rock layers as these dinosaurs!"

When Dr. Werner personally questioned paleontologists if they had found birds and dinosaurs buried together, the truth flowed out: "I interviewed a scientist at a major Museum of Paleontology who discussed a parrot fossil they had found in Cretaceous layers (dinosaur rock). But the parrot fossil was not on display in the museum." This general testimony repeated itself over and over in his interviews with scientists across the country, Warner finding additional evidence that modern birds and a plethora of other fauna have been unearthed with the dinosaurs, even larger mammals, yet kept out of the public eye. Werner noted that of the museums he visited, none displayed out front the evidence scientists related to him in his back office interviews.

Dr. Werner also physically visited a number of well-known dig sites and observes: "At the dinosaur dig sites, scientists have found many unusual extinct mammal forms, but they have also found fossilized mammals that look like squirrels, opossums, Tasmanian devils, hedgehogs, shrews, beavers, primates, and duck-billed platypus." He goes on to mention: "Paleontologists have found 432 mammal species in the dinosaur layers; almost as many as the number of dinosaur species. But where are these fossils? We visited 60 museums but did not see a *single* complete mammal skeleton from the dinosaur layers displayed. These fossils include nearly 100 *complete* mammal skeletons."

Werner further relates: "Cartilaginous fish (sharks and rays), boney fish (such as sturgeon, paddlefish, salmon, herring, flounder and bowfin) and jawless fish (hagfish and lamprey) have been found in the dinosaur layers and appear the same as modern forms. Modern-looking frogs and salamanders have been also found in dinosaur dig sites yet are classified with completely different Latin taxis. All of today's reptile groups have been found in the dinosaur layers, and they look the same or similar to modern forms: snakes (boa constrictor), lizards (ground lizards and gliding lizards), turtles (box turtles, soft-shelled turtles), and crocodilians (alligators, crocodiles and gavials)."

Such associations are not expected if these creatures entered the fossil record in the course of natural death, each supposedly slowly covered over great time periods. However, if the Flood as described in Genesis was the cause of their demise, the findings in these deposits fit quite well. One of scientists interviewed by Dr. Werner stated:

We find mammals in almost all of our [dinosaur dig] sites. These were not noticed years ago…We have about 20,000 pounds of bentonite clay that has mammal fossils that we are trying to give away to some researcher. It's not that they are not important, it's just that you only live once and I specialized in something other than mammals. I specialize in reptiles and dinosaurs.

As for the Age of Dinosaurs, one paleontologist explained:

In a sense, the Age of Dinosaurs is a misnomer. Mammals are just one such important group that lived with the dinosaurs, coexisted with the dinosaurs, and survived the dinosaurs. "[1]

Dr. Warner continues his quest for truth in publishing *Living Fossils Two* (New Leaf Press, 2009) and a coming volume on human remains, where he convincingly and systematically documents fossil after fossil given ages of dozens of millions of years, each perfectly indistinguishable from their modern counterparts. This Warner accomplishes this well, powerfully exhibited side by side with contemporary species in 270 pages of living color.[2] Adding to this evidence is quote after quote in context from working professionals, maintaining the association of dinosaurs and all the primary zoological subclasses of fauna within the dig sites. In summary, Warner's combined works confound the basic premise of the Geologic Chart, that of progressive upward evolutionary change among the layers of time, portrayed in the images of different animals (such as reptiles becoming birds or mammals) currently taught as scientific fact.

In conclusion of these matters and in consideration of the aforementioned find of sharks and fish located with dinosaurs within the Hell Creek dinosaur dig site, Dr. Tim Clarey of ICR summarizes well:

Most dinosaurs are found with marine fossils or buried in marine sediments in the rock record. [3]

With this we leave our subject reptiles in their buried millions, all in hope this treatment provides the observer a better understanding aligned with the facts of the matter, rather than the misinformation and biases that surround these amazing creatures and their demise.

---

[1] Interview with Dr. Zhe-Xi Luo, Carnegie Museum, Pittsburgh, PA. by Dr Carl Werner, 17 May 2004
[2] See www.youtube.com/watch?feature=player_embedded&v=C5eTNoTHewY Modern Birds Found With Dinosaurs - YouTube
[3] lcr.org/aaf Timothy Clarey, *Acts & Facts* June 2015 iss. vol. 44 no. 6 p. 16

XI
The Alaska Dinosaurs: the Recent Finds

U. S. GEOLOGICAL SURVEY   BULLETIN 815   PLATE 2

A. MAMMOTH TUSK ON COLVILLE RIVER NEAR ETIVLUK RIVER

Fig. 79 This mammoth tusk was collected in 1926 near the current dinosaur digs by the
USGS (United States Geological Survey) in Alaska

*Alaskan river banks abound with mammoth fossils and their tusks.
More lay below the surface across the state, covering hundreds of
thousands of square miles—another testament to the great Flood of Noah's
day. The tusk here was found on the Colville River near a recent dig site
containing di-nosaurs, said to be "washed in place" by "flooding."*

Dinosaur remains were discovered in Alaska after a misplaced bone
found in a warehouse was identified from a 1961 discovery by geologist
R.L. Liscomb, who unfortunately perished the year following the find, his
discovery locked away in time for over 30 years! The remains were found
in the far north section of the state, near the North Slope oil fields. This
area is known intimately to the author and contains the remains of
mammoth, broad horned bison, horses, great ox and a number of other
extinct species, each that perished only a few thousand years past in flood
deposits.

In another complication for evolution, these dinosaur bones have been found in an un-fossilized state, appearing as any of the mammals buried around them! In reality, the dinosaur remains were found catastrophically deposited *above* and in other words *with* the mammoths. The geology known there is Pleistocene and recent, identified as such by a long string of geologists since Dr. Dall, all the way back to the 1800s. Further, the reptile remains are sandwiched above and below coal layers, with the mammoths beneath, representing another case where the famed Geologic Column has failed as any representation of what is observed in the rocks. Reporter Chris Schmitt comments on the find of the Texas team led by Dr. Fiorillo, that finding 14 dinosaurs in a single pile in this water forced deposit - *"leading him to believe they were washed down a river channel in a flood."*[1]

The primary remains were found so described. A complete skull was found pushed upside down in this jumbled heap, thus buried *catastrophically*, hardly a contradiction to the Flood. There is every indication these dinosaurs were drowned and buried by the same event that overcame the mammoths and other animals at this location, explained by no better causative then the great Flood of Noah's day! In an interesting turn of events, the USGS and State of Alaska recently re-identified the reptile holding *Pleistocene* strata to that of dinosaur holding *Cretaceous*. Somehow, the same strata identified one day as a few thousand years old becomes 70 million the next, even while the bones are still un-fossilized!

Quoting the Eskimos who lived toward the Colville River:

The water having poured over the terrestrial disc, human dwellings disappeared. They fastened several boats to one another. The wind carried them away. The waves traversed the Rocky Mountains. Presently the moon and earth disappeared. Men died in the terrible heat; they also perished in the waves. Men bewailed what had hap-pened. Uprooted trees floated about in the waves. Men having fas-tened boats together trembled with cold. A man threw his bow into the water and said, "Wind, this is enough, be still!" —Appendix II

---

[1] www.pbs.org/wgbh/nova/evolution/filming-dinosaurs-in-alaska.html quote by Chris Schmit, Nova

XII

The Geologic Chart and Phylogenic Tree Falsified

One should stand in awe of the power of the Geologic Column! Its paper capable of hypnotizing entire teams of professional geologists ever willing to bow down and worship its powerful potions and toss away their senses! In the same moment they ready to mock the creationists for their obvious blind and unscientific faith; how foolish are those folk they say, believing in Bible myths and miracles! The real question remains, who is believing what myths? How sad! What untold wealth in the depths of the earth have these passed over following such delusions called science? What disservice to man and nations has their blind dogma produced? What casualty to morality have they inflicted while in the same breath wave a wand declaring a billion tons of clean fill millions of years old, simply in order fit the paper on the Chart, yet knowingly mock the paper of the Scriptures! What millions have they deceived? How many trusting and innocent children have they turned away to these falsehoods? Have they any concept of what Christ Himself says about these matters?

In reality, the "chart" is nothing more than a sequential list of grave markers, disproven with the revelations herein and those as quoted from Dr. Warner's investigations. His work proves that many secular researchers struggle and contort the evidence to make the paper fit. It seems that the layers are *stacked* so to speak, designed only to promote a dead dogma and worse, one that ends in the deception of little children!

The Column with its pictured layers was actually deposited by Flood currents, as mentioned first and most correctly by Woodworth, as the specific gravity of each material is sorted by current action, making up the layers then repeating. More specifically, as sandstone (like the massive Tapeat's and Tyee to be described herein), shale or limestone were laid down, each simply repeating in no specific order as the currents of the Deluge ebbed and flowed by the workings of tides, gravity, and other movements known only to God in the catastrophe *general*. And note: each and every layer *sedimentary* in nature, which means they being *water deposited*, some stretching across millions of square miles and full of entombed fauna and flora! The only possible causative? A Flood of Global proportions!

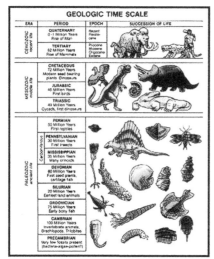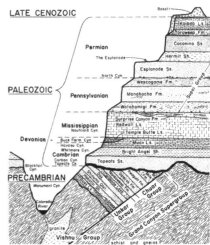

Fig. 80 Left, the infamous "Geologic Chart" the layers representative
of annihilation in the Flood year, not evolution over eons of time. Right, the Grand Canyon
showing flood layers. (images courtesy Creation Ministries International www.creation.com)

*The Chart assumes evolution and eons of time formed these layers, a
grossly mistaken deduction.*
   In the above image, on the right is the Grand Canyon, noting the
uniform sequence of the layers, consistent with a *single* event. A similar
but smaller sequence was formed in one day as part of the Mt. St. Helens
eruption, com-plete with current formed layering. Modern geology tells us
each layer rep-resents millions of years, yet field observations indicate the
reverse! Note the absence of erosion between these strata, indicating little
time passed be-tween layers. The chart sequence better represents the
burial sequence of these creatures: first, the sea bottom dwellers—worms,
trilobites, snails. Sec-ond, the more mobile—nautiloids and fish. Third, the
aquatic reptiles and creatures of the estuaries. Fourth, the marine
mammals; and fifth, the land dwelling animals, birds, snakes and
dinosaurs. And finally, the mammals and birds.
   The Bible teaches that the earth was made "out of water and with
water" (Genesis 1, & 2 and 1 Peter 3:5), then was subsequently destroyed
by water in the great Flood. Note that 75% of the earth's surface is made of
sedimen-tary rocks, deposited through and by *water*. Note over 90% of
these were laid down by water action in the Continental and larger in scale.
Most of these layers contain fossils and artifacts of every sort.

Interestingly, deep down in these layers geologists have found remnant sections of an earlier earth, these sediment layers called "Pre-Cambrian" or pre-life. (Note the tilted layers of the Unkar/Chuar "Supergroup," lower half of the Canyon crosssection in Fig. 80) These defined "pre-life" because they contain *no fossils*, except pollen,* the same pollen we find in modern rocks! As there was no mass death recorded *before* the Flood event, we should expect to find a virgin layer without fossils at such depths, the earth of the primal creation week. In truth, the evolutionists are again mistaken, as life existed and was more prolific back then!

As such, these supergroup sediments in the canyon bottom would be the ground Adam walked upon in the First Earth. Why are they fossil free? That's simple, when you look at their structure you see above them thousands of feet of uniform water driven layers, full of fossils or dead things, exactly what we would expect if there was a worldwide flood, its prime directive: the destruction of all air-breathing life! These layers the geologist refers to as the *Cambrian* or *Life* layers, but actually they have it backwards again! These are the *death layers*, where life ended in a watery mass destruction, including those of the dinosaurs and large mammals, like the mammoths!

*The Roraima pre-Cambrian formation contains pollen in South America.

In consideration of the evidence, note this statement recorded by Dr. Warner from an experienced paleontologist who informs us:

> *In a sense, "The Age of Dinosaurs" is a misnomer… Mammals are just one such important group that lived with the dinosaurs, coexisted with the dinosaurs, and survived the dinosaurs.*[1]

We now have a quandary—which is true? The evidence from the field or the paper of the "Chart?" Note that reptiles immediately sink when drowned, but mammals bloat and float, naturally depositing them on higher ground and the former lower in a flooding catastrophe. In truth, the chart is merely a depiction of the death and burial sequence from the beginning to the end of the Flood, and an incorrect one at that! With transitional forms absent (like worms becoming moles), it's now known each fossil from bottom to top is unique! In reality, the general sequence of the Geologic chart represents a short period of catastrophic work, e.g. the Flood year, *not* millions of years of time at all. As Dr. Werner points out, many dinosaur fossil sites are intermingled with the fauna of the entire chart, including mammals, birds, snakes, shells, insects and so forth, these finds invalidating the entire premise of evolutionary based geology!

239

Important Discoveries
Concerning the Origin of Life

Fig. 81 On the left, Darwin's Phylogenic disproven tree of common ancestry.
On the right, the new based on the actual fossil record

Is Darwin's famed evolutionary tree turning into a Creation orchard?[2]
Mammals, reptiles, birds, fish, insects and all basic "kinds" have now been
found in the geologic basement layers!

These simple questions beg asking:

Q. If the account of a worldwide Flood is true, what would be expected
to be found in the earth's crust?

A. The remains of millions (and even billions) of trapped and buried
animals.

Q. What do we *in fact* find?

A. Millions and billions of trapped and buried animals, mixed and tan-
gled in no ascending evolutionary order, now found in a *million* documented
sites alone! (See world fossil map this link).[3]

Q. Has institutional science gone too far with their mistaken view of
origins?

A. This quote is telling:

Science is fundamentally a game...with one overriding and defining
rule: Rule #1: Lets see how far and to what extent we can explain
the behaviors of the physical and material universe in terms of
purely physical and material causes, without invoking the supernat-
ural [4]   —R.E Dickerson 1992

Without their great eons of time, the magical complexity in the living
world becomes a threat to them, not having enough time for evolution

to "create" it! Seems they wish to hold the keys of truth and so called "science" entire, able to disallow *any* thinking contrary to their beliefs, no matter how powerful or logical the evidence! So with blind faith, Evolutionary Geology and Biology bows to the failed geologic chart and now disproved phylogenic tree, and like the game of rock-paper-scissors, the paper of the column more powerful than the rock! The "Chart" then actually is an oxymoron, that is, on one hand we have the idiom of geology that holds that "the rocks don't lie," and on the other, we have the mistaken "logic" of the so called *Geo-logic Column!*

No matter what the opinion of man, the evidence pointing to the Flood is clear. That said, with such illogic, dogma, low threats and evidence contending, the author now dismisses *evolutionary based geology* as a valid authority relating to origins science. The sum of its great ages, misinterpretations, dogma and contradictions, the perpetrations of falsehoods and worse; the leading of so many school children to trust in its guarded precepts as "science" is in every respect *deplorable.* In its absence, we now offer a new and better model of origins to assist man to better understand a more correct truth. This truth is in part only, as man will never completely understand all what happened in the Flood year, or any other un-witnessed story of the past. Men are but an ant crawling round these stones atop the mountains, having no right to question *God*, but only to use the mind He gave us as Hugh Falconer asserts, with awe and fear, grateful for life, the ability to study and the air we breathe. With this approach, we may be certain not to fall the way of the foolish but have the understanding of the wise, therein finding favor with God and receiving His true blessing with it!

---

[1] Interview with Dr Zhe-Xi Luo, Carnegie Museum, Pittsburgh, PA. by Dr .Carl Werner, 17 May 2004

[2] See http://creation.com/is-the-evolutionary-tree-changing-into-a-creationist-orchard

[3] Fossil Sites of North & South America: A Paleontology Primer in a Google Map - Google Maps —Link mentioning 1 million fossil beds.

[4] Safarati, Jonathan Refuting Evolution, (Creation Book Pub 1999), p.18 quoting Dickerson, *Perspectives on Science and the Christian Faith* 1992

Geologists Comment on the "Chart"

Finally, we leave the infamous chart to be described by those more experienced and wiser, no longer inclined to allow paper to cover what the rocks truly tell us.

Dr. Edmund Spieker, well known expert on petroleum geology and no advocate of the biblical flood, responds concerning the usefulness of the "Chart," here states: "Does our time scale, then, partake of natural law? No, I wonder how many of us realize that the time scale was frozen in essentially its present form by 1840? How much world geology was known in 1840? A bit of Western Europe, none too well, and a lesser fringe of eastern North America. All of Asia, Africa, South America, and most of North America were virtually unknown. How dare the pioneers assume that their scale would fit the rocks in these vast areas, by far most of the world? It was only in dogmatic assumption, a mere extension of the kind of reasoning developed by Werner from the facts in his little district of Saxony. And in many parts of the world, notably India and South America, it does not fit. But even there it is applied! The followers of the founding fathers went forth across the earth and in Procrustean fashion made it fit the sections they found, even in places where the actual evidence literally proclaimed denial. So flexible and accommodating are the 'facts' of geology."[1]

To this statement hydrologist Dr. Henry Morris responds, writing in his signatory work *The Genesis Flood* (1961) reflecting on Dr. Spieker's comments: "Had the above charges been made by George McCready Price or some other modern opponent of uniformitarian geology, they would have been indignantly discounted as the ratings of an ignorant fundamentalist! But the fact is that Dr. Spieker is such a through-going uniformitarian that this purpose in thus exposing the weakness of basic geological theory is primarily to deny that any revolutions or other geologic events of worldwide significance ever occurred and, therefore, that the boundaries between the various systems are meaningless. That is, he insists that there is no actually identifiable boundary between the Cretaceous and Tertiary, for example, or between the Cambrian and Ordovician, or between any other two supposedly adjacent systems."[2]

Notes concerning diagrams on succeeding pages 244-245:

*The Young Himalaya: The first European expeditions into the Himalaya commented on their youth in unison. Swiss Geologists Arnold Heim and August Gansser in their classic volume *The Throne of the Gods* (1939) mentioned: "The highest mountains in the world are also the youngest... With their topmost peaks the mountains have shattered the entire scheme of the geology of the long, long ago." (p. 220) Suggesting they were uplifted in historical times.

**Concerning the Matterhorn Geikie observes: *"In the Alps, where the rocks composing huge mountain masses have been so completely overturned that the highest beds appear as if regularly covered by others, which ought properly to underlie them."* [3]

D.N. Wadia, Author of *Geology of India* notes in a paper entitled *The Himalaya Mountains Their Age, Origin and Sub Crustal Makeup* (1965) in-cludes a chapter *The Extreme Youth of the Himalaya,* comments that in his view, the Himalaya uplift occurred in three phases, then admits: "There is a body of competent evidence, both physical and biological, to indicate that parts of the Himalayas have risen *at least 5,000 feet* since the Middle Pleis-tocene (recent times). Early man thus witnessed the growth of this northern barrier." Wadia mentioned the fact that these massive edifices are made of an earlier sea floor, prolific with fossils of creatures from both land and sea are found on the flanks and summits of these high ranges.

Hugh Falconer reports that the natives of the country maintain that a number of passes across the Himalaya are rarely or no longer crossable, forcing the abandonment of pastures and villages of known an-tiquity, their being thrust up into altitudes of perpetual snow. Locals point out now frozen slide areas were forests once stood. He suggests an uplift of approximately 8,000 feet occurred, lifting the range and the interlaying Tibetan plane. (*Memoirs*, Vol. I p.181-83) Such rapid uplift coincides with the observations of Dr. Walt Brown concerning the Andes, (see *Whales in the Mountains* Appendix VIII) suggesting an uplift period for that range of an *hour*.

The following images depict several well known earth features that stand in contradiction to the Geologic Column

Fig. 82 Chief Mountain of the 360 mile long Lewis Range. Note the older strata sit atop the younger with a missing gap of 400 million years

Fig. 83 Mt Everest summit rocks contain trilobites, brachiopods and chronids, said to be of the 600+ MY old Ordovician age (above blue line). These sit atop much younger limestones of the Cretaceous, dated between 14 and 40 million years using isotope methods in the "Yellow Band" (above redline).[4] See preceding note concerning the "extreme youth" of the Himalaya. What happened to the missing 500 MY?

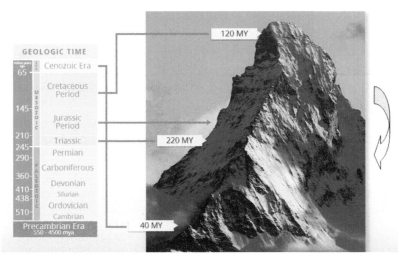

Fig. 84 Matterhorn rocks of supposed 40 million year age sit at the base of the pinnacle, directly under rocks of the 220 MY old Triassic period. Theorists claim the upper layers came from Africa [4]** See preceding notes p. 243

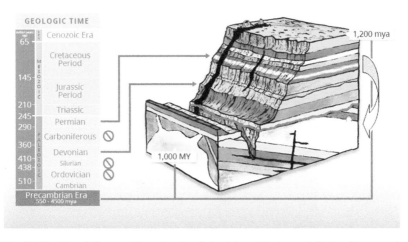

Fig. 85 The Grand Canyon. Note that the Ordovician, Silurian and Carboniferous units representing 270 million years are missing. Isotope dating of flows show the upper fresh flow (black) date older than the canyon bottom (intrusive) by over 200 MY!

Conclusions

Geologist George McCready Price summarizes regarding the subject of the purported Geologic Chart, telling us:

> *"There is no man on earth who knows enough about the rocks or the fossils to be able to prove in any fashion fit to be called scientific that any particular kind of fossil is actually and intrinsically older or younger than any other kind. In other words, there is no one who can actually prove that the Cambrian trilobite is older than the Cretaceous dinosaur or the Tertiary mammal."[6] "The fact is, the current geology is wholly built up, from the Cambrian to the Pleistocene, on the dogmatic denial that any such catastrophe has occurred to the world in which man lived; for one such event happening in our modern interdependent world is enough to make the whole pretty scheme found in our textbooks tumble like a house of cards."[7]*

Yes, this is the great worry of the advocate of evolutionary based geology, and as we shall soon show, his worries have only just begun, for now comes not a worry for such mistaken geology, but its worst nightmare: *The Great Unconformity.*

The Great Unconformity

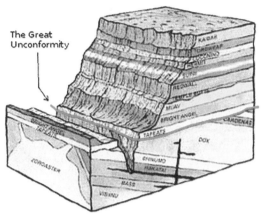

Fig. 86 The Grand Canyon and the Great Unconformity, red line
(Image courtesy Answers in Genesis www.answersingenesis.org)

There is a well known place where one can read the Flood story written in the rocks, and it's right here in America, **The Grand Canyon.** Within its depths we find the evidence fully supporting the biblical narrative imprinted in stone, where they may be felt, touched and seen. Further, we find these primal layers tilted and fractured, sitting at angles indicating the crust was smashed at this locale. I suggest this occurrence was not accidental: that God Himself picked this very location in order to prove to man the Bible account reliable in a volume written on a million tons of rock.

Fig. 87 "You are here." The Tapeat's Sandstone (top) Granites (bottom) Event Horizon near the canyon bottom. These indicate tremendous forces and heat enough to melt granite, not the action of a calm and tranquil sea.
The Great Unconformity— close up and personal. Note the heat tempering caused by the fric-tion and extreme weight of

millions of tons of water laden sediments from the Flood. They acted cutting off the tops of these granite blocks (actually mountain ranges) by the Tapeat's Sandstone near the bottom of the Grand Canyon. The Park Service signs tell the public the Canyon was formed by 10 or more "calm and placid seas" over many millions of years, a concept not at all supported in the rocks. The Great Unconformity contact zone exhibits heat, severe compression and a perfectly defined event horizon, only ½" thick in places. The Unconformity and these water deposited layers tell a history story in the rocks, a serious story that is anything but *"calm and placid."*

The Great Unconformity shows that flows *eroded* the surface of huge blocks parallel to gravity across the earth's surface (at the red line). Observe the tilt and faults of the *Unkar/Chuar* groups of sediments in that area stacked below the red line (lower center). These were the earth's surface before this event, now sliced, broken, buried and tilted. This is the crust of First Earth, the ground that Adam walked upon. It's obvious a huge fault occurred where the Supergroup Rocks were catastrophically thrust up. These were likely temporary mountain ranges before the silt laden flood waters eroded them at the Great Unconformity contact plane. Note that the tilted Unkar/Chuar zone was in place *before* the Canyon forming event and is *fossil-less* (below the red line). We see that only a portion of the "original earth" remains. Without a doubt, this cataclysmic feature is *the* Event Horizon of Earth Geologic History.

The evidence is clear: the earth experienced a cataclysm unequaled in history based on these formations. The event that caused this erosion plane followed the following sequence:

•   The initial crust shattering as shown by the tilted structures (All the Fountains of the Great Deep "bursting" Genesis 7:11)
•   The broken and tilted blocks were subsequently eroded near level by water/sediment action noted at the unconformity contact
•   The currents sorted sediments into layers, depositing in parallel with gravity and quickly layering above the horizon after the initial event when the currents slowed
•   Lastly, a final run-off eroded the Canyon while the new layers were soft in the last 150 days of the Flood, exposing the sediment layers of another earth at the bottom, one that existed before the catastrophe; the earth Adam walked upon. The entire face of the early earth here was scraped flat. The water-carried sediments were re-deposited, leaving behind what we see today in the Grand Canyon and the geologic structure

of the entire planet! This statement cannot be refuted nor disproved. Sometime in history, we know the super-group layers were positioned horizontal. One cannot imagine nor conceive the colossal scale of these events and the environment on earth while this was happening. *The total annihilation of all life on earth was at stake.*

All the layers are water-deposited with current action evidence. If there was a worldwide flood, what should a cross section of the crust look like? *Exactly this!* The Bible teaches the earth was made "out of water and with water" (2 Peter 3), thus explaining these lower mystery layers. These show no sign of any fossils, a portion of which is open to view in the Canyon (which the author has studied firsthand). Does this make sense according to the biblical accounts? The answer is a resounding *yes*—here in the Grand Canyon, *we see the Origins Story of earth and subsequent destruction clearly stamped on millions of tons of rock!*

Though rarely documented in school textbooks, we have at the bottom layers of the canyon the original earth eroded off flat, as if by a giant rock saw. What layer sits directly above this cut? Hundreds of feet of near pure sandstone, which geologists named the 'Tapeat's, and not only sandstone, but a sandstone full of marine fossils! Note this layer is intercontinental in size, extending over a *million* square miles. Plainly, this line of evidence points nowhere else. What student of flood geology could construct a better model if he had ordered the billion tons of rock in place himself, all demonstrating that the Flood was true!

To conclude this short treatise on proofs showing how earth's geologic features align with the biblical narrative, the words of George McCready Price, master of Geology and tireless advocate for reason, summarized:

> *"Inductive geology, therefore, deals not with the formation of a world, but with the ruins of one; it furnishes us no materials for constructing a cosmogony – that is, nothing as to the details or order in which creation took place, though, as we have see, it indirectly proclaims the general fact of a literal creation in no uncertain tones. But this latter problem lies across the boundary line, in the domain of philosophy and theology; and to these systems of thought we may cheerfully leave the task of readjustment in view of the facts here presented."*[8]

249

[1] Edmund M. Spieker: "Mountain-Building Chronology and Nature of Geologic Time-Scale," *Bulletin American Association of Petroleum Geologists,* Vol. 40, August 1956, p. 1803.

[2] Whitcomb, J and Morris, H. *The Genesis Flood* (pp. 209-211). Phillipsburg: Presbyterian and Reformed Publishing Company (1961)

[3] Archibald Geikie Text-Book of Geology 1885, sec. ed. Selections

[4] Geology of the Summit Limestone of Mount (Everest) of the Yellow Band 2005 Harutaka, Sakai et al Univ. of Tokyo 12/2005; 14(4):297

[5] Morris & Whitcomb *The Genesis Flood* 1961 Pres & Reformed Pub p. 199

[6] Price, *The New Geology*

[7] Price, George McCready *Evolutionary Geology and the New Catastrophism* Pacific Press Pub. Association (1926): p.335

[8] Price, George McCready, *Evolutionary Geology and the New Catastrophism* Pacific Press Publishing Association (1926): p. 337

XIII

The Grand Canyon Event Horizon and Tyee

Fig. 88 Grand Canyon (image by author)

What an amazing place! The formation of this beautiful Canyon poses a question—was it formed with a *lot of water over a short period of time or a little water over a long period of time?* Looking across the Canyon, one may imagine an ocean of water spilling across the continent heading downhill, taking everything in its path. More importantly, an Event Horizon exists in the depths of the Canyon; so in word and image travel down and see for yourself.

Can a river eroding one grain of sand at a time leave jagged edges in solid granite and lava? No, rivers and creeks erode smooth walls. It's been proven a catastrophic gush of flood water can rip apart basaltic or metamorphic formations; the Missoula Flood and Mt. St. Helens events support this. The Missoula Flood theory was mocked for decades before geologists determined that water alone can cut through solid lava like butter, even opening broad gaps in mountain ranges. Both these events made history, forcing the rewriting of geology texts relating to geologic feature formation in light of these amazing cataclysms that were witnessed. We now know that often creeks and rivers exist due to catastrophic events that first created the features, then water took a course within them. For science to be valid, it must be vulnerable to change when new discoveries are made. If not, it becomes as the Bible teaches "science, falsely so called" (1 Tim. 6:20). How many other feature forming processes that occurred during the flood year are we yet to understand?

Fig. 89 Comparison of the Grand Canyon (LH) and Mt. St. Helens (RH) erosion paths. The Mt. St. Helens Gorge (right) was cut out in only three days, the Grand Canyon (left hand) was eroded as the waters ran "continually off the earth for 150 days" in the Flood. On the left, notice the exposed rough walls cutting through granites, indicative of a past catastrophic event. Can a river eroding one grain of sand at a time leave such jagged edges (dark rock - center)? No, river erosion leave smooth walls. The Missoula Flood taught geologists a catastrophic gush of flood water is capable of ripping through mountains!

Fig. 90 The Tapeat's Sandstone is a widely distributed sandstone layer deposited by water and full of fossils—covering millions of square miles. Classified a *turbidity* (a high speed underwater mud flow) as can be determined from the wide distribution of this formation, a "local flood" was not involved in this mega deposit. (RH map courtesy Alpha Omega Ministries *www.aomin.org*)

The Western Oregon Tyee Deposit

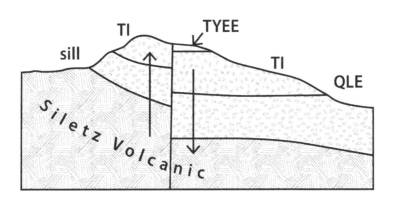

Fig. 91 The Tyee deposit (top arrow) extends across a thousand square miles of the Oregon Coast range and here at 4,000 feet elev. Its material is from the Rocky Mountains (Geology cross-section after Baldwin, 1976)

A section of water deposited hi-speed mudflow with fossils makes up the RH peak of the Mary's summit at the 4,000 foot level. How did this material get up there? Deep sea drilling revealed its thickness is in excess of 10,000 feet!

Distribution of the Tyee on Top of Oregon's Coast Range

Fig. 92 Tyee Distribution
(USGS Snavely et al 1964)

Mary's Peak is located near Corvallis, Oregon. The hump just to the right of the summit in the upper image is actually a sandstone *turbidity* deposit (a high-speed underwater mudflow). This layer is part of the Western Oregon *Tyee* formation found here at the 4,000 feet level, extending west into the Pacific Ocean. (See fig 91)

What is a water pushed flow containing fossils doing up it this altitude? Notice in the drawing the fault line (center vertical) indicates more of the Tyee was higher on the formation but was somehow eroded. This means our entire Peak here was under *moving water* for a period. The Coast Range in Oregon is a result of the Pacific Plate being rapidly pushed under the North American Continental Plate, which bulged this area vertically. The Tyee shows up atop many of the mountains near and south of Mary's, substantially thicker in places and tilting to the south.

A recent study using spectral analysis of the granules that make up the Tyee pinpointed a new origin of the material—the Rocky Mountains![1] This finding has thrown off the cosmology of much of the Northwest, giving strong support to the Flood model of origins. It would appear the Continental Divide uplift caused a westward current off-flow, eroding the Rockies. Their particles became the Tyee, flowing to the west to the ocean, not from the south, as postulated for 100 years.

A 1964 USGS study completed by Dr. Parke D. Snavely, Jr., Holly C. Wagner, and Norman S. MacLeod[2] documents the Geology of the Tyee, showing the area was reformed by a tremendous catastrophe involving volcanism, pyroclastic flows, ash and water in the not too distant past. This study elaborates for pages, describing how this part of the west was catastrophically destroyed volcanically and redistributed by water, leaving deposits like the Tyee behind, building to a thickness of up to *10-15,000 feet!* A "pyroclastic flow" of ash debris infused with superheated water is mentioned in this report. Such massive geologic work would have affected the *entire world, doing more geologic work than Krakatoa itself!*

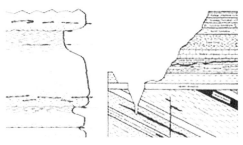

Fig. 93   The Tyee deposit (left) is a 10,000 ft+ homogeneous turbidity deposit, compared here to the Grand Canyon layers (right) for reference. Grand Canyon layers reach 7,000 feet above the canyon floor. The Tyee is a single deposit of 6,000-15,000 feet was deposited and eroded "rapidly" per the late Dr. Ewart Baldwin, Geology of Oregon 1976 & per Dr. Parke Snavely, et al 1964.

Events similar (yet thankfully smaller) were witnessed firsthand at Mt. St. Helens in May 1980, requiring the rewriting the feature forming theories in the geology textbooks. At St. Helens, it was found by *observation* that textbook descriptions and theories of topographical origin had been in error for over *150 years.* Such explanations were falsely based on "one-grain-of-sand-at-a-time" erosion concepts, held in suspicion by flood geologists for years, while class after class of trusting university students were taught these false theories for decades! What actually forms many valley features (as determined from the St. Helens and Missoula Flood events) is that these high speed clastic or other flows of debris simply dredge out valley channels as they move (some up to 60 MPH). In other words, *drainages formed is a result of fast formed channels, not from stream water erosion over eons of time!*

Helicopter crews patrolling the St. Helens post-eruption area witnessed this process, observing cars fleeing before these advancing flows, landing and extracting the terrorized passengers just in the nick of time! The flows are made up of a rolling mass of scalding ash/mud and debris, carrying trees, parts of homes and vehicles along, sweeping away everything before their might! No geology textbook on earth was found to describe this process, yet the valley structures they leave debunk the notion they were formed over millions of years.

Professor Ewart Baldwin, University of Oregon's Geology Department Director for many years, stated that the Tyee was formed quickly and eroded rapidly.[3] The Tyee carried the land borne sediment to the sea as the "waters ran continually off the earth," thus leaving our little but troubling piece of sandstone turbidity atop Oregon's Mary's Peak at 4,000 feet!

Dr. Baldwin mentions the Tyee formation's great thickness and states: [it] "must have been deposited catastrophically."[4] He stating this massive water deposited formation as uncomfortable and catastrophically deposited, then he asserts [it was] *"quickly eroded,"* confounding the Geologic Chart and in agreement with the latest science on the formation! So we have the Tyee, another monument to catastrophe on Mary's Peak, the *Last Mountain Standing.*

See www.genesisalive.com website Last Mountain Standing - Genesis Alive! http://www.genesisalive.com/last-mountain-standing.html

[1] Heeler, P. et al 1985. *Isotopic Provenance of Sandstones from the Eocene Tyee Formation, Oregon,* (Geological Society of America Bulletin, 96), 770-80. (http://gsabulletin.gsapubs.org/content/96/6/770.abstract)

[2] Snavely, Park et al 1964 see http://www.kgs.ku.edu/Publications/Bulletins/169/Snavely/index.html#

[3] Geology of Oregon, Baldwin, Ewart M. 1964 fig. 9 "Cross Section through the Central Coast Range" Tyee deposition map image

[4] Baldwin, Ewart M. *Geology of Oregon* (Kendall Hunt Publishers, 1964 and 1976), p. 7, 24

XIV

Other Formations Supporting a Grand Cataclysm

For the benefit of the reader, included is a brief section relating to the plethora of evidence in support of the flood model as found in the field of geology.

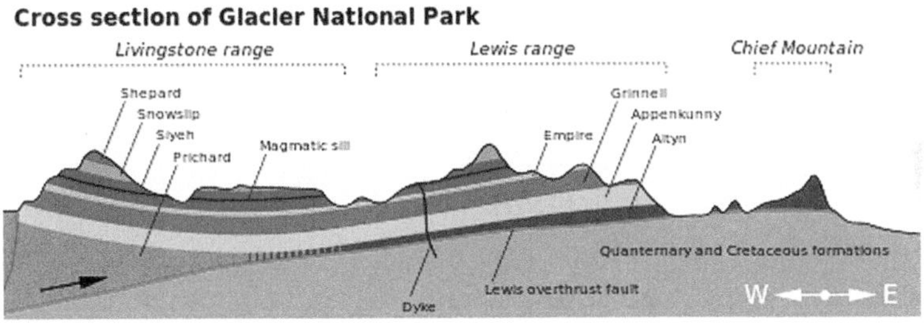

Cross section of Glacier National Park

Fig. 94 Cross section of the Lewis Overthrust, this 360 mile range famous for its implications vs. the Geologic Chart (chart US Park Service image)

The Lewis Range has trilobites and other "older" fossils within the top layers, and far younger fossils according to the "geologic chart" in the base. The best explanation: silence, the next, make up a good pushing story, a billion tons worth.

Turning to more oppositions of the Geologic Chart relative to the actual stones, we showcase the concept of *Overthrusts*, the notion that large geologic formations, including mountain ranges, somehow pushed over younger structures in variance to the shrine of the Geologic Column. The classic example of this interpretation is found in Montana and British Columbia in the *Lewis Range*, where uniformitarian geologists maintain billions of tons of rocks containing older fossils of the Cambrian may sit uncomfortably atop younger rocks, and no one amongst institutional geology dare question it.

In the book, *The Origin of Mountains* (London, 2000) geomorphologists Cliff Ollier and Colin Pain provide a study of the origin and development of the earth's surface features, theorizing about earth's feature forming processes. Researcher Michael Oard states of the authors: "Their decades of international experience give them insights into the origin of mountains

257

that are valuable to creationists attempting to model the Genesis Flood." Commenting on the chapter concerning "Thrust Faults" (such as the Lewis above and other anomalies) compared to uniformity, Michael Oard[23] comments:

"As the mountains uplifted, the authors point out that some of them spread laterally, thrusting rocks over the surrounding lowlands (cited ref. p. 12). This would account for *all the thrust faults, if indeed they are real.* Do the authors (Oard says), or anybody else, know the cause of such recent vertical tectonics? Does the lack of a mechanism nullify the authors' field deductions? The answer is no. They provide a list of 20 possible mechanisms for vertical tectonics, *none of which can be demonstrated to be occurring today"* [emphasis added].

Mountain Building

Many geologists agree that most of the earth's mountain ranges are relatively young, G.M. Price, quoting Willis states as follows: "Contemporaneously, similar movements were in progress over the other continents: along the Andes, affecting half, at least, of South America; the Pyrenees, Carpathians, Alps, and a large part of Europe; the Himalayas and much of Asia."[1] In commenting about a report submitted by Willis, G. M. Price relates: "In his trip through Asia, he came back with the wonderful announcement that throughout that continent the greatest mountain chains challenge credulity by the evidence of their extreme youth."[2] Further commenting about the relative youth of earth's mountains, Dr. John Morris in his volume *"The Global Flood"* (ICR publishing, 2012) mentions that geologists estimate 90% of all the ranges are less than 5 million years old (some less than two), a mere tick on the evolutionary clock of billions of years in the scheme of evolutionary time.[3] The answer is simple: the tectonic forces of the Flood created them quickly, accordion style! One capable researcher, (see Appendix VIII *Whales in the Mountains*) Dr. Walt Brown of MIT fame, even goes so far as to suggest they pushed up within a single day![4]

North America

New research explaining the unlikely long-range transportation of rounded quartzite rocks has lately emerged, Oard also leading the charge. In a series of papers entitled "Flood Transported Quartzites—the Failure of Uniformitarian Interpretations,* Oard et al assert: "The origin of far-transported, resistant, well-rounded quartzite rocks in the northwest United States and adjacent Canada has been documented.[5] These gravel to boulder-sized rocks have been transported up to 1,200 km (745 miles) east of the Rocky Mountains and 650 km (400 miles) west, and have filled deep paleovalleys with over 4,500 meters (15,000 feet) of thick conglomerate in eastern Idaho and northwest Wyoming. The Bighorn Basin is about 190 km (118 miles) north-south and 110 km (68 miles) east-west, an area of 20,900 km², not an insignificant area...a widespread erosional event must have removed at least 744 m (2,440 feet) of the basin fill in the eastern half of the basin...it must have been transported a great distance, perhaps all the way off the continent."[6]

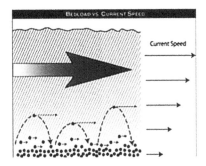

Fig. 95 Current flow off the east and west flanks of the continental divide have left peaned quartzite rocks for hundreds of miles, even on top of the Wallowa Mountain of Northeast Oregon. (Image courtesy www.creation.com*)

As another example of sediment transportation in the Bighorn Basin, Oard mentions: "Some of the gravel is quartzite, but the closest source of quartzite is central Idaho about 400 km (248 miles) away. What post-Flood mechanism could have accomplished all of this geological work?"[7]

Note also that Michael Oard[4] et al, determined that these quartzite minor sized boulders, which originated from the continental divide in Idaho, are found pushed east and west for hundreds of miles, some sitting thousands of feet high atop the Wallowa Mountain range in Oregon! These boulders are rounded and pock-marked as they were pounded along the bottom under *water force, not glacial action*. In many cases they are attributed to have eroded major features of both hard and soft sediments as they ball-preened away everything in their path as the fast moving flood waters swept off the continent into the sea. The author has noticed the same material throughout the hills of the Eastern Oregon Desert at all altitudes. It is theorized that as the Rockies (and likely the massive Coast Ranges of British Columbia,

259

Yukon and Alaska) rapidly rose during the great Flood and created off-flow currents, these remnant stones rapidly eroded off their flanks, carried along by water up to 700 miles in one documented instance.

*Image and text in part Flood transported quartzites: Part 3—failure of uniformitarian interpretations—creation.com

Europe

The Caspian Basin in Europe is a huge "sink" that contains many uniform layers of water deposited sediments: It is filled by sedimentary rocks measuring up to 17.4 miles or 28 km thick.[8] The structure's existence is virtually unexplainable by long-age uniform means. "The South Caspian Basin provides a more dramatic example of late Flood activity. It lies in the southern part of the Caspian Sea. This deep sedimentary basin is somewhat circular with a diameter roughly 400 km[9] or 350 km by 550 km."[10] Oard concludes: "Needless to say, this presents a significant challenge to uniformitarian geologists…"

Quoting Russian geologist Artyushkov concerning the Caspian:

*The Caspian Sea basins of Central Eurasia constitute one of the major petroleum provinces of the world (Devlin et al., 1999), and one of the most **enigmatic** basin systems worldwide[8]* [emphasis mine].

Only water action of the magnitude of the Flood could explain the transportation and filling such a massive trough. The geology around the perimeter of this area shows no sign of the ability to seasonally transport sediments to fill it. The size and volume of this basin staggers the imagination as reflected in Artyushkov's assessment.

Asia

Oard comments: "Although the coarse gravel in south-central Asia was not transported as far [as in the United States] it accumulated in thicker sheets, often reaching 1,000 meters (3,280 feet) with a maximum of around 3,000 meters (10,000 feet!). All of the erosion of the mountains and the accumulation of thick gravel occurred in the Late Cenozoic." Oard continues: "Similar gravel deposits have been found in south-central Asia.[11] The transport of resistant rocks from the erosion of the surrounding mountains in that locale is somewhat different from that in the northwest United States and Canada because the gravel mainly forms an apron around the edges of the surrounding basins. Although the coarse gravel in south-central Asia was not transported as far, it accumulated in thicker sheets, often reaching 1,000m with a maximum of around 3,000 m!"

Africa

Concerning Africa, and large-scale planation surfaces [level plains] especially those existing at altitude, are difficult to explain by any other mechanism than the withdrawal of the Flood's waters in its late stage. Oard states: "These occur all over the world, although one of the most remarkable is that found in Africa.[12] The African Surface, as it is called, covers most of Africa. *Mountains, rift flank uplifts, and volcanoes were all once eroded down* to from this planation surface up until the Mid Cenozoic [emphasis added]. Then it was tectonically deformed, causing the erosion that created the Great Escarpment that circles southern Africa—also within the Late Cenozoic. The Great Escarpment is up to 9,800 feet or 3,000 meters high in southeast Africa and is called the Drakensberg. It is difficult to imagine a post-Flood hypothesis (in other words, the geologic work involved would be hard to image happening today) that would explain such widespread erosion, both in creating the original large planation surface and the subsequent Great Escarpments. The strong implication is that the Flood created these features and the Flood/post-Flood boundary in much of Africa is in the very late Cenozoic."[13]

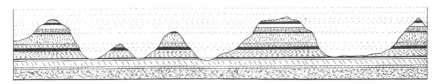

Fig. 96 A typical geologic cross-section, the horizontal lines of water deposited stone intersecting the adjacent terrain cross-valley.
(Image Nelson, *The Deluge Story in Stone* - Bethany Pub. 1968)

The material was deposited level at the onset of the Flood, the missing material eroded as the Flood waters rushed off the earth's surface. Such hill structures are the most common in the world.

Plains and Hills

Oard[14] reports that Ollier and Pain maintain that after the base strata were folded by tectonic events, they were planed down to form flat surfaces, called planation surfaces, *on all the continents, including Antarctica* (cited text p. 214). This process cut across most previously folded sedimentary rocks and smoothed both the hard and soft rocks evenly. "Even massive granites were 'planed' over in many areas, as in the Tien Shan Mountains of central Asia" (p. 144). The original surfaces were planed down to what is called *base level*, which the authors show is usually considered *sea level* (p. 3). It's interesting that one area occupied by the Apennines Mountains of Italy today, was planed *below* sea level!"

Some planation surfaces are very flat, such as the plains of Australia and Africa (p. 1). Oard explains: "Ollier and Pain marvel how such plantation could have occurred at all and that it was 'widespread' citing the authors:

The remarkable thing is that plains of great perfection are even made, despite all the obvious possibilities of complications. But they are real, and planation surfaces were widespread before the uplift of the many mountains of Plio-Pleistocene [recent] age (p. 302).

Erosional processes known today do not produce the immense landscapes the authors report. Only an event on the scale of a global Flood could do such geologic work. Oard comments: *"The authors expressed surprise because the observed surfaces are inconsistent with their uniformitarian worldview."* Present processes roughen surfaces, forming rills, coulees and valleys. Planed surfaces do not develop today except on a very local scale when perhaps a river suddenly shifts its course and moves across tilted sedimentary rock. Furthermore, the field relationships show that planation in the past mostly occurred in the Late Miocene-Early Pliocene period (p. 302), suggesting that it occurred *rapidly,* the authors stating: *"At present, the cause of the observed high rate of planation remains a mystery."*

Australia

"The Kimberly Plateau of north central Australia that was planed in the Proterozoic (ancient rock) has apparently not been covered by protecting sediments since then (p. 27). It defies imagination how such a surface could have remained so flat for 600 million years or more, when present processes could dissect a continent and erode it to near sea level in 10 to 33 million years." Oard further notes, "The presence of such 'old' planation surfaces is objective evidence that the dating methods, both fossil and radiometric, used to date the time of planation are wrong."[15]

Mountains Uplifted Globally in Plio-Pleistocene

Oard continues: "Ollier and Pain believe this time frame is the origin of *nearly all mountains* and have an impressive amount of evidence to back up their conclusion." He says: "In the mountains today we observe all stages of this past dissection. Some planation surfaces were dissected completely during uplift, leaving behind rough mountains with no sign of a planation surface. In other mountains, the planation surface is left on the top as an erosional remnant. Sometimes these planation surfaces are at different altitudes in the mountains due to differential uplift. The highest mountains in Montana, the Beartooth Mountains, are an excellent example of this. They display impressive flat topped granitic peaks at a height of about 4,000 m (13,000 ft.)."

Oard mentions the shocking fact that the authors assert: *"practically all the uplift occurred in the Pliocene and Pleistocene, the most recent epochs of geological time!"* As examples he noted the Andes Mountains (cite ref. p. 127) and the Tibetan Plateau, which is considered to be one vast erosion surface that uplifted in the Pliocene-Pleistocene (p. 128–129, 137–138). Oard summarizes: "Furthermore, they present an impressive table of mountains from all over the world that uplifted during this time frame (p. 304– 306)."

The Mountains Will Melt and Gold Deposits

The fact is, with the recent ringwoodite find (see chapter 6), there is now proof that plenty of water was available to cover the planet. An early account of the Flood onset mentions that the percolating water "scalded" the feet of the mockers standing outside the Ark. As Noah was exhorting them to repent, he also mentioned that the "[the] High Mountains...be dissolved.. shall melt like wax before the flame." (Final sermons, chapter 7.) The researchers mentioned the estimated water temperature of this deep aquifer as being nearly 2000^0 F. Interestingly enough, silver, copper and gold all melt just below this temperature (silver, 1763^0 F; copper, 1984^0 F; and gold, 1947^0 F). Considering such, water percolating through the crust at these temperatures could account for many of the placer gold deposits found around the globe, including the richest finds in America, such as those of the California gold rush of '49, the subsequent Juneau, Alaska, finds of the 1870s and the Klondike rush of 1898 (the "98ers").

One account from Alaska seems to confirm this probability. While in the process of searching for gold on the Seward Peninsula near the Nome, Alaska, gold fields, a miner reported the following observations:

[While] tunneling under a recent lava flow that had covered a stream bed with rich placer gold. There were significant tree root remains under the lava cap, however, that area is treeless tundra now. Biologists' analysis of the roots indicated they were varieties normally found in temperate climate zones today. [16]

This find shows us that, a) placer gold is found in association with a tropical environment and many fossil remains in Alaska and on the Seward peninsula, b) that the general area was undergoing a catastrophe at the time the gold was deposited, and c) was covered by a lava flow indicating tremendous heat. Note that the Seward peninsula has extensive fossil deposits, including those of the mammoth; neither these nor any other remains being found in state, they seemingly have had the flesh boiled off them compared to their Siberian counterparts to the West. Such may be said of the majority of Alaskan placer deposits that span area of over 300,000 square miles. (See Alaska section in Appendix XI and Mammoths App. XV.)

53 Pounds of Gold a Day

One of the largest gold deposits in the world is on the Pacific island of Lihir, which contains one of the most massive gold deposits known—the Ladolam deposit. Geologist think this formed below ground as magma (molten rock), heated mineral-rich water, and forced it under great pressure toward the surface, dissolving all sorts of minerals, including gold. Geologists think many of the world's gold ore deposits are formed in this way. When geologists sampled the super heated water, they found it contained 1000 times more suspended gold than in typical geothermal sources; as such they estimate that 53 pounds of gold per *day* is being added to the deposit. One geologist, Mr. Greg Hall stated to the *New Scientist*, "My gut feeling looking at Lihir is that it formed in the same time it took Mount St. Helens to blow up—a month, a day, maybe as short as 5 hours."[17]

Such placer finds were critical to the development and wealth of the United States and were no accident; they were a blessing from God given as a gift for America's future growth and wellbeing, and apparently, were deposited as part of the general Flood disaster. It's startling to ponder what geologic work that could be accomplished with water at those temperatures moving about earth. Such would explain much of the unexplainable that geologists ponder today in the rocks, also the evaporates and other mineral deposits found in the earth's crust that are difficult to account for in a uniform interpretation. As Noah stated, the "mountains..will melt!"

With this impressive array of testimony from a variety of experts, we end our discussions relative to Geology, a geology that fits well into a creation and subsequent Flood model, moving on to explain the glaciers and finally; the silent testimony of the mammoths and their companions, *lost.*

[1] Price quoting Dana, *Manual*, p. 365

[2] Price, George McCready quoting Willis, *Research in Asia*, Vol. 2, p. 24.

[3] Morris, John D, *The Global Flood* 2013 p

[4] Dr. Walter Brown *In the Beginning* Center for Scientific Creation 2008

[5] *J. Creation* 21(1):98–110, 2007. p 105

[6] Duller, R.A., Whittaker, A.C., Swinehart, J.B., Armitage, J.J., Sinclair, H.D., Bair, A. and Allen, P.A., Abrupt landscape change post–6 Ma on the central Great Plains, USA, Geology 40(10):871– 874, 2012.

[7] Oard, M.J., Hergenrather, J. and Klevberg, P., Flood transported quartzites east of the Rocky Mountains, *J. Creation* 19 (3):76–90, 2005

[8] Knapp, C.C., Knapp, J.H. and Connor, J.A., Crustal-scale structure of the South Caspian Basin revealed by deep seismic reflection profiling, *Marine and Petroleum Geology* 21:1073–1081, 2004.

[9] Artyushkov, E.V., Formation of the super deep South Caspian basin: subsidence driven by phase change in continental crust, *Russian Geology and Geophysics* 48:1002–1014, 2007 Oard, M.J., The geological column is a general Flood order with many exceptions; in: Reed, J.K. and Oard, M.J. (Eds.), *The Geological Column: Perspectives within Diluvial Geology*, Creation Research Society Books, Chino Valley, AZ, pp. 99–121, 2006.

[10] Nadirov, R.S., Bagirov, E., Tagiyev, M. and Lerche, I., Flexural plate subsidence, sedimentation rates, and structural development of the super-deep South Caspian Basin, *Marine and Petroleum Geology* 14:383–400, 1997.

[11] Oard, M.J., Retreating Stage formation of gravel sheets in south-central Asia, *J. Creation* 25(3):68–73, 2011

[12] Oard, M.J., The remarkable African planation surface, *J. Creation* 25(1): 111–122, 2011.Oard, M.J., The geological column is a general Flood order with many exceptions, *J. Creation* 24 (2):78– 82, 2010.

[13] Oard, M.J., Is the geological column a global sequence? *J. Creation* 24(1):56– 64, 2010

[14] http://creation.com/mountains-rose

[15] Oard, M.J., Antiquity of landforms: objective evidence that dating methods are wrong, CEN Tech. J 14(1):35–39, 2000

[16] Private correspondence, between author and Mr. James Hansen of Nome, Alaska 7-1-2015

[17] http://creation.com/rapid-gold-deposit Quoting an article by Mr. Daniel Devine May 2007

XV

The Mammoth: Index Fossil of the Flood

Fig. 97 The mammoth, index fossil of the Flood. Found entombed across the globe from sea floor to 12,000 ft in the Andes and higher in the Himalayas!

The mammoth: true Index Fossil of the Flood. Millions of mega-fauna like this mammoth were killed by intense cold, heat and/or flood water in a very short time across the entire globe. Mammoth remains are piled in heaps from Alaska to Florida and Africa to Tibet. They are similarly found across both coasts of South America and from England to Asia. The world over the story is the same, their demise best understood by no other means save the great Flood.

One thing is certain to all: there is no mistaking a mammoth from a snail, the index fossil of the evolutionist! Typically and mistakenly associated as living among the barren plains of ice and snow, it now appears quite strongly that this was *not at all* the environ the mammoths thrived in, and thrive they did, by the *millions*. Rather, the standing fossil trees and other flora indicate a quite mild climate existed where they walked, with birch, palm, larch, redwood and conifers of considerable size with them, interspersed with beautiful savannah[1*] grasslands (similar to the African version) and meandering

266

rivers. We have them living by their thousands in the First Earth, found in areas covering *millions* of square miles above the Arctic Circle alone, all in temperate weather, not snow!

Past this, our mighty quadruped was likely the most widely dispersed animal in the world before the Flood, their remains appearing in the most unlikely places. Speaking of Alaska and Siberia in specific, it's said an estimated five million mammoths lie entombed in those places. The soil of Siberia is so full of mammoth bones that ivory mines were kept working for many years. At least 20,000 tusks were taken from one mine alone. Besides mammoths, the Arctic soils contain the remains of over 60 animal species, including the woolly rhinoceros, camels, horses, oversized tigers, lions, buffalo and antelopes. Many of them lie in frozen silt, mixed together with boulders and tree roots to great depth. Entire islands were found consisting of their masses, these intermixed with silts, gravel, trees and vegetation. What short of a Flood could account for such deposits?

*Richard Stone *Mammoth, the Resurrection of an Ice Age Giant*, Pesues Pub (2001) p. 176 making mention of "Pleistocene Park," an attempt to bring back the environment called the *Mammoth Steppe* by Russian scientist Sergei Zimov, in hopes to restore their old habitat in Siberia.

One testimony concluded: "Apparently, at one moment the mammoth was munching away peacefully at buttercups growing lush in the sunshine of a temperate plain: the next it was subjected to cold so bitter it was *deep frozen* where it stood, buttercups in mouth." Their body tissues and stomach contents had not even begun to decompose, even thousands of years later. Sir John Richardson tells us: "It is easier to imagine that the animals whose osseous remains now engage our attention ranged, while living to the shores of an icy sea, and that by some sudden deluge, or vast wave or succession of waves, they were swept from their pasture-grounds."

In regards to Siberia and the mammoths, we return to Professor Howorth, member of nine expeditions to those realms and writer of the great and exhaustive work, *The Mammoth and the Flood*, in 1887.

Giving us observations from the now barren plains of the Arctic regions, we may envision Howorth, peering out across the barren tundra and penning these words: "These facts, I claim, prove several conclusions. They prove in the *first place* that a very great cataclysm and catastrophe occurred at the close of the mammoth period by which that animal, with its companions was overwhelmed over a very large part of the earth's surface. *Secondly,* that this catastrophe involved a widespread flood of waters which not only killed the animals, but also buried them under continuous beds of loam or gravel. *Thirdly, that the same catastrophe was accompanied by a very great and sudden change of climate in Siberia, by which the animals which had previously lived in fairly temperate conditions were frozen in their flesh under the ground and have remained frozen ever since."*

Looking across the hemisphere to the Americas, we again find the skeptics and scoffers disappointed by their floodless ages and meaningless "charts," as the mammoths keep speaking their terrible tale.

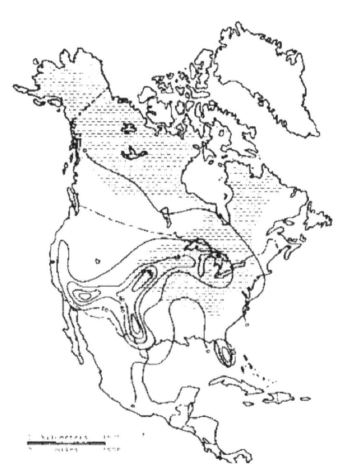

Fig. 98 Distribution of North American mammoths and mastodons
(After L. D. Agenbroad, *The distribution and chronology of mammoth in the New World*, in *Acta Zool. Fennica* 170:223 (1985), Helsinki.

North American Mammoths

Madison Grant, in his *Conditions of the Wildlife in Alaska,* wrote: "Bones of large extinct animals more or less fossilized occur in abundance throughout the entire valley drained by the Yukon River from Dawson down, and in the valley of the Colville and Porcupine Rivers, and in still greater abundance in the Seward Peninsula. Within 60 miles of Siberia, Bison skulls are quite common and indicate an animal much larger but probably ancestral to our own living buffalo." A check of the Alaska expanse referenced covers over 300,000 square *miles* in area.

Alaska Geological Survey number 280 states: "In the gravels are many bones of bison, musk ox, mammoth and horse." Another official source, the *Alaska Geography Bulletin* no. 449 makes note of the streams of Norton Sound containing a quantity of these relics: "Inglualik River derives its name from the Eskimo word meaning 'river of bones' in reference to the number of mastodon and other bones found in the terrace of gravels along its course." Remains of giant bear and lion are also recorded, mixed with other animals caught in the general destruction.[12]

Along the Koyukuk River, the remains are so prominent, parts of the river emit strong odors locally referred to as "stink banks," the river pilots able to position their craft by the smells.[13]

MAMMOTH TUSKS AND BISON SKULL FOUND IN ALASKA MINING CLAIMS.

Fig. 99 Alaskan mammoth and bison horns unearthed from the Yukon mining district. Thousands were found across the Yukon Basin; all were recovered from *flood deposits*.

269

Howorth on the Mammoth in the Americas

"In America, as in Europe, the number of the remains [of mammoths], and their universal distribution, contrast notably with the scarcity and local character of the debris of mammals in other sub-aerial beds, on other geological horizons, and point, there, as here, to their having been the victims of a catastrophe. The un-weathered bones, the intact skeletons, the fact we cannot understand how the horse now revels in the prairies, and which was unknown to the Indians at the Spanish conquest, and yet which was very widely distributed by evidence of the fossil record, could have disappeared from so congenial a country save by a widespread catastrophe. Such a catastrophe I have no hesitation in invoking." Howorth states (Dr. Warren) says very rightly: "The cause of the disappearance of the mastodon seems to be mysterious. We are naturally disposed to believe that an animal of so large a size, of so great a strength, and such extensive distribution in various parts of the earth, must have required some great and general catastrophe to overwhelm and annihilate it." Howorth resumes, "I have no doubt that scientific men will presently accept no other conclusion from the facts.[1] What we have seen in the nature of this catastrophe in Europe and Asia is evidence that points precisely to the same cause in North America. If we are to meet the facts, we need a cause which destroyed animals old and young, great and small, aggressive and helpless, in common doom. In many cases we find them destroyed in herds or schools, mammoths and even their cousin mastodons buried deeply in such tough material as gravel and clay, intact. Occasionally we find them buried very deeply: in cutting the Great Western of Canada Railway, elephants' remains were found buried sixty feet deep near Lake Ontario and buried with them shells, both land and fresh-water, under deposits which continuous strata, unbroken and undisturbed, over many miles of country. It seems to me there is no other agency available to produce this result save a flood of water. As with the mammoth in Siberia and in Europe, so in North America the carcasses of the mastodon are often found in an erect position. Thus Cuvier states that the mastodons found in the river of the Great Osages were nearly all in a vertical position."[2]

"Since that time, says Mr. Southall,* many others have been found in swamps a short distance beneath the surface in an erect position.[3] This is assuredly consistent only with the animals having been overwhelmed in a deluge of mud and gravel while in an upright position, the attitude being that of swimming. This observation is forcibly demonstrated in a case quoted by Dr. Warren is his *Memoir on the Newburgh Mastodon* [where] he states:

'The anterior extremities were extended under and in front of the head; the posterior extremities were extended forward under the body.'"

Howorth quoting *The Epoch of the Mammoth and the Apparition of man upon the earth*: by James C. Southall, 1878

The American Museum of Natural History displays the "Warren Mastodon" unearthed near Newburg, New York, in 1845. Experts noticed its position was upright and apparently gasping for a breath of air when it perished. A mastodon skeleton discovered in 1823 near Long Branch, New Jersey, is described as: "Its position, corresponding with that of the skeleton found on the Wabash, was vertical, the feet resting on a stratum of sand and gravel, and the head to the west-south-west. There is every reason to suppose that the animal was mired in that situation." Dr. Warren, in his *Memoir on the Mastodon*, realizes the gravity of the problem. He says: "Notwithstanding, therefore, the possibility of conceiving many causes which may partly account for the destruction of the mastodon, we cannot find any one adequate to the annihilation of the whole race." [4] Howorth continues: "We must consider some great catastrophe to account for their universal extirpation, and from those who deny the occurrence of such a catastrophe, it may fairly be demanded why these extinct animals have not continued to live on to the present; they not a small and feeble species."

South America and the Pampas

Speaking of South America concerning their caves, fissures and fossil deposits, we have Howorth describing the geography for us: "In South America the Pleistocene beds are developed on a very large scale. The distribution of these beds is exceedingly widespread over South America." Burmeister says: "The diluvial deposit containing bones of animals of this age extends over the whole Brazilian plain, from the flanks of the Cordilleras to the borders of the Atlantic. They [the mammoths] have also been found abundantly in Bolivia, on the great plateau; and also west of the mountains, both in Peru and Chili. From Caracas in the north, to the sierra of Tandel in Patagonia in the south. *They have, in fact, occurred in more or less abundance over the whole continent.* In the great Argentine plain they are found close to the sea-level, while in Bolivia they occur, according to D'Orbigny, at a height of 4000 meters, and they are found with a singular similarity if not uniformity of contents in all latitudes" [emphasis mine].

"North America is, in fact, largely identical with that from the beds we are now discussing: the megatherium and mylodon, the tapir and capybara, the mastodon and horse, etc., being found in both, and every observer, from Darwin to Burmeister, is agreed in assigning them to the same horizon."[5]

Wide South American Distribution

From the various recorded discoveries of the remains of mastodons in South America, it appears that they once had a geographical range over nearly the whole of that continent, since they were found by Humboldt as far north as Santa Fe de Bogota, especially at the Camp des Geans, where they were collected in great numbers. They have also been discovered as far south as Buenos Aires, on the Atlantic, by Admiral Dupotet, at Concepción de Chili, on the Pacific, and at various intermediate points in Peru, Chili, La Plata, Brazil, and Columbia, by Dombey, Gay, Alcide d'Orbigny, Darwin, and others. Thus, their remains extend from 5° north to about 37° south, and on both sides of the great chain of the Cordilleras, from ocean to ocean.

What is still more remarkable, the bones of mastodons have been discovered at unusually great elevations, according to D'Orbigny, even up to the borders of perpetual snow.

Darwin's Perspective—the South American Mammoth

The conclusion of uniform and catastrophic destruction of the mammoths had already been reached by Charles Darwin, who speaks of then saying: "From the bones in one of the skeletons, and likewise from those in parts of another, being embedded in their proper relative positions, the carcasses of the animals, when they perished, were *probably drifted to this spot in an entire state." This involves precisely the same conclusions as follow from the similar occurrence in the European loess and the Siberian tundras.* So does the finding of the remains in great masses or caches. Mr. Darwin, speaking of the deposits at Bahia Blanca says: *"It is a remarkable circumstance that so many different species should be found together; and it proves how numerous in kind the ancient inhabitants of this country must have been.* Speaking of the frequency of the occurrence of the bones in the Pampas deposits, that any line whatever drawn across the Pampas would probably cross the skeleton of some extinct animal."[6]

Darwin summarizes on the Pampas: "The number of bones embedded in the grand estuary deposit of the Pampas must be very great. We may therefore conclude that the wide area of the Pampas is one wide sepulcher for these extinct animals."[7]

D'Orbigny cites Darwin's interesting summary: "It is impossible to reflect on the changed state of the American continent without the deepest astonishment. Formerly it must have swarmed with great monsters; now we find mere pigmies, compared with the antecedent allied races. The greater number, if not all, of these extinct quadrupeds lived at a period and *were the contemporaries of the existing sea-shells.*" Orbigny continues: "What, then, has exterminated so many species and whole genera? The mind at first is irresistibly hurried into the belief of some great catastrophe; but thus to destroy animals, both large and small, in Southern Patagonia, in Brazil, on the Cordillera of Peru, in North America, and up to Behring Straits, we must shake the entire frame-work of the globe."

Fig. 100 "Zhenya" on the Yenisi River, North Siberian Coast, September 2012.
Notice the "Adamovchiva Wood" along the adjacent coast. Hardly evidence of extinction
by dust storms, yet strong evidence the mammoths perished in the Flood
(Photo courtesy Peter Prokosch www.grida.no/photolib/detail/driftwood-at-the-shores-of-the-yenisei-
river-at-dikson-taimyr-siberia-russia-1991_8b79)

Universal Observation of Extinction

Howorth continues: "If the animals died sporadically and at different times, how is it their remains are invariably so fresh and so intact across the continents from sea to sea? This conclusion also follows from the finding of entire skeletons in their natural position standing upright. While the discovery of defective skeletons turned upside down, prove that the animals were in other cases killed before they were swept away and buried in the mud, especially when the head, tail, and extremities are missing, these being the portions of the trunk most easily separated." Some cause which dealt with these carcasses in a violent way and deposited them according to the laws of gravity. Such animals do not turn on their backs to die, and they were evidently turned over by a violent cause."

As previously cited, Alcide D'Orbigny (1802-1857) spent eight years

273

on the South Continent. This naturalist comments on the absurdity of those who suggest large animals like dinosaurs or mammoths drown accidently in great numbers: "I ought to add, that the effects of rivers as transporting agencies have been greatly exaggerated in arguments about the distribution of the great mammals. In my journeys on the great rivers, such as the Parana, the Paraguay, the Plata, and all the Bolivian effluents of the Amazon, and during eight years, I do not remember having seen a single floating animal in the vast solitudes of America. Animals never voluntarily enter the great rivers, and it is very seldom they are overtaken by inundations."[8] *

*In reading the signs posted at the National Dinosaur Monument at Vernal, Utah, the river drowning explanation is precisely the story the US Park Service claims is responsible for the destruction of the dinosaurs there and that of a variety of other creatures so found in the Morrison Formation. This formation is uniform for hundreds of thousands of square miles, and exhibits the characteristic of a turbidity high-speed mud flow, not a stream!

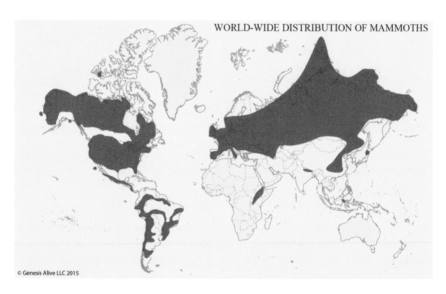

Fig. 101 Worldwide distribution of the mammoths and mastodons, their flood buried remains found globally from sea bottom to the Andes into *the Himalayan perpetual snow*

They have, in fact, occurred in more or less abundance over the whole continent. In the great Argentine plain they are found close to the sea-level, while in Bolivia they occur, according to D'Orbigny, at a height of 4000 meters.
　　　　　　　　　　　—H. H Howorth, *The Mammoth and the Flood*

Howorth's summarizes his work on the mammoth in the Americas: "A huge hecatomb covering two continents with the corpses of a myriad herds can only be imagined as the result of a sudden, complete, and widespread catastrophe; and this is even more certain when we remember how cosmopolitan in constitution and habits such animals as the horse, the mastodon, the megatherium, etc., must have been to have lived in the extremely diversified terrestrial provinces where their remains occur.

M. d'Orbigny's Final Comments on Bolivia

"This seems to me to describe very neatly the ordinary results of a great flood. It would seem…that one cause destroyed the terrestrial animals of South America, and that this cause is to be found in great dislocations of the ground caused by the upheaval of the Cordilleras. If not, it is difficult to conceive on the one hand the sudden and fortuitous destruction of the great animals which inhabited the American continents, and on the other the vast deposit of Pampas mud. I argue that this destruction was caused by *an invasion of the continent by water* [emphasis mine], I find an evident proof of this in the immense number of bones and of entire animals whose numbers are greatest at the outlets of the valleys, as Mr. Darwin shows. This proves that the animals were floated, and hence were chiefly carried to the coast." Again he goes on: "This hypothesis necessitates that the Pampas mud was deposited suddenly as the result of violent floods of water, which carried off the soil and other superficial artifacts."

A Calamity Experienced Becomes a Wakeup Call

"After having seen at Callao the ravages which a simple earthquake may make, I am justified in believing that the upheaval of the Andes would suffice to destroy at one stroke by a movement of the water all the terrestrial faunas of the globe. At Callao, during the earthquake which occurred at the end of the last century, the waters carried over the land ships there at anchor and changed the whole aspect of the country, still covered with pebbles.

"My final conclusion from the geological facts I observed in America is that there was a perfect coincidence between the upheaval of the Cordilleras, the destruction of the great race of animals, and the great deposit of the Pampas mud. Thus these three questions of immense importance for American geology and for the chronological history of faunae may be explained by *one cause*, namely, the upheaval of the Cordilleras, to which we may perhaps attribute the analogous phenomena of which Europe has been the theatre."[9]

Mammoths in the Himalayas— Fairholme, Falconer and McClelland

Professor George Fairholme, in his *"New and Conclusive Physical Demonstration of the Fact and Period of the Mosaic Deluge"* (1840), describes the deposits of the Arno River in Italy, where remains of nearly every wild land mammal from mouse to elephant and rat to rhinoceros, are buried together with members of the deer and cat family, including lions, tigers, hyena and rabbit found buried in heaps. This conflagration created a great task for the world's foremost zoologist of the day, none other than Cuvier himself, who toiled for years to untangle and identify all the species represented.

> *Speaking of elephant fossils, I am assured that their fossils are found at the highest elevations that man has attained in Tibet, under the zeal of my friend Dr. Falconer and Capt. Cautley.*
>
> —Professor George Fairholme

Testifying to the deposition of fossil elephants found up to 15,000 feet in the Tibetan plains, Professor George Fairholme writes, quoting McClelland in *The Geology of Kemoan,*[10] providing these observations: "In evidence that these animals did not perish on the spot, but were carried and deposited by mighty currents, which it is evident by the spread over this entire country by dozens of extinct species having every exposed cavity full of marine shells plants and fossil substances, having been found not only mixed with the bones but adhering to them to being tightly wedged in the cavities of the skull, and where were once eyes, were stopped up by shells and pieces of coral." Mentioning the elephants, mammoths and mastodons, Fairholme goes on to comment: "In speaking of elephant fossils I am assured that their fossils are found at the highest elevations that man has attained in Tibet, under the zeal of my friend Dr. Falconer and Capt. Cautley." [11]

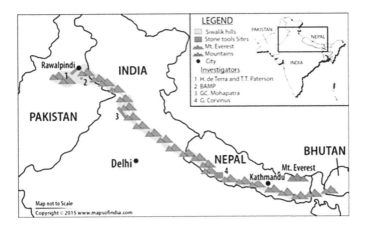

Fig. 102 The Siwaliks, the 1400 mile fossil graveyard of the Himalayas, the red legend
locations 1-4 signify dig sites where stone implements were found along with fossils

The Siwalik Hills

The Sewalik Range runs parallel along the south edge of the entire Himalayan system, from the Ganges to the banks of the Beas (Bias). All the great rivers of India run at right angles through the Sewaliks—the Ganges, Junina and Sutlej—and have worn themselves valleys through this chain, exposing the fossil beds in height from 400 to 600 feet.

D.N. Wadia in his volume *Geology of India*[1] states: "The sudden and widespread reduction by extinction of the Siwalik mammals is a most startling event for the geologist as well as the biologist. The great carnivores, the varied races of elephants belonging to no less than 25 to 30 species ...the numerous tribes of large and highly specialized ungulates [hoofed animals] which found such suitable habitats in the Siwalik jungles of the Pliocene epoch, are to be seen no more in an immediately succeeding age."

He also mentions "uniformity of lithologic composition," meaning they were deposited and perished *simultaneously*, identical to the other massive graveyards found around the globe.

It is in these hills that extensive fossil remains of mammoth were discovered by Dr. Falconer and Captain Cautley[2] as mentioned. One of the carnivore found is the great sabre-toothed tiger, *Machairodus latidens*, now extinct, remarkable for its enormous canine teeth and wide distribution. Falconer mentions it has been found in Kent's Cavern, Torquay, in the Norfolk forest beds, in the tertiary deposits of Germany, the Auvergne in France, the Val d'Arno in Italy, the Pampas deposits and bone caves of South America, and the upper miocene fresh-water limestone's of the Sewalik Hills. These hills also contain remains of extinct species of the Proboscidea or elephants, various species of Mastodon have lived there, and also in Burma, and also in Armenia, many parts of Europe, and North and South America. Dr. Falconer described 13 species of fossil elephants in the Siwaliks, 9 of which are from India. Amongst these are Elephas ganesa, with tusks 10-14 feet long, probably the largest of all the extinct elephants. Also found were the heads and horn cores of fossil oxen and antelopes and the bones of a fossil ostrich, and remains of a huge crane, *Argala Falcoueri*. The tertiary rocks of India have also furnished remains of alligators, crocodiles, and gavials. Some of the existing tortoises are large, but the extinct *Colossochelys atlas* (a large tortoise), discovered by Dr. Falconer in the Siwaliks, is notable, measuring 20 feet long x15 feet in lateral girth.

In Burma over 1,200 miles east of the Siwalik Hills, fossil deposits opened by the Irrawaddy River "may reach 10,000 feet" according to Wadia who tell us: "Two fossiliferous horizons occur in this series separated by about 4000 feet of sands." He noting these are similar to one of the beds in the Sewaliks that include ox, hippo and mastodon. He notes: "The sediments are remarkable for the large quantities of fossil-wood associated with them. Hundreds and thousands of entire trunks of silicified trees and huge logs lie in the sandstones."[1] Echoing those found on the Siberian Arctic coasts, many fossils were found associated with paleolithic stone implements of man. These are located along the entire length of the Siwaliks in all the countries mentioned. Based on the comments of investigators, both modern and past, the immensity of these beds cannot be overemphasized; they containing a broad representation of life forms swept into disorder by water in a single event along the foot of the Himalaya, stretching for over 1400 miles.[3] These deposits are clearly homogenous, and related to the same catastrophe.

[1]Wadia D. N. *Geology of India* p. 269 as cited from Velikovsky, I *Earth in Upheaval* 1955 used by permission
[2]Falconer, Hugh & Cautley, Proby, Capt. Sengal Art. *Fossil Zoology of the Seliwalk Hills of North India* 1846 vol. I, II
[3]Adapted from *Nature*, 5th September 1878; British Museum Catalogue; with notes from Falconer

In his convincing summary concerning the fossils of elephants and concurring with Howorth, Fairholme submits: "Now if we were desirous of pointing out any one strong point in the phenomena of the earth surface which seems more conclusively that any other to corroborate the record of a general deluge, we would not desire one more remarkable than the fact of the remains of the innumerable elephants being scattered over the earth, invariably confined to the superficial diluvium bed, but so far from being peculiar to such tropical latitudes as they must have inhabited when in life that we now find them not only at *every latitude*, from the equator to the pole, but also in *every degree of elevation* from the sea's level up to the alpine plains of Mexico and the glaciers of the Himalayas" [emphasis added].

Geologist George McCready Price makes these concluding remarks relating to this matter of the Mega-Fauna, now gone from the face of the earth: "The fossil world is a unit and simply represents the ruins of an older state of our present world; and whatever geological changes they indicate, must have taken place since man was on the earth, for there is no possible line of scientific reasoning to convince us that any single type of fossil is older than the human race." Price continues: "The mammoth, the rhinoceros, the camel, the huge ground sloth, the saber-tooth tiger, and the mastodon, together with 'not less than thirty distinct species of the horse tribe,' Marsh says, 'all disappear from North America at one time, and the most ingenious disciple of Hutton and Lyell has been puzzled to invent a plausible explanation.'

"When we consider that at this same 'geological period,' similar events were occurring on all the other continents, the huge ground sloths of South America, wombats the size of tapirs and kangaroos the size of elephants in Australia; the mammoth and woolly rhinoceros in Eurasia; together with the enormous hippopotamus, as far as England is concerned; to say nothing of those great bears, lions, hyenas with semi-tropical vegetation *all disappearing at the same time*, it becomes like a deliberate bribe to our intellectual honesty to be approached with offers of 'explanations' based on any so called 'natural' action of the forces of nature. None but a mind long debauched by unscientific theories and illogical methods of reasoning would ever attempt to defend geological uniformity [e.g. the Geologic Chart] in the face of such facts as these. But when we consider the fact that those human beings of the deposits of central Europe were contemporary with the animals mentioned above and disappearing along with them at the same time, while mountain masses in all parts of the world, crowded with marine forms of the so- called 'older' types, positively cannot be separated in time from the others, it becomes as certain as any other ordinary scientific fact, like the capture of Babylon or the burning of Carthage, that our once magnificently stocked world met with some sudden and awful catastrophe in the long ago; and is it in any way transgressing the bounds of true inductive science to correlate this event with the Deluge of the Hebrew Scriptures and the traditions of every race on earth!"[14]

Price, George McCready, *"Evolutionary Geology and the New Catastrophism"*

The Ark Bound Animals Were Blessed by God

Stepping out of the Ark and into the new world, the animals would need time to multiply and spread out to their new ranges. From the biblical account we know there were no spares, just one pair per "kind," suggesting the hand of God watched carefully over them. So the question arises, why would God "bless" and multiply these, saying go and fill the earth, and further, *"My covenant shall be with you and every beast of the earth with you"* (Genesis 9:10) and promise *"I will never again destroy every living thing as I have done"* (Genesis 8:21), then subsequently destroy the mammoths by the millions in calamities such as "dust ages" as some suggest (Oard 2015), if they lived *after* the Flood? Such a theory makes no sense at all from a biblical perspective and further, has no support in human observation. From the evidence of the field, that of the global field, the evidence is conclusive as brought by so many competent observers, that is, their destruction was widespread and complete, simultaneous and worldwide. It reached the mountains of Tibet, the plains of Siberia, it engulfed all of Alaska, Canada and the full of the Western Hemisphere and from one end of the Andes to the other. It struck Europe, the Isles and moved across all of the Mediterranean and Africa. It swept the earth clean of all life, save those in the Ark, and we should thank God for that.

The Mammoths Are Missing Cold Weather Anatomy

The coat problem: it seems the mammoths simply weren't made for the cold. All known elephants lack sebaceous or oil glands. An object of study concerning the mammoths for over a hundred years, scientist after scientist examined mammoth anatomy in search of these glands, all to no avail. Ca-pable French scientist and elephant expert Me. H. Neuville, stated such in his 1919 report[15] on the mammoths, quoted as follows: "It appears to me im-possible to find, in the anatomical examination of the skin and pelage, any argument in favor of adaptation to cold. The man of science is struck by the absence of the glands. The physiological function of these glands is very important: The effect of the sebum is to lubricate the fur, thus protecting it against disintegration, and that of the sweat is to soak the epidermis with an oily liquid, protecting it also against desiccation and disintegration. In reality the deposit of sebum on the surface of the skin,...contributes also to the protection of the integument. The absence of the glandular secretions puts the skin in a condition of less resistance is well known in dermatology."

Note; a recent study by a newly formed laboratory in Russia has claimed to have found these glands in the mammoth, but their findings remain in question and are unverified by independent study.

Arctic animals have the unique anatomy to cope with such conditions not found in the mammoths, their inner "wool" little different than that of the African elephants of today, with their very limited temperature range and climate.

Summary

Comparing the well-studied moisture needs of the caribou and muskox living at those latitudes today, we find these animals require only a fraction of the water needs of a mammoth. From this perspective, the water intake, food needs and skin type of the mammoth preclude the idea of their living in the deep cold of today's Arctic. This also leads us to better understand why they quickly perished in the cold snap caused by the Flood, and poten-tially why many of their contemporaries lived on, past not being offered a seat on the Ark.

Temperate Index Species— the Ferret

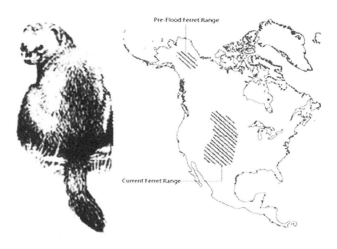

Fig. 103 "I hate the Cold!" The temperate "shift." Shaded areas indicate pre-flood (upper) and current (lower) range of the Ferret and Badger due to a climate change

On the right, the range[16] of black-footed ferrets (Mustela Nigripes) and badgers. Both now live far south of the arctic permafrost. They are found with the woolly mammoth in Alaska and the Yukon, why?

Ferrets and badgers require reasonable soil depths and moderate winters in order to survive, as do their food sources. As they have been found entombed in those upper latitudes along with the mammoth fauna, this raises an obvious question; why don't they reside at those latitudes today? The Steepe and North American black-footed ferret are unable to live in an Arctic or subarctic climate, so how did they live and roam the Arctic zone in that supposed sub-zero world with our large friends, as fantasies portray?

The burrowing ground habitat that ferrets and badgers require is permanently frozen in those areas today. This fact strongly suggests that when the ferret was living in the Alaska and Yukon Territories, together with the woolly mammoth, lion, horse, etc., the climate must have been mild and temperate and the vegetation lush. From this evidence, we can understand there was no permafrost in the Yukon and Alaska districts, meaning also they experienced no Arctic winter. Not a few experts on this subject agree.[17]

Fig. 104 Our mammoth

Howorth, our hero of the mammoths, the premier "index fossil of the Flood" concludes for us:

What cause competent to do this is known to us? Water would drown the animals and yet would not mutilate their bodies. It would kill them all with complete impartiality, irrespective of their strength, age or size. I submit with every confidence that I have proved the position that the extinction of the mammoth was sudden, and operated over a wide continental area, involving a widespread hecatomb in which man as well as other creatures perished; that this destruction was caused by a flood of waters which passed over the land, ... that this catastrophe forms a great break in human continuity no less than in the biological records of animal life, and is the Great Divide, when history really begins.
—Henry Hoyle Howorth *The Mammoth and the Flood*

Now we leave these great beasts and men that studied them so completely. It is sad that we will never hear their trumpets that once echoed across the vast expanses! But still they speak to us: *Catastrophe! Flood! Freezing! Heat! Judgment! Death!* Their bones and graves are a testament and a *warning*, markers of destruction forged by the great Deluge, apparently not allowed space on the Ark, their Creator deciding instead to pick their smaller cousins, likely knowing they had no place in the Second Earth. The vast forests where they once dwelled now gone forever, the wide Arctic growing only the lichen, willow and moss today, the temperatures diving below *minus 80 degrees.** In those places, they were unable to survive it, but still what a loss! One must consider the spectacle they would have made, their sounds carrying as they moved across the great expanses together with all the horses, rhinos, antelope and others, now forever lost to us, how so sad indeed!

*The North American record was set at Prospect Creek camp on the Alaska Pipeline: Minus -87^{0}F.

A young pilot once flew the great expanses of the Arctic, perplexed at the contradictions offered before him. He wondered what it must have been like way back when the herds of trumpeting mammoths and great horned buffalo roamed these plains. The horses, lions and antelopes, were now all *vanished,* how, and further, why? Left to us are the remnants, a token by comparison of what was: the musk ox, caribou and sheep, the moose and the fox, who sing not at all. The closing chorus left to the wolf for us, her lonely cry like to *mourning.* What's left appearing as ants to the pilot, dots among these immense spaces of grandeur, now almost empty. What a sight they must have been! What vocals must once have echoed across these Great Plains! The challenges and immensity of the place, often harsh and deadly, but then he reasoned, sobered by the idea as he took it all in: *"How could a loving God make such a place, allowing all this death and suffering, at times so much hardship, at others so inexpressible and exhilarating!"* The unimaginable beauty of it all—the stirring vistas and countless summits; the magnitude of McKinley; the power of the Yukon; the horrific weather as nowhere else on earth! The animals, so content with their magical complexity and habits, things taken for granted, but how by chance? Who is behind it all? No one, he thinks to himself and continues on his way.

Then one snowy night on a flight gone wrong, facing the terrors of a mountain crash at night, the pilot posts a question in the cockpit, the last of his life before contact, it's simple and desperate: *"If there's a God, I need your help now!"* Instantly an answer flashes back to his mind, *"Son, you said the right thing!"* An hour later his wheels safely touch down, he pondering that voice a thousand times since, his journey for truth begun. As it turns out, Gramma was right all along!

The Mammoth: Index Fossil of the Flood

[1] Howorth *Mammoth*, p. 311
[2] Warren *Memoir on the Mastodon* p. 165
[3] Cuvier Vol. i. p. 222.
[4] Warren, *Memoir on the Mastodon* p. 166
[5] Cited from Howorth, *Mammoth* Sir John Richardson, Zoology of the *Voyage of the Herald* p. 315
[6] Voyage of the Beagle. 4 Id. iii. p. 96 and other.
[7] ibid 9 p. 155.
[8] Cited from *Mammoth*, Howorth, Op. cit. from D'Orbigny iii. 3, 86
[9] M. d'Orbigny Op. cit. iii. 3, 82. 13A Cited Wood—*Mammoth* p. 379
[10] Citing Nelson, Byron C. *The Deluge Story in Stone* Bethany Fellowship 1968 p. 93
[11] George Fairholme, *New and Conclusive Physical Demonstrations of the Mosaic Deluge* p.19-20 James Ridgeway Pub, London Sec edition, 1840
[12] *Old Yukon*, Judge James Wickersham (Washington Law Press 1938) p. 379-397
[13] *Old Yukon*, Judge James Wickersham, (Washington Law Press 1938) p. 387
[14] Price, George McCready, *"Evolutionary Geology and the New Catastrophism"* (Pacific Press Publishing Association 1926), p. 331, 333-335
[15] La Anthropologie, July, 1919
[16] After R. D. Guthrie, *Frozen Fauna of the Mammoth Steppe* (1990 p. 248,49).
[17] C. Richard Harington 1977:423 "The discovery of black-footed ferret remains in the Old Crow Basin and central Alaska strongly indicate the presence of dry grasslands with abundant rodents in those places during the Pleistocene. The preferred habitat of the species is arid short grass prairies or steppe, and is a good paleontological indicator of that kind of habitat." Another source tells us: "Vast herds of mammoth and other animals in the New Siberian Islands yielded... woolly rhinoceros, musk ox, antelope, reindeer, tiger, fox, bear and horse and 66 animal species.. required forests, meadows and steppes for their subsistence; could not have lived in a climate like the present..." *The Quaternary Era*, Vol. II, London (Edward Arnold Co. 1957), p. 650

XVI

The Early Earth and Ice Age in Perspective

Fig. 105   Glaciation occurred after the Flood

One of the Norwegian Flood accounts recalls that after the Flood, it snowed continuously for three years…

The Great Ice Age, the Only Ice Age

As part of the Flood's massive precipitation, for the first time in earth's recorded history, **snow** blanketed the higher latitudes and polar regions. We know the First Earth had little or no rain nor snow; so how do we get a glacier and more than that—an Ice Age? Think of it, how warm would the oceans be if we had fruit growing and a tropical climate in both the Arctic and Antarctica, each zone now found to have redwood forests? Dana[1] determined by the presence of coral beds known to exist at 80° North, the water temperature would have been no less than 69° Fahrenheit! What would happen if a previously temperate, but now *a minus* -150° F atmosphere (space temperature) made contact with +70⁰F oceans? When you place hot water in a freezer, what is the result? *Steam and evaporation.* So it stands to reason with this warm moisture raising and contacting the cool atmosphere, it resulted in precipitation, initiating *massive snowstorms at the higher latitudes.* Glaciologists call this the making of an Ice Age—we contend the *only* Ice Age of such magnitude on earth.

Fig. 106 Consider the outcome if a previously temperate, but now *a minus* -150⁰F atmosphere, (space temperature) made contact with +70⁰F oceans? The result: steam and evaporation, steam that rose and created massive snowstorms after the flood.

The oldest book in the Bible—Job—mentions ice, frost and snow in the Middle East! Over time, earth's weather systems would have stabilized, leaving us the cycles and temperate zones we have today. But now even those are changing, getting slightly warmer over the hundreds of years. We know in general the glaciers are receding and the deserts are growing! Flying in the 1970s to the present across the largest ice fields in North America, the author observed the retreating massive glacier moraines, showing that ice covered much more of Alaska in the past. The fact is that the glaciers are slowly melting in a general sense. There's some panic over this natural process, but if one thinks that global warming is an issue, try global cooling!

The Ice Cores—Showing Catastrophe

Dr. Maynard Miller, one of America's foremost glaciologists documented[2] that no ice on the planet exists older than 5,000 years. When asked about the polar ice sheets and their age, Miller stated to the author that old age ice calculations were inaccurate, this due to homogenization of the deep cores that make them difficult to discern weather cycles exactly. When reading the literature, researchers often switch from actual to assumed deposition based on *core depth* and average rates of snowfall, not annual increments marked in the ice. Spectral analysis of these cores vary greatly depending on equipment resolution settings, the cycles based upon the incremental sensing of dust layers, dust that could easily be part of the initial disruption of the atmosphere at the onset of the flood.

Physicist Dr. Jake Herbert mentions that secular scientists maintain "deep cores from central Greenland provide irrefutable evidence for an old earth. However, the difficulty of correctly identifying annual layers negates the argument."[3] Further, Herbert mentions the recent reset of dating one core down to 9,300 years, this in a 1500 meter sample, he stating this a "remarkably low age" for this core sample in secular terms. He goes on to cite T. H. Jacka,[4] a scientist working the Antarctic sheet, who admits violent storms are apparent in the lowest readings, having an affect on these counting methods, throwing the results.

Secular scientists maintain that "deep cores from central Greenland provide irrefutable evidence for an old earth. However, the difficulty of correctly identifying annual layers negates the argument." —Dr. Jake Herbert

Also documented was the appearance of more intense dust storm activity in the bottom half of cores, ranging from "3-100 times" more activity. Considering that the high spraying aquifer water and volcanic activity at the onset of the flood, which injected massive amounts of aerosols into the atmosphere, it's not a stretch to assume what the cores are revealing is no less than a signature of the early Flood breakout. (Also reflected in sea bottom cores.[5])

Such eventually created massive snow deposits and reoccurring storms, jumpstarting the *Ice Age,* and account for the polar and Greenland ice caps being formed from *fresh water.* Consider the record setting US snowfalls near Mt. Baker, Washington in the 1972 and 1998 seasons, which produced over *1,100 inches* or nearly *100 feet*[6] of snowfall in a single winter season. How fast could snow accumulate if such conditions existed over places like the Canadian shield zone? Note the fact that a wing of US warplanes flying to England were forced down on the Greenland ice sheet in WWII, later found over 200 feet down in the ice, giving us perspective on the age of earth's glaciers and ice caps in general. A period of only few years (as the Norwegian Flood account mentions, think of Mt. Baker!) could explain their origin. Already mentioned was the find of pine

pine needles in Greenland under the ice sheet, further evidence earth's poles were once ice-free. (See Chapter 2– Alex Heilberg section)

Conflicts with simplistic views of Ice Age origin have not escaped the notice of a number scientists. Yale Geologist/Glaciologist R. F. Flint comments: "Examination of Britain's record of the Ice Age levels discloses a complex inter-bedding of drift sheets derived from different sources. When we add the additional complications imposed by thin drifts, scanty interglacial deposits, and the frequent presence in fossil-bearing beds of secondary [displaced] fossils derived from the reworking of older horizons, we get a truly difficult overall problem... All in all, British glacial stratigraphic research has encountered exceptional difficulties."[7]

Michael Oard, meteorologist and Ice Age researcher comments: "Mammoth remains in the northern hemisphere are associated with events during the Ice Age. However, uniformitarian Ice Age models cannot explain the mammoths, or even the Ice Age itself. However, the unique creationist post-Flood Ice Age offers a reasonable solution for the mammoth mysteries." Oard goes on: "The Ice Age was caused by the climatic aftermath of the Genesis Flood."[8]

Video on the Ice: http://www.icr.org/ice-age/

Article Link in full: http://www.icr.org/article/ice-age-genesis-flood/

The Erratics, Flood Remnants or Glacial Origin?

Fig. 107 The Madison Stone in New Hampshire,
dropped by a glacier or rolled along by the Flood?

Geologists are unable to pinpoint the origin of the Madison Stone, at the last count four locations were on the table for consideration...interesting that scientists can be so dogmatic concerning how this monster was borne of glaciations, yet cannot tell us from whence it came. Take note we have no record from our ancestors concerning ice ages, only that of a flood!

Misplaced boulders are found all over the globe, some transited many hundreds of miles from their host formations. Erratics are understood to have transported from Finland across the Baltic to Poland, and further to Moscow, and even to the mountains of Germany. R. F. Flint[9] cites Finnish Geologist Pentti Eskola who identified 961 stones from just south of Riga in Latvia to those sourced in Finland, making the striking discovery that the percentage of each rock type were comparable with those in Finland. The Madison erratic (pictured) near Conway, New Hampshire, is a piece of granite measuring 90x40x38 feet and probably weighing over 10,000 tons.

The Ototoks erratic, 30 miles south of Calgary, Alberta, is the largest known erratic in North America.[10] This monolith is a massive quartzite derived from structures "at *least* 50 miles to the west." The stone measures 160x55x25 feet and is calculated to weigh over 16,000 tons. A single erratic near Dam, Washington, has a surface area of more than 20,000 square feet, its thickness averaging about five feet weighing approximately 13,500 tons. It seems that it was somehow transported at least 4-1/2 miles from its source. According to R. F. Flint, how this was accomplished without breaking the monolith "has never been explained." It's clear that a glacier was not the prime-moving agent in this case.

Velikovsky in his *Earth in Upheaval* (1955) mentions an erratic in Sweden "three miles long, one thousand feet wide and from one hundred to two hundred feet thick" which was mined for commercial purposes. It is out of place with the local strata being transported an "indefinite distance." Another mega-block is found in England, on which "a village had been unwittingly built." He citing G. F. Wright in his work *The Ice Age in North America and its Bearing on the Antiquity of Man* (1911). Further mentioned are erratics transported from the mountains of Norway to the British Isles, these across the expanse of the North Sea.[11]

An erratic was found in Sweden "three miles long, one thousand feet wide and from one hundred to two hundred feet thick" being transported an "indefinite distance." —Earth in Upheaval, Immanuel Velikovsky 1955

Speaking of the Alps, Swiss naturalist Horace Bénédict de Saussure explained the presence of stones broken off from that range being catastrophically carried and deposited on the Jura Mountains far to the west of the Alps. He tells us: "The waters were carried toward these abysses with extreme violence, falling from the height they were before; they crossed deep valleys and dragged immense quantities of earth, sand, and debris of all kinds of rocks. This mass, shoved along by the onrush of great waters, was left spread up the slopes where we still see many scattered fragments."[12] He mentioned transported till filled the valleys of the Jura, full of fossils and differing in mineral composition from the local geological environ. Some of these blocks are thousands of cubic feet in size, such as the Pierre à Martin, being itself a mass of over 10,000 cubic feet, moved according to de Saussure, by no other agent than water, and deposited two thousand feet above the valley floor near Lake Geneva. Though this theory was later challenged by uniformists as a work of glaciers, the deposition of sediments suggests Saussure had the more correct story.

In North America, granite blocks from Canada have been found across the Northeast states, even deposited in the cornfields of Iowa. Modern students of geology have been dogmatically taught that all of these stones fell on top and then were transported by glaciers, yet experience tells us that glacial till consists of *rounded* boulders, not massive stones like these erratics. If a glacier did carry one of these giants piggy back, then stopped and melted, other moraine and till should be stacked to the brim in a line for hundreds of miles where the face of the glacier halted. It's true a line of boulder till may be found in such terminal moraine dropping in a path but not in these diameters. If rainfall and melting runoff were the only sweeping elements involved, deposits of many sizes should be left in abundance at the terminal moraine zone, but no, the area around many of these boulders is swept clean, exactly what we would expect if flood waters hundreds of feet high rushing at speed of 100 feet/second were sweeping and tumbling them along, like those blocks in Cherborg, France (mentioned in chapter 8), a mere fishing sinker in fast water.

No erratic in the range of these huge sizes has *ever* been witnessed riding on a glacial surface and carried for any such distance, though glaciers are abundant. These would also show striation marks caused by contact with the valley sides or bedrock floor, absent in many of these boulders. Yet once institutional geology (like biology following the mistaken tenants of evolution) took hold of the glacier idea, reversing the course is now difficult, even without any witnessed evidence! In the case of the author, informed in geology class that the erratics found in Oregon's Willamette Valley (made of material that originated near Missoula, Montana) were part of mega-flood cycles and floated in place on icebergs—a theory now challenged by a plethora of modern evidence from multiple investigators showing only one event was involved.[13]

As one who spent years hiking many miles at the foot of numerous glacial outlets in Alaska and flying among the largest glaciers on earth for many hundreds of hours, this observation is irrefutable—glaciers are great grinding machines making round objects and not "erratic" ones. With the advent of isotropic analysis, material making up the erratics can now be matched to their source. As a result, there has been a notable shift in summarily applying the glacial transport idea to all such stones (as noted in the text by Oard[14] and considering the Tyee deposits in Oregon). Such methods may be used to positively identify the host source of the misplaced rock, often found to have moved in the *opposing or lateral direction* of generally accepted ice sheet movements, which modernist interpretations claim were their transporting mechanism.

Dr. Archebald Salker, prominent Canadian geologist of the 1950s concluded that the foothills erratics had been transported by glacial ice originating in the Rocky Mountains, holding back saying that: *"transport by mountain glaciers alone could not explain the great length, narrowness, and changes in elevations which characterize it.*"[15] One source for the Ototok Dr. Stalker considered was "800-1300 km to the Northeast," but he discounted it is as out of the question due to its *distance*, not its *geology*. It is obvious to many that these monster blocks were not always related to glacial transport, as Horace Bénédict de Saussure rightly observed. They are telltale of catastrophe, their movement unexplainable by known forces save one—the great Flood of Noah's day as described in the pages of the Bible. In addition, we have no reason to believe that the Ice Age was not singular and global. We know that ice sheets moved away from near the poles then receded in many places on earth for one period, not many. As the early scientists testify to a previously warm earth, glaciation seems an intervening event in history, that of between First Earth and the present world, yet God could have saved space for them in First Earth somewhere. Today they are doubtless a showpiece of the greatness and power of the Almighty, not a distraction from His perfect works.

[1] Dana, D.D *Manual of Geology,* p. 793

[2] Maynard M. Miller *Recent Climatic Variations, Their Causes and Neogene Perspectives,*1985

[3] Jake Herbert, *Acts&Facts* June 2015 vol. 44 no. 6 p. 15

[4] Jacka, T. H *Antarctic Ice Cores and Environmental Change*, Australian Antarctic Div. www.chem.hope.edu Mar. 31, 2015

[5] Larry Vardiman, *THE SANDS OF TIME*, 1996 "DSDP extracted cores from 624 sites on the ocean floors of the globe. Cores from most of these sites showed only recent sediments from the Tertiary and Quaternary periods. Of the 624 total sites only 186 contained sediments from the Cretaceous period or earlier." http://www.icr.org/research/index/researchp_lv_r01/

[6] George Taylor et al June 2001 http://www.nwas.org/digest/papers/2001/Vol25No12/Pg15- Leffler.pdf

[7] Flint, R. F., *Glacial Geology and the Pleistocene Epoch*, 1947, p. 337

[8] Oard, Michael December 1, 2000 https://answersingenesis.org/environmental-science/ice-age/the-extinction-of-the-woolly-mammoth-was-it-a-quick-freeze-9849/

[9] R. F. Flint, *Glacial Geology and the Pleistocene Epoch* 1947, p. 116-17

[10] http://www.history.alberta.ca/historicsites/

[11] Velikovsky, Immanuel, *Earth in Upheaval,* Paradigma Pub, London 1955, 2009 p. 25-27 used by permission

[12] Horace Bénédict de Saussure, *Voyages dans les Alpes*, 1779 cited by Velikovsky, Immanuel, *Earth in Upheaval,* Paradigma Pub., London 1955, Digital 2009 p. 25-27 used by permission

[13] Dennis B. Bokovoy CMI article *The Mystery of the Megaflood* http://creation.com/the-mystery- of-the-megaflood 2005, downloaded 5-2015

[14] Oard, Michael et al, 1 of 4 articles concerning drift remnant of the Flood http://creation.com/flood-transported-quartzites-part-1east-of-the-rocky-mountains downloaded 5-2015

[15] Dr. Archibald MacSween Stalker, Geological Survey of Canada: in Barendregt, R. W. et al., eds., *The Palliser Triangle, a region in space and time*: Alberta, University of Lethbridge, p. 63-76.

XVII

World Coal and Oil Deposits

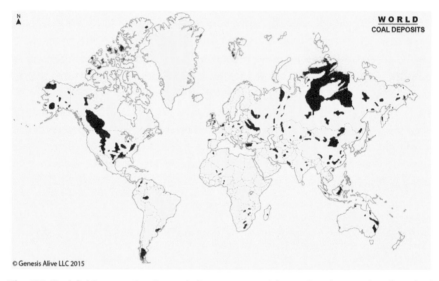

Fig. 108 Coal fields cover the planet, their source material now found to consist of tree bark and vegetation, dropped from massive floating log mats held up by mountain ranges. Oil and natural gas are often found in close proximity—"fossil fuels"

In Alaska, we find fossil evidence of mega fauna and flora, giant ferns, nautilus, the mammoths and others living in a past warm and lush climate. We also find massive oil and coal reservoirs beneath the surface—"fossil fuels"—that formed from what? Coal has been found to be comprised of *tree bark* and vegetation deposits. When over-weighted with heavy sediments and compressed, coal is quickly forms by this process measured in hours. These beds are not the result of millions of years acting on ancient swamp material as evolutionary textbooks claim. As a result of the Flood, huge floating log mats bumped the bark off that then sank. A subsequent covering by sediment slurry would provide the compression needed. Most all coal fields have a sandstone overburden, now hardened to stone. Geologists watched this very sequence before their eyes in the waters of Spirit Lake at the base of Mt. St. Helens. Here, a floating log mat consisting of a million logs dropped their bark within a year, piling on the bottom. Coal formation researcher and expert Dr. Steve Austin connected the dots.[1]

Appalachian, Alaskan, and Rocky Mountain Coal

From the line of coal deposits, it's apparent these floating log mats (in the case of coal made from tree bark/vegetation mats) were driven by winds and current then covered in sediments, which later became trapped against the mountain ranges worldwide. Any coal miner will tell you they often run into petrified stumps and need to dynamite them away on occasion. In one mine the author worked, dinosaur prints were found inverted in the sandstone ceiling at the 10,000 foot level in the Rocky Mountains.

In addition, when coal is subjected to carbon dating, the results show thousands of years in age, the strata from which they came dated in the hun-dreds of millions, according to the failed Geologic Chart. A typical coal spec-imen will Carbon 14 (C-14) date at less than a few thousand years old![2] In 2011, a complete shark skeleton was found in coal, stated to be over 200 million years old. Of course, no Carbon 14 testing was undertaken on either the skeleton or the shark remains; the state paleontologist merely looked at his "geologic chart" on the wall, moved his finger to "Carboniferous"* and announced the age to the media. Carbon 14 typically dates coal samples around eight thousand years old.[3]

*Coal is considered by uniformitarian geologists to have formed during the carboniferous period, between 250 and 318 million years ago.

In Alaska, the author witnessed coal in Pleistocene beds near and above mammoth remains (Colville River), confounding the notion of such ridicu-lous ages suggested for coal to form from "peat bogs." Another example is found in the Powder River coal deposit, which covers over 10,000 square miles across Wyoming and Montana. This seam may run up to 150 feet in thickness. Have you ever heard of a peat bog 150 feet deep? The thickness of an un-solidified vegetation mass required to form such a deposit would be enormous, potentially ten times or more the compressed mass, or 1,500 feet thick! Coal has been known to form in a short period of time under com-pression.[4]

The World's Oil Deposits

What is the origin of the oil deposits? They are a leftover from the Flood, formed in this single and *global* event. Oil and gas deposits may be found in abundance on every continent of the world, many overlapping the other. These are known to be derived from organic material, such as buried ani-mals, micro-organisms and vegetation. Oil has also been found associated with coal deposits. Oil once formed in less than 80 years in a leather processing disposal pit.[5] In 2009, an underground coal mine in eastern Kentucky (Mine 28) was advancing and struck oil, forcing a cessation of activities. These chemical reactions have been found to occur elsewhere, such as Aus-tralia, showing oil to be sequentially forming with depth in coal and seeming to be quite active today.

In Washington State, a company has been successful in converting sewage waste into commercially useable fuel oil in hours in quantities making the venture profitable. What other event resulted in the formation of these fossil fuels? Like coal, these resources would be needed for man to survive in the new and cooler planet; we shouldn't take them for granted. Coal and oil are a gift from God to sustain mankind in the new and cooler earth. Neither existed in the First Earth or before the Flood event, nor were they needed. They are recent in age, water sediment covered, and all a result of the great Flood.

Evidence of Rapid Petroleum Formation

Two factors must be considered in answering this question 1) what type of material is need to derive hydrocarbons and 2) what geologic structures are needed in order to "trap" the residue or "oil." Long age theorists insist that the rocks surrounding oil formations are geologically "old" and thus defeat recent formation as a flood model demands, but this is not true. Research conducted by P.V. Smith and others show otherwise. Citing Morris in *The Genesis Flood* quoting V. P. Smith:

> One of the surprising results of this study is the discovery of [oil] in recent sediments from the Gulf of Mexico.[6]

As shown in the Himalayas, earth's rock structures are in a dynamic state. This in mind, as oil attempts to surface, natural traps form. Oil formation theory includes models that show many pools are refilling and dynamic, hardly proof of long-age. The author has worked with coal and other mineral/metal deposits in some of the largest and deepest mines in the world. We should be in awe of these massive, catastrophically formed deposits. They fit perfectly with the events as recorded in the Bible: first of a world made with and out of water, then a stasis, and then the *Flood*. We see no such deposits forming today, save the precursor elements observed forming under the waters of Spirit Lake after the Mt. St. Helens eruption. Subsequent to the flood event, processes of uniform erosion and local deposition show us earth has been generally in stasis.[7] The evidence pointing to vigorous agents involved in the formation of Earths coal and "fossil fuel" deposits, not a process derived over eons of time.

Quoting Georges Cuvier, we find him best to conclude this matter of Fossils, The Flood and Catastrophe:

I conclude with M. De Luc, and M. Dolomieu, that if there be any fact well established in geology, it is this, that the surface of our globe has suffered a great and sudden revolution, the period of which cannot be dated further back than five or six thousand years. This revolution has, on one hand, engulfed, and caused to disappear, the countries formerly inhabited by men, and the animal species at present best known; and, on the other, has laid bare the bed of the last ocean, thus converting its channel into the present habitable earth. - Disc. Prelim [8]

[1] Snelling, Andrew A http://creation.com/how-fast-can-oil-form

[2] Snelling, Andrew A http://creation.com/stumping-old-age-dogma

[3] http://www.icr.org/article/shark-jaw-opens-questions-about-coal/

[4] www.creation.com/how-fast-can-oil-form

[5] *Creation Ex Nihilo,* Vol. 12 No.4

[6] Morris and Whitcomb *The Genesis Flood* 1961 (Pres. & Reformed Pub. 1988 edition), p. 436 citing P.V. Smith "Occurrence of Hydrocarbons in Recent Sediments from the Gulf of Mexico" *Science,* 1952 Vol. 116 p. 437

[7] Video: Origins - Mount St. Helens - Explosive Evidence for Creation with Dr. Steve Austin http://www.youtube.com/watch?v=flrhqjN5BHo

[8] https://en.wikipedia.org/wiki/Georges_Cuvier

XVIII

The Question of Time: Earth and Solar System Age

Fig. 109 The Sands of Time—earth's hourglass is likely small

Radiometric and other Dating Methods

Much we hear about origins attaches millions or even billions of years to every animal, vegetable and mineral in the universe. How can we verify the accuracy of these methods and further, can they be trusted? A recent 8-year study[1] conducted by a group of experienced scientists visited and re-sampled the US sites used to date the earth in the 1960s and 70s. They worked to validate the radioisotope dating methods, using the best science possible. Double-blind samples were sent to nationally known laboratories (often without the knowledge of who obtained the rocks) to maintain objectivity. When the results came in, the scientists first determined the four major isotope dating systems were discordant among each other, and secondly, several varied over 500 million years on the same sample! Further, each was found inconsistent with non-nuclear dating methods yet contradicting among the same samples. We take for granted that "nuclear isotope" meas-urement suggests some type of accurate super-clock, but in fact that's not the accuracy range of these dating methods at all. Quoting from the extensive "RATE" report mentioned, results using multiple isotope dating methods on a single Grand Canyon sample found:

"The diabase sill in Grand Canyon displays discordant isochron 'ages' ranging from 841.5±164 Ma (K-Ar whole-rock isochron) to 1379±140 Ma (Sm-Ndmineral isochron)"[1]

299

This finding means that across the four primary isotope methods used to measure age on the same sample, they ranged along a *500 million year time span, providing an accuracy tolerance of 50%!*

In addition, measurements taken from a fresh lava flow that waterfalls over the top edge of the Grand Canyon dated 270 million *older* than a flow exposed at the canyon depths, clearly not the "atomic clock" accuracy these methods are purported to be. Finds such as these suggesting billion year isochron dates in the wrong part of the Grand Canyon befuddle evolutionary time charts, this in a structure which should be the long-age geologists best model![2]

In summary, it's accurate to state that the various isotope combinations used in the isochron method of dating are clearly discordant—they do not produce the same age for a given rock formation. Secondly, isochron methods provide inaccurate ages for rock formations of *known age,* such as known lava flows mentioned in historical records.[1] For example, according to Dr. John Morris in his volume *The Global Flood* (2012), samples from Mt. Ngauruhoe in New Zealand provided a set of dates using one isotope method ranging between 270,000 to 3.5 million years, a second of over 133 million years, a third of nearly 200 million years, and the last, using the Pb-Pb (lead isotope Pb^{238} to Pb-pure lead method) dated 3.9 *billion* years old! Another conflicting example comes from the east African Rift Valleys.[2] These lavas are said to be Pliocene (<5 million years) or younger, and gave a Rb-Sr (Rubidium/Strontium) isochron age of 773 million years![3]

Closer to home, Dr. Steve Austin, who has undertaken extensive study of the Mt. St. Helens area, tells us that isotope readings from flows only 10 years old show dates as late as 2.8 million years.

Contributing nuclear physicist for the Institution for Creation Research Dr. Vernon Cupps tells us,[4] "In the end, the isochron model for radioactive dating is only a hypothesis and a rather poor one at that. Models, no matter how elegant their mathematics, are only as good as the assumptions that go into them and how well they reproduce reality through observation and experimental data." Dr. Cupps' conclusion:

The scientific method simply does not allow isochron-model dat-ing to be presented as scientific fact. —Dr. Vernon Cupps

Evolutionists attempt to discredit biblical chronologies referring to the accuracy of these isochron systems. Herein is the value of supporting the work of institutions such as Institute of Creation Research, they offering professional objectivity in their analysis of the rocks.

References:
1. Morris, J. 2007. *The Young Earth* Green Forest, AR: Master Books, 52.
2. Faure, *Principles of Isotope Geology*, 146-147. As cited in 3 below
3. Morris, J. 2007. *The Young Earth*, p. 58-59.
Quote: Cupps, Vernon, *Acts and Facts* Vol. 41 No. 11 Nov. 2014
http://www.icr.org/i/pdf/af/

Challenges to the Isotope Methods:

• HE (Helium) and AR (Argon) gases, whose known escape rates in rocks indicate the earth's crustal rocks are =/<10,000 years in age.
• Carbon 14 found in diamonds, coal and even dinosaur bones, suggest dates in the thousands.
• PO[214] (or Polonium 214) as reported by Dr. Robert Gentry[4] demonstrated scientifically that PO[214] exhibits a 1/2 life measured in *seconds*. They are found to etch decay halo's in many minerals including the crystalline granites said to require millions of years to form, but the presence of these particles indicates otherwise.[5]
• Note the critique of the isotope methods by Dr. Vernon Cupps (2014) link http://www.icr.org/article/8486/

Note: Most uniform chronometers such as ocean sea-salt and C-14 in the atmosphere suggest ages of less than 100,000 years. The isotope types are in the minority by a 20:1 factor verses other uniform measurements that are verifiable. Dr. Henry Morris lists 75 that fall into this category. See Article "The Young Earth" by the Late Dr. Morris @ http://www.icr.org/article/64/

The 2013 Isotope Clock "Anomaly"

The RATE team was encouraged by anomalies reported around the world from 2006-13[6 7], where these nuclear clocks "hiccuped" after a solar flare, placing in question the entire premise of isotope decay trustworthiness. As these nuclear clocks are based solely upon the rate of decay never altering, such decay accelerations would throw these measurements far off in a short time period, invalidating their resultant long-ages. The RATE project team suspected such in their published report, detecting a "fast forward" of the parent/daughter elements in their research.[8] Could the 2013 burp be a clue to a past *major anomaly?* We simply don't know at this time, but one thing is certain: these supposedly infallible dating methods are now deeply *in question.* As our experience over time watching isotopes is limited, no one can really know their true accuracy. Origin science is especially tentative, as no one can ever know if all the evidence has been found and further, has said evidence been correctly interpreted. One thing is stable and certain, the unchanging Word of God, where science is vulnerable and tenable, like the 2013 time slipup, new evidence can contradict seemingly air tight assumptions in a moment of time.

One must consider why *none* of these young-age dating chronometers (there are dozens, ocean sea salt input, surface erosion etc.) so mentioned were outlined in our 9th grade earth science classes, and conversely, why were only the isotope methods explained? This is concerning, and demonstrates how establishment science could care less about developing creative thinkers among our youth, only followers!

In the end, man may apply any bias he wishes to make the evidence fit his theory, then write it up to make a desired point. In the case of the radiometric techniques, held immutable for a generation, the perception dies hard, but perceptions don't equal truth. For those unsatisfied with the mainstream and ready to approach origins openly, the isotope methods are easily falsified.

Earth's Decaying Magnetic Field = the Earth Is Young!

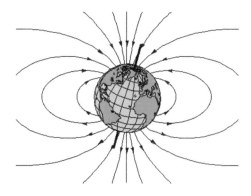

Fig. 110 The earth's magnetic field is decreasing at a rapid rate,
its protective shield vital to life survival on earth. We should never take it for granted.

The earth's magnetic field acts as a protective net and navigational guide. What is little known is that the earth's magnetic field is decaying so rapidly that aeronautical charts require updating every 90 days due to isogonic line shift. Reversing this known decay rate, we would find the earth too magnetic to support life only 20,000 years ago. This fact of earth physics has never been countered yet remains concealed from the public view and missing from every basic earth science textbook from junior high through college. Why? I would assert that because modern "science" is unable to tolerate the implications such knowledge would cause. Such a basic measurement so opposite from the isotope methods may generate questions that the evolutionist wishes not to answer!

The Steen's Mountain magnetism study data is a serious enigma for long ages. The Steen's formation is considered a "scarp face" exposure of the "Columbia Basalt" lava flow edge, thus making them an ideal formation to study the past. Here was found (as Dr. Russ Humphreys predicted in 1983) that rapid reversals of the magnetic poles occurred. As mentioned, this finding was a shock to rank and file geologists, who taught for 70 years such reversals took 50,000-700,000 years to cycle. These polar magnetic reversals are also found in the cores of the mid-ocean rifts, suggesting these changes occurred *simultaneously* with the Columbia Basalt flows, smoking gun evidence of their common origin—the Flood catastrophe.

More confirmation of the solar system's young age, as 30 years of space probe flybys show a dramatic reduction in Mercury's magnetic field.

As part of Dr. Humphrey's model, Mercury, due to its unique makeup, should exhibit the fastest decay rate of any planet in the system. It turns out Humphreys' calculations have now been proven in *three* NASA probe missions—Voyager II in 1975, Mariner 10 in 1990 and more recently, Messenger, collecting data from 2008 through 2013. His theory inspired by Thomas Barnes and the Bible, traces measurements made back as far as 1835 showing the earth's magnetic field is rapidly collapsing at a rate equal to a *1400 year half-life.*

Fig. 111 *Messenger* Probe data collected from Mercury flybys indicate an 8% magnetic decrease over 30 years.

This graph shows magnetic measurements of Mercury, the final data in-dicating a whopping 8% decay in only 30 years (1975-2013), indicating Mercury's magnetic 1/2 life is a mere 320 years!

When the results came in, Humphreys was amazed, as the values validated his theoretical plots, showing this planet's field strength did decrease with each flyby, even spaced so closely in time (30 years). To better understand the physics involved, his theory would expect such a decrease due to the electrical resistance in a planet's core decreasing the electrical current causing the magnetic field, just as friction slows down a flywheel. The smaller the core or greater the resistance, the faster the field will decay [like Mercury].

Suggested video:
Magnetic Fields, part 1 of 2 with Dr. D. Russell Humphreys - Origins - YouTube
https://www.youtube.com/watch?v=7manZ1WF-Lc

The 2012 Vindication: All Five Predictions Play Out!

Humphreys comments: "Magnetic fields in the cosmos serve as God's signature on His creation, and like everything in the heavens, they give glory to Him (Psalms 19:1) Measurements from *Messenger* compared with the 1975 *Mariner 10* data show that Mercury's magnetic field has weakened by **nearly 8% in the past 36 years,** an astonishingly fast decrease." This data supports Humphrey's prediction in the 1984 paper where he stated: "Mercury's decay rate is so rapid that some future space probe could detect it fairly soon. In 1990, the planet's magnetic moment should be 1.8 percent smaller than its 1975 value." The observed rate agrees shows Mercury's core has an electrical conductivity close to that of earth's core. This fast rate of decay (a half-life of *320 years*) implies the crust was magnetized only thousands of years ago. As reported in 2013, this figure Humphreys now obtained, times two![9]

Establishment Science Takes Note

As of August 2014, there seems to be some uncertainty among institutional scientists regarding current theories about how the earth creates and maintains its magnetic field. A well recognized geophysicist, David Stevenson of the California Institute of Technology [as quoted in *Discover* magazine] expressed concern that problems do exist relative to earth's magnetic field and long-age based theories, quoting Stevenson:

Right at this moment, there is a problem with our understanding of Earth's core and it's something that's emerged only over the last year or two. *The problem is a serious one. We do not now understand how the Earth's magnetic field has lasted for billions of years.* We know that the Earth has had a magnetic field for most of its history. We don't know how the Earth did that. We have less of an understanding now than we previously thought we had a decade ago of how the Earth's core has operated throughout history.[10]

Does this revelation suggest that resistance to Dr's Barnes and Humphreys' work is quietly eroding? It appears so. Do these comments indicate that our magnetic field decline rate has lately accelerated? We don't presently know. If this comment is related to such, nothing can be done by man to stop it. The result would be that earth's protective shield would likely fall and we will be left unprotected from the sun's harmful radiation flares. Such could completely disrupt life as we know it on this planet. Weather now or later makes little difference; God has declared that a final judgment is coming on the earth since the Pillars of Seth onto the Bible. The warnings are there, and it's up to every individual to take the necessary action to save themselves from this last and final calamity as clearly outlined in the Bible.

*Cited from Folger, T., *Journeys to the Center of the Earth: Our planet's core powers a magnetic field that shields us from a hostile cosmos. But how does it really work?* Discover, July/August 2014.
For further updates see: http://www.genesisalive.com/the-question-of-time.html

Let us not forget what Jesus Christ said:

"Just as in the Days of Noah, so shall the coming of the Son of Man be!"

[1] http://www.icr.org/article/rate-news-release/

[2] Excessively Old "Ages" For Grand Canyon Lava Flows www.ICR.org

[3] Steve Austin *Excess Argon Mt. St. Helens* 1996 http://www.icr.org/research/index/researchp_sa_r01/ *"the dacite which formed in 1986 give K-Ar 'ages' from 0.34 ± 0.06 Ma (feldspar-glass concentrate) to 2.8 ± 0.6 Ma (pyroxene concentrate). These 'ages' are, of course, preposterous."*

[4] www.halos.com

[5] http://creation.com/new-radiohalo-find-challenges-primordial-granite-claim

[6] Fischbach, E., Jenkins, J.H. and Sturrock, P.A., Evidence for time-varying nuclear decay rates: experimental results and their implications for new physics, arXiv preprint arXiv:1106.1470, 2011

[7] Stober, D., The strange case of solar flares and radioactive elements, news.stanford.edu/news/2010/august/sun-082310.html, accessed 25 August 2010

[8] http://phys.org/news201795438.html

[9] http://creation.com/mercury-more-marks-of-youth

[10] Cited in: Folger, T., *Journeys to the Center of the Earth*: Our planet's core powers a magnetic field that shields us from a hostile cosmos. But how does it really work? *Discover*, July/August 2014.

XIX

Ten Earth-Age Time Measurements

This chapter covers ten earth-age time measurements to be considered from uniform, observable and logical factors derived from the physical and other sciences. These suggest that the earth and our solar system may be quite young compared to the eons generally taught in science today.

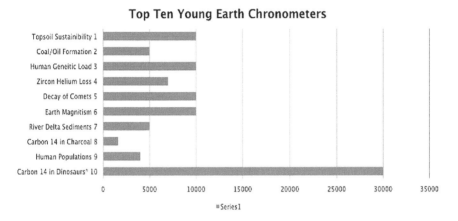

Fig. 112 Ten Young Earth Chronometers

*Note: Due to the Pre-Flood moist atmosphere, C14 would have been absorbed prior to entering the food chain, providing only trace levels and an "appearance of age" in samples from the First Earth as compared to today.

AREA OF CONCERN FOR SOIL DEGRADATION

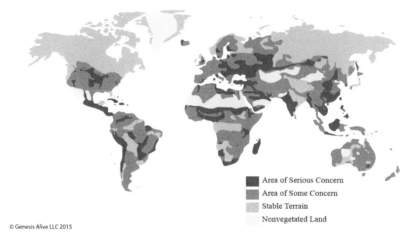

Area of Serious Concern
Area of Some Concern
Stable Terrain
Nonvegetated Land

© Genesis Alive LLC 2015

Fig. 113 Areas facing critical topsoil losses, inexplicable in a long age earth.

1. *World-wide Top Soil Problems.* China's agricultural soils[1] are known to be 40% depleted, 30% threatened, with approximately 16% contaminated. In the US, both Kansas and Iowa[2] are at crisis depletion levels, as 30% or more of their acreage is in the "red zone." Most of the world's major crop producing areas are estimated to contain less than 200 years use remaining, some less than 60 according to the latest reports (2012). Such data suggests earth would have been a soil-less landscape in only a few thousand years. Our hydrological cycle works to take soil only one-way—straight into the oceans, this by design after the Flood.

www.china.org.cn/environment/news/2008-11/21/content_16803229.htm
www.nytimes.com/2013/12/31/world/asia/good-earth-no-more-soil-pollution-plagues- chi-nese-countryside.html?_r=0

2. *Coal/Oil formation*: Coal has been replicated in the laboratory in a period measured in hours, oil in weeks. For example, Argonne National Laboratories reported that lignin (the major component of wood), water and acidic clay heated in a sealed container to only 150°C produced brown coal in just two to eight months. [1-4]

www.creation.com/coal-volcanism-and-noahs-flood (Coal, volcanism and Noah's Flood - creation.com),
www.creation.com/how-fast-can-oil-form (How fast can oil form? - creation.com)
Hayatsu, R., McBeth, R.L., Scott, R.G., Botto, R.E. and Winans, R.E., Artificial coalification study: Preparation and characterization of synthetic materials, *Organic Geochemistry* **6**:463–471, 1984.

Saxby, J. D. and Riley, K.W., 1984. Petroleum generation by lab-scaled pyrolyysit over six years simulating conditions in a subsiding basin. *Nature,* vol. 308, pp. 177-179.

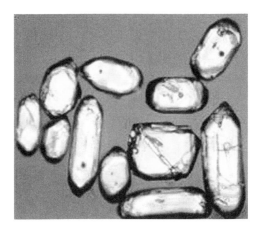

Fig. 114 Zircon crystals emit a measurable level of helium, indicating a half-life of only a few thousand years.

4. *Deep Crust Zircon Crystals.* These emit a sustained amount of helium with a 1/2 life of only a few thousand years.

Humphreys, Austin, Baumgardner, and Snelling, on Helium Diffusion Age of 6,000 years supports accelerated nuclear decay, *Creation Research Society Quarterly,* 41(1):1–16, 2004 http://www.creationresearch.org/crsq/articles/41/41_1/ Helium_lo_res.pdf.

5. *Comets Disintegrate Too Quickly.* According to evolutionary theory, comets are supposed to be the same age as the solar system, about *5 billion years.* The fact is, each time a comet orbits close to the sun, much of its material is lost. Based on this factor, it's been calculated that a comet's life cycle is less than 100,000 years and many have typical ages of 10,000 years.[1] Evolutionists explain this discrepancy by assuming that comets come from some unobserved spherical "Oort cloud," this well beyond the orbit of Pluto. To date, none of these assumptions has been substantiated either by observations or realistic calculations. Lately, there has been much talk of the "Kuiper Belt," lying in the plane of the solar system supposedly just outside the orbit of Pluto.

Even if this body of ice existed in that proposed location (now disproved by the latest images from the NASA "New Horizons" space probe) such would not solve the evolutionists' problem, since the Kuiper Belt would quickly become exhausted if there were no Oort cloud to supply it!

Steidl, P.F., *Planets, Comets and Asteroids, Design and Origins in Astronomy*, pp. 73–106, G. Mulfinger, ed., CRS books.

Whipple, F.L., "Background of Modern Comet Theory," *Nature* 263 (2 Sept 1976) 15.

See the detailed technical article: www.creation.com/comets-and-the-age-of-the-solar- system. Comets and the Age of the Solar System.

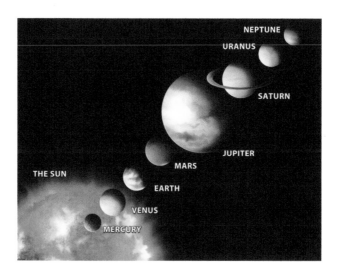

Fig. 115 A planet's mass and structure creates a magnetic field. All the planets in our solar system suggest a young and rapidly declining magnetic "age"

6. The Earth's Magnetic Field Is Collapsing Rapidly. Due to this factor, aeronautical maps issued by the FAA must be updated every 90 days, as earth's magnetic field is measured to have a half-life of only 1600 years! Proceed in reverse 20,000 and the earth would have been too magnetic to be life habitable. This factor also applies to a number of the outer planets like Mercury, that orb showing a whopping 8% decline in a 30 year time period, confirming a theory put forth as noted by Dr. Russ Humphreys.

Big Bang—on another note relating to the "big bang" and the cosmology of the Universe, Dr. Danny Faulkner of AIG (Answers in Genesis) posted these comments about the latest challenge to the theory in the AIG March 2015 newsletter, he states:

"A very distant galaxy shows evidence of much dust, while a quasar nearly the same distance contains the most massive black hole ever detected. In a big bang cosmology, we are viewing these two objects from a very early epoch in the universe. There is not enough time in the current understanding of cosmic evolution for either of these ob-

jects to exist. Hence, these observations present tremendous problems for the standard cosmology.

Are these recent studies an embarrassment for the big bang model? Hardly, Faulkner asserts the big bang model has had so many iterations and unanswered challenges, each explained away by model changes that simply amount to *"rescuing devices."* Faulkner concludes: "Any theory that can be modified to fit any new data is no theory at all. For an idea to be a theory it must be possible to disprove the idea, at least hypothetically. If that is not possible, then the idea is dogma, not theory."[1]

Big Bang, Dr. Danny Faulkner Article *"Big Bang Cosmology Challenged by Dust and a Massive Black Hole"* www.answersingenesis.org March, 2015
See: www.creation.com/the-earths-magnetic-field-evidence-that-the-earth-is-young and Video! https://vimeo.com/72675702

Fig. 116 The world's river deltas contain less than 7,000 years of deposits, fully aligned with the time of the Flood event (circle denotes delta zone)

7. *River Deltas.* Delta deposits around the world suggest a single general age range between 5-7,000 years old.[1] As an example, the largest river in the world, the Mississippi[2] exhibits about this volume of sediments across its diverse set of deltas. So do the Nile and Po River in Italy, all well studied delta systems. If the entire planet was engulfed in a flood, it makes sense these deltas would have a new start date, these found well within the timeframe of the Flood, adjusting for seasonal variations.

311

www.adammandelman.net/tag/the-basics/
Benjamin F. Allen, "The Geologic Age of the Mississippi River" *Creation Research Society Quarterly*, Vol. 9 (September 1972), pp. 96-114.

8. *Coal and charcoal typically exhibit C-14 ages less than 5,000 years.** Many man-made artifacts found in coal indicate a young formation. Such stand in defiance of the notion that coal formed in the so-called "Carbonif-erous Age" of 200-300 million years ago. As referenced elsewhere, coal has been formed in the laboratory in hours and C-14 dates coal only thousands of years old.

*http://grisda.org/origins/51006.htm

9. *Human Populations** Conservative statistical analysis of population growth allows man a presence on earth of only a few thousand years.[1] Humanists claim that mankind evolved from apes about a million years ago. This unfounded inference is easily refuted based on the lack of buried human bones alone, their being *billions* unaccounted for if people reproduced for that time period. Speaking for human kind only (not counting the animals), if the population had grown a very conservative 0.01% per year since (doubling only every 7,000 years), there could be up to 10^{43} total people that have lived up to today. In other words, the entire universe couldn't hold all the bones left in one generation of that many folks! This is only a very tiny fraction of 10^{43}.

Consider that the current world population could fit in just two counties in Florida today, with three feet of space around each person. If the Pentagon was 10,000 feet high, every person on earth could have a desk. US experts calculated that the Mekong River Delta (in Vietnam) alone could feed and clothe the world in 1960. There is plenty of livable space on earth and space enough to grow the food needed for all. Mankind is simply too sinful to work together for the good of the whole. God cannot be held accountable for that!

*see www.creation.com/where-are-all-the-people

Noah's Flood and Population Genetics

New research relating to population genetics has found support in the regime of genetic entropy, suggesting a "jump start" in population occurred at the time of the Flood in 2300 BC. The study data is related to the known quantity of genetic error passed from one generation to the next. Mankind is showing genetic entropy, or running down, to the point where genetic mistakes overwhelm the cells ability to filter out errors. Sometimes these mistakes are expressed in genetic diseases, now numbering in the several thousands. Such entropy or *Genetic Load* are calculable using computer modeling, and suggest a very short timeline for mankind's presence on earth.

Factors relating to Genetic Load (After Sandford[1])

* Three new mutations occur each time a cell divides in your body
* Average cell of a 15 year old has up to 6000 mutations
* Average cell of a 60 year old has 40,000 mutations
* 60-175 mutations are passed on to each new generation

These studies[2-7] used demographic models of human populations over time and geographical space, rather than assumptions based upon evolutionary models. The resulting data showed a very recent "burst" of human genetic diversity associated with systemic genetic loading. One author commented, "The *maximum* likelihood time for accelerated growth was 5,115 years ago" [emphasis mine]. Such a timeframe is closely associated with the Genesis Flood, when earth began its repopulation through Noah's family. God directed them to "be fruitful and multiply, bring forth abundantly and multiply in it" (Genesis 9:7). After this, people rapidly spread across Asia, the Mideast and Europe. It appears now that an echo in genetics based on good science supports such. One researcher commented:

Amazingly, this recent explosion of human genome variation mostly associated with genetic entropy, also fits the same pattern of human life expectancy rapidly declining after the Flood as recorded in the Bible. [12]

Another genetic indicator is found in the mitochondria. mDNA contains its own DNA molecule separate from a creature's main genome. It's like a backup copy of your mother's untouched DNA. mDNA mutation rates can be measured to give us molecular-genetic clock. Jeanson[11] demonstrated that a creation time of not more than 10,000 years ago is confirmed by these ge-netic clocks.[9] [10] The results of these studies fit perfectly with the predictions of a young-earth creation age range. Adam and Eve were originally created with pure, uncontaminated genes. It seems when sin entered the world after the fall, our genes have been on a downhill slide ever since. According to Nathan Jeanson of the Institute of Creation Research: "We are not gradually evolving better genomes. Instead, the recently measured degradation patterns and rates clearly match the biblical model and timeframe."[13] [14]

[1]Sanford, J. C. 2008. Genetic Entropy and the Mystery of the Genome, 3rd ed. Waterloo, NY: FMS Publications

[2]Sanford, J., J. Pamplin, and C. Rupe. 2014. Genetic Entropy Recorded in the Bible? FMS Foundation. Posted on kolbecenter.org July 2014, accessed July 25, 2014. Also see Dr. John Sanford's' volume; *Genetic Entropy and the Mystery of the Genome*, [3]http://creation.com/store_redirect.php?sku=10-3-506 3rd edition, FMS Publications, New York, 2008.

[4]Tomkins, J. Genetics Research Confirms Biblical Timeline. Creation News Update. Posted on icr.org January 9, 2013

[5]Tomkins, J. Human DNA Variation Linked to Biblical Event Timeline. *Creation Science Update* Posted on icr.org July 23, 2012.

[6]Tennessen, J. A. et al. 2012. Evolution and Functional Impact of Rare Coding Variation from Deep Sequencing of Human Exomes. *Science*. 337 (6090): 64-69.

[7]Fu, W. et al. 2013. Analysis of 6,515 exomes reveals the recent origin of most human protein-coding variants. *Nature*. 493 (7431): 216-220.

[8]Keinan, A and A. G. Clark. 2012. Recent Explosive Human Population Growth Has Resulted in an Excess of Rare Genetic Variants *Science*. 336 (6082): 740-743.

[9]Thomas, Brian. 2012. A Recent Explosion of Human Diversity. *Acts & Facts*. 41 (9): 17.

[10]Jeanson, N. T. 2014. New Discoveries from 2,700 Species Comparisons *Acts & Facts*. 43 (2):9.

[11]Jeanson, N. T. 2013. Recent, Functionally Diverse Origin for Mito-chondrial Genes from ~2700 Metazoan Species. *Answers Research Journal*. 6: 467-501.

[12]Nathanial Jeanson is an ICR genetics researcher with a PhD from Harvard University

[13]Dr. Jeffrey Tomkins is Research Associate at the Institute for Creation Research and received his PhD in genetics from Clemson University. *Acts and Facts*, Vol. 43. 11 Nov 2014 p.16

[14]Kondrashov, A., *Contamination of the genome by very slightly deleterious mutations: why have we not died 100 times over? Journal of Theoretical Biology* 175:583–594, 1995.

Notes: Mutational Load. Francisco Ayala postulated a 10,000 year maximum for humans due to mutational failure 30 years ago that has recent support. There are over 3,000 genetic diseases in human populations today.

10. *C-14 in Dinosaur bones*[1.] This revelation created an uproar in professional circles when a French research team, simply following the evidence where it led them, found that dinosaur bones from a number of samples dated a mere 22-39,000 years old. Opposition to these findings resulted in censoring several papers at a recent conference (see note 1). The subject is currently a hot topic, quoting the news story: "A team of researchers gave a presentation[2] at the 2012 Western Pacific Geophysics meeting in Singapore, August 13–17, at which they gave ^{14}C dating results from many bone samples from eight dinosaur specimens. All gave dates ranging from 22,000 to 39,000 years." The lead presenter, Dr. Thomas Seiler, is a German physicist with Ph.D is from the Technical University of Munich.

Note that ancient wood samples buried deep in Oregon's Coast Range and most Siberian mammoth bone trace along the 20-35,000 year timeline, suggesting they all perished in the same timeframe as the dinosaurs.

[1]See (C14 dinos - creation.com). http://creation.com/c14-dinos
[2]The video of his presentation
http://kgov.com/carbon-14-and-dinosaur-bones

Pre-Flood Carbon 14

Understanding that C-14[1] is not a positive health element in the life cycle of modern earth, we would not expect its presence in any quantity in the First Earth. In those times, it would be reasonable that only small traces would exist in the animals and plants. This the case, using the yard stick of the relatively high rates of C-14 entering the earth's system today, hence an "appearance of age" would be indicated, due to the absence or very low readings of C-14 in the early "very good" earth samples. As such, any low C-14 readings, (suggesting great age) in organic matter from the early earth act as circumstantial evidence of earth's chronology as outlined in Genesis, not great eons of time.

[1]See http://creation.com/images/pdfs/cabook/chapter4.pdf

Link: chapter4Radio_dating.pdf

In the discussion of C-14 and its increasing presence pointing to a young earth, the following is a summary excerpt from a paper prepared by Dr. Andrew Snelling, a working geologist from Australia and Creation Ministries International contributor, sharing basic information related to the Carbon 14 cycle.

Snelling tells us: "Studies by renowned atmospheric physicists Seuss and Lingenfelter show that C^{14} is entering the earth system some 30-32% *faster* than it's leaving. What does this mean? It implies that C^{14} is still 'building up.' These factors place an upper limit age of the atmosphere of some 7 to 10,000 years. Also, it suggests that a thousand years ago, the C^{14}/C^{12} ratio in the atmosphere was less than today (because the C^{14} was still building up). Therefore a specimen which died a thousand years ago will show an *older than true age*. Two thousand years ago, specimens would have still less C^{14} to start with, so they have an even greater error. In other words, the further you go back, the more you have to shrink the radiocarbon dates to make them fit the facts. Remember that this correction is based on *measurable scientific data*." As previously suggested, if there were more moisture and a different air mixture around the earth before the Flood, such could have shielded and/or absorbed the C-14 and the cosmic radiation. Therefore, the amount of C^{14} in the pre-flood world could have been minimal. So a specimen from before the Flood would have an appearance of C-14 age, invalidating the test. Barnes and Humphries suggest that as you go back in history, the strength of the magnetic field increases rapidly. A stronger magnetic field would *increase protection* against these harmful particles, providing futher artificial readings.

Important C-14 Considerations:

• The Carbon 14 in the atmosphere is not in stasis but is building up rapidly. A protective vapor canopy, moisture laden atmosphere and/or increased magnetic field will decrease Carbon 14 levels, invalidating these tests, a serious embarrassment to evolutionists by giving ages which are much younger than expected in terms of earth history.

• It was expected that most deposits such as coal, gas, petrified trees, etc. would be un-dateable by this method, but in fact, of 15,000 dates in the journal *Radiocarbon* to 1968, only three were classed un-dateable. This is amazing with samples of coal and gas supposedly produced 100 million years ago providing C^{14} dates of a few thousand years!

Examples of C¹⁴ Dates that Contradict Long-age Views:

- Charcoal from Kyrgyzstan from the Pennsylvanian age, supposedly 330 million years old, dated at 1,680 years.
- Natural gas from Alabama and Mississippi gave dates of 30,000 and 34,000, respectively.
- Bones of a saber-toothed tiger from the LaBrea tar pits, supposedly 100,000 years old, gave a date of 28,000 years (predicted with the First Earth moist atmosphere content).
- A block of wood from the Cretaceous (supposedly more than 70 million years old) found encased in a block of Cambrian rock (hundreds of millions of years earlier), gave a date of 4,000 years.*

*http://creation.com/carbon-14-dating-explained-in-everyday-terms

Book Blog:

http://www.noahcode.org/blog/the-noah-code-adventure-begins#comments

Website: www.noahcode.org

Facebook: http://www.facebook.com/genesisalivehangout

Bibliography

The Genesis Flood, Henry Morris and John Whitcomb, 1961, P&R Publishing

The Global Flood, John D. Morris, 2012 Institute for Creation Research Pub. www.icr.org

Science & Human Origins, Ann Gauger, Douglas Axe, Casey Luskin, Discovery Institute Press, 2012 http://www.discoveryinstitutepress.com/

Darwin's Black Box, Michael Behe, Free Press, NY 1996, 10th printing

Mammoth, Resurrection of an Ice Age, Giant Richard Stone, Basic Books, 2001

The Mammoth and the Flood, Henry H. Howorth 1887, reprint available through Kissinger Publishing on Amazon or www.kissinger.net

Forbidden Archeology, Michael A. Cremo and Richard L. Thompson, Torchlight Pub. 1993 in its 15th edition 2012

Ancient Man: Handbook of Puzzling Artifacts, William Corliss, 1978 www.sceince-frontiers.com

Earth in Upheaval, Immanuel Velikovsky, 1955, Paradigma Press, London, Digital Ed. 2012

Bones of Contention, Marvin Lubinow, Baker Books 2004

The Genius of Ancient Man, Evolutions Nightmare, Editor Don Landis, Mas-ter Books, 2012

Gobekli Tempe, Genesis of the Gods, Andrew Collins, Bear and Company 2014

In The Beginning - Compelling Evidence for Creation and The Flood, 8th edition, Peggy & Dr. Walt Brown, Center for Scientific Creation, Phoenix, Arizona www.creationscience.com A free web viewer of this title is available online

Free download of above from Creation Ministries International: http://downloads.creation.com/free_resources/pdf/Stones_and_Bones.pdf

Index

Index

Index

Coming Title by Mark D. Rose

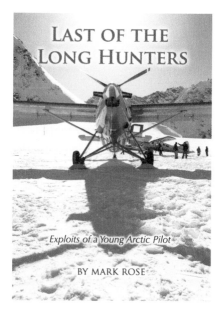

Last of the Long Hunters records the life of a young pilot flying in Alaska's Frontier Arctic. You'll experience the front seat thrills of bush planes and helicopters operating in the most dangerous conditions on earth, flying in minus 60⁰F temperatures and horrific storms among the magnificent mountains, glaciers and rivers that only Alaska has to offer. Once read you'll not be satisfied until you visit the Great Land yourself! Includes true-life experiences of accidents, rescues, comradeship, humor, heartbreaks and life in Arctic Alaska, gone forever when dismantled into parks and native lands in the 1970s.

It opens with an interesting early history of the 49th state, leading to the eventual use and development of a new tool of transport—the single engine airplane—but not without extracting a terrible price. Experience what it was like to grow up among the deadly big game, hunting the massive caribou herds and absorbing the greatness of the country. Aviators will gain from the flying experiences related and a full appendix relating to safe flying procedures. Every boy, man and aviator won't be able to put this one down, and more importantly, be compelled to grapple with its final truth. First in a series.

New Pamphlet

The Origins of Life and You
A common sense look at the complexity of life

If the evidences of life's origin covered in *The Noah Code* appealed to you, we now have available this all new resource. Covers most Noah Code chapter one topics plus: Orca and Bat Sonar, Cell types and division processes, dinosaurs, QR code links and more, with a section for notes. Beautiful images, 36 pages, convenient 4.75"x4.75" size, 10pt cover

Ordering Information

By mail: Genesis Alive Publishing, PO Box 91, Corvallis, Oregon 97339

email: info@genesisalive.com

Web: www.genesisalive.com

Book Website: www.noahcode.org

epub order: Download *The Noah Code* on .epub including live links - www.noahcode.org

Kindle for *The Noah Code*: http://www.amazon.com/dp/B00V9QK0RC

Note: Electronic (ePub and Kindle) versions include live links of selected topics at your finger tips, including *videos*

Volume discounts are available —Thank You!

About the Author

Mark Rose is a patent holding engineer and commercial pilot. He studied geology and has engaged in field work around the world, specializing in technology used in underground mining operations for 30 years. He founded *Genesis Alive* in 2014, an organization dedicated to championing truth in origins thinking. He lives near Albany, Oregon.

Notes

Notes

Notes

Notes

Notes

Notes

CPSIA information can be obtained
at www.ICGtesting.com
Printed in the USA
FSOW03n0835080316
17607FS

9 780996 066549